PHYSIOLOGICAL FOUNDATIONS
OF BEHAVIOR

PHYSIOLOGICAL FOUNDATIONS
OF BEHAVIOR

BY

CHARLES M. CHILD

PROFESSOR OF ZOÖLOGY IN THE UNIVERSITY OF CHICAGO

HAFNER PUBLISHING COMPANY
New York and London
1964

First published 1924
Reprinted by arrangement 1963

———————

Printed and Published by
HAFNER PUBLISHING CO., INC.
31 East 10th Street
New York 3, N.Y.

Printed in U.S.A. by
NOBLE OFFSET PRINTERS, INC.
NEW YORK 3, N. Y.

INTRODUCTION TO REPRINT 1963

The reprinting of C. Judson Herrick's *Neurological Foundations of Animal Behavior* has naturally suggested the reprinting of an equally classic and detailed study, namely, *Physiological Foundations of Behavior*. It is fitting and proper that these two outstanding books should again be made available to the present-day student in the field of behavior, for these two scholars, C. M. Child and C. Judson Herrick, were gifted in their ability to put to nature proper questions concerning the organism's response to its environment in development and adult reactions. These questions are still with us. The partial answering of these queries by Child and Herrick whets one's imagination to follow through in an attempt to clarify the answers.

The two books were the result of a friendly and co-operative collaboration. Child's book concerns itself with the general physiological foundations of behavior while Herrick's specifically limits itself to the neurological foundations and mechanisms of animal behavior. Both go to the roots of behavior, which are:

(1) its genetic aspects,
(2) its instinctive processes,
(3) its social situations,
(4) its modification (learning), which is certainly the most practical.

With the growing interest in behavior (psychology) much work is now being increasingly undertaken on a greater number of invertebrate forms. Since the late Professor Child spent most of his scientific career on these lower forms, especially the planaria, this reprint will be of considerable usefulness to those who are now pioneering in protopsychology. If these lowly forms, according to recent investigation,

v

show the beginning signs of boredom, interest, decision making, anxiety, conflict, frustration, rebellion, learning, etc., Child's book, depicting patterns of primary reactions, will be invaluable to all who are interested in behavior in this fruitful area. The book is not limited in its scope. On wide avenues it leads the reader into broad expanses of social integration in which the democratic process is placed on a natural scientific base.

It is pleasing, convenient, and profitable to have within one book, by one man, a subject treated so thoroughly. Without disparaging present-day efforts, some feel that our modern symposia frequently lack unity of style and thought. *Physiological Foundations of Behavior* has a rare unity of style and content. It was published originally at a time when interest in behavior was taking shape. It has not lost either its charm or insight.

Lawrence, Kansas   **PAUL G. ROOFE**
October, 1936   *University of Kansas*

PREFACE

The work of recent years on the problems of heredity and genetics has modified in many ways our conceptions of the mechanisms of inheritance, but has to a large extent ignored the problem of the mechanisms by which particular hereditary potentialities are realized as characteristics of particular individuals. Since knowledge of heredity and its mechanisms can be attained only through the study of individuals, any advance in our knowledge of the individual and its mechanisms must necessarily contribute in one way or another to our knowledge of heredity.

If the organism and the "germ plasm" are physico-chemical systems, the development of an individual organism in any specific protoplasm involves an orderly sequence of physiological activities and for such activities relations between the protoplasm and its environment are necessary. In recent years students of heredity have given but little attention to the rôle played by reaction to environmental factors in the realization of hereditary potentialities in an individual organism. If we admit that such reaction is behavior in the broad sense, this question is the question of the significance of behavior in individual development. And if behavior in this sense plays any essential part in individual development, such behavior and its effects at any given stage must be concerned in determining the behavior of later stages.

This book is a consideration of the general physiological features of individual pattern from the viewpoint of behavior, that is, of reaction to environment. The question underlying the whole discussion is: given the hereditary potentialities of a particular species, how are certain of these potentialities realized as characteristics of an individual of the species? Current theories of heredity leave us, I believe, no other basis than relation and reaction to environment on which to formulate an answer in physico-chemical terms to this question. The conception of the early stages of the process by which hereditary potentialities become real physiological and morphological features of an individual which is developed in this book is based on many different lines of evidence and throws light on many problems of individual development. Doubtless the advance of our knowledge of the physiology of protoplasms will modify in many ways the terms in which the conception is stated, but that individual development must be interpreted in terms of reaction to environment of a specific protoplasm cannot, I believe, be denied without ignoring many facts.

The book is a further development of the views advanced in Chapter IX of "Senescence and Rejuvenescence," "Individuality in Organisms" and "The Origin and Development of the Nervous System." Chapters I-VI are concerned with a general discussion of organismic pattern and integration. Chapters VII-X comprise a new presentation of the evidence for the conception of physiological or metabolic gradients. This presentation is made necessary by the progress of investigation since the publication of "Individuality in Organisms" in 1915. Chapters XI-XV are concerned with various aspects of physiological integration in the individual in their relation to environment. And finally in Chapters XVI and XVII the idea is developed that social integration as a reaction process among human beings is in many respects very similar to physiological integration in the development of the individual.

The appearance of the book at the present time and in the present form is due in some measure to the suggestion of my colleague Dr. C. J. Herrick that we should collaborate in some way in a discussion of the foundations of behavior in organisms. This collaboration has turned out to be the writing of two books, this one concerned with the general physiological foundations of behavior, the other, with the neurological foundations and mechanisms of behavior in animals. The two books are primarily concerned with different aspects of the problem of individual behavior and in that respect are in large measure independent and there has been no sacrifice of personal views for the sake of unity. Nevertheless, they are conceived, and it is hoped, may be accepted as a collaborative study of some of the fundamental factors in organismic behavior.

To many of my colleagues and co-workers I am deeply indebted for suggestions and criticisms and the use of data and figures: first of all to Dr. C. J. Herrick for repeated reading of the manuscript and for many suggestions and criticisms; to Dr. W. C. Allee, Dr. A. W. Bellamy and Dr. L. H. Hyman for reading and criticism of the manuscript; to Mr. J. N. Gowanloch for permission to make use of unpublished data and figures. I take this opportunity of expressing my appreciation of the work of the artist, Mr. Kenji Toda, in the redrawing of a number of figures.

For permission to reproduce published and copyrighted figures acknowledgments are due to the following publishers and authors: Messrs. A. and C. Black; The Carnegie Institution of Washington; The Columbia University Press; Henry Holt and Co.; The University of Chicago Press; Dr. A. W. Bellamy, Dr. Otto Glaser, Dr. R. G. Harrison, and Dr. H. S. Jennings. The sources of all figures reproduced from the work of other authors are indicated in the legends.

C. M. CHILD.

Chicago,
January, 1924.

CONTENTS

LIST OF ILLUSTRATIONS

LIST OF ILLUSTRATIONS

PHYSIOLOGICAL FOUNDATIONS
OF BEHAVIOR

PHYSIOLOGICAL FOUNDATIONS OF BEHAVIOR

CHAPTER I

THE PROBLEM

Each living thing represents an order and unity of some sort maintaining itself with more or less success in a changing environment. It is the character of this order and unity and its ability to adjust itself to a wide range of changes in its environment which place the living organism in sharp contrast to the rest of the world. We speak of organisms as individuals, meaning that each organism represents a more or less definite and discrete order and unity, in other words, a pattern, which not only determines its structure and the relations of its parts to each other, but enables it to act as a whole with respect to the world about it. It is this action of the organism as a whole with reference to its environment which constitutes its behavior as the term is usually employed. The behavior of the organism comprises in fact its reactions and responses to the action of environmental factors upon it. Often, however, we limit the term behavior to those reactions which involve movement, or changes in movement, whether accomplished by specialized locomotor organs as in animals or by growth, changes in turgor, etc., as in plants.

It may be pointed out in passing that while such reactions of organisms constitute a more or less definite reaction group, accomplishing certain results for the organism as a whole, they really constitute only a part of the behavior of organisms. Reaction to environmental factors by change in rate or kind of metabolism or in rate or course of development is just as truly behavior as the motor reaction of an animal to light or the movements of pursuit following the sight of prey by a carnivore. The conception of the organism as a machine which is first constructed and only after completion begins to function, i. e., to behave as a machine, has been widely held in the past and still has its supporters. According to this conception the earlier stages of development are determined by heredity, that is to say, the factors concerned in the construction of the machine

1

are predetermined in the protoplasm, and only at a certain stage of development does function in the proper sense begin (Roux, Weismann. See Chap. XIII). This conception is fundamentally preformistic and fails to take account of the facts of physiology. Actually the organism is not at any stage a closed system, but is functioning and behaving at all times as long as it is alive. Reaction to environment is occurring at all stages of development, though of course the kinds and complexity of reaction differ at different stages according to the mechanisms present. Moreover, such behavior or reaction is itself a factor in development and therefore in the construction of the behavior mechanisms of later stages. The behavior of the various developmental stages as well as the specific hereditary constitution of the protoplasm is a factor in determining the behavior of the fully developed organism.

When we analyze the behavior of the organism we find that it consists of the integrated [1] or coördinated behavior of parts, organs, tissues, cells and protoplasms. From this fact it follows that in the integration of behavior different degrees, scales, or orders of magnitude exist. Different sorts of protoplasmic behavior are integrated into the behavior of cells and different sorts of cellular behavior are integrated into the behavior of multicellular organisms. From this viewpoint the term "organismic," which has been used elsewhere (Child, '21 a, p. 3) is as necessary as the term "protoplasmic" and has as definite a meaning. It will be used here, as previously, with reference to those particular degrees of integration, order, unity which constitute the whole organism as contrasted with its constituent parts. Organismic behavior is then behavior of the organism as a whole as distinguished from the behavior of single parts.

---

[1] Ritter ('21) maintains that the term "integration" is unsatisfactory for biological purposes because of its implications. His argument is essentially that what we mean biologically by integration is the antithesis of differentiation, and not of disintegration, and he suggests the term "conferentiation" as the antithesis of differentiation in place of the term "integration." I am unable at present to appreciate fully the reason for such substitution. According to my point of view, differentation is not biologically the antithesis of integration, but a part, a feature, a phase of it, and disintegration is biologically, as well as otherwise, the antithesis of integration. If, for example, we call the appearance and development of the unity and order which constitute the wholeness of the individual organism a process of integration, differentiation is certainly not physiologically the antithesis of this process, but one aspect of it, and it is certainly first of all a process of "disintegration" when that individual divides into two or more parts or individuals. The disintegration may not be complete, or it may be followed by new integrations, but it is none the less a disintegration, so far as the original individual is concerned.

Behavior is of course not limited to living things. The reactions to environment of colloids, electrolytes, molecules, ions, atoms, electrons are as truly behavior as the driving of an automobile, or communication by speech or writing. On the other hand, the integration of behavior is not limited by the individual organism. Organisms may be integrated into social groups of various sorts and orders of magnitude and in such groups the behavior of the constituent individuals is more or less integrated into the social behavior of the group.

While it is by no means always possible to predict the behavior of a given kind of organism under given external conditions, there can be no doubt that the character of the behavior is determined by the character of the organism. Organismic behavior presupposes the existence of an organism, and is dependent upon the mechanisms present in that organism and their pattern of integration. The behavior of an *Amœba* when exposed to white light of a given intensity is different from that of a starfish and this again from that of an earthworm. The behavior of a green plant under the same conditions differs widely from all of these. Such differences in behavior, whether of different individuals of the same species, of different related species, or of members of widely separated groups have their foundation in differences of some sort in the make-up of these different organisms.

Some of these differences in behavior, *e. g.*, the characteristic differences between different species, result from differences in the hereditary constitution of the protoplasms and are stable to a high degree. Others, particularly some of the individual differences in the higher animals and to a still greater degree in man, are individually acquired. That is to say, they result from the effects of individual experiences determining the realization of potentialities given in the hereditary mechanisms. For example, many behavior mechanisms are determined in rough outline, so to speak, by hereditary factors reacting to a certain environment, but complete their development only through use: the bird learns to fly, the child to walk. Again, the memory of a past experience alters later behavior: "the burned child dreads the fire." In such a case the past experience serves merely as the factor which determines that among the potentialities of action of the mechanisms a certain one shall be realized.

In all these cases, however, it is the organism which is behaving and the constitution of the organism is the primary factor in determining the character of the behavior. In short, the problem of behavior, considered from the general biological viewpoint, involves the problem of the order and unity, the integration which constitutes the organism. We cannot go very far in the biological analysis of organismic behavior without knowledge of the organism which is behaving, and the organism in its relation to behavior appears in two different aspects, the physiological and the historical.

The physiological problem is concerned with the relations between protoplasms and organisms and the external world, the processes concerned in development and maintenance of the different parts of the organism and the relations between them. Physiology is often defined as the study of function, but life and organisms are functions of protoplasms in a certain sort of external world. Physiology is life viewed as action in protoplasmic substrata, but its task is not completed when it has determined all the different actions in all the different protoplasmic substrata. It must tell us how these actions are related, how they are ordered and integrated into organismic mechanisms and how these mechanisms are integrated into what we call the organism. The problem of physiology is, in fact, the problem of the organism as a physico-chemical action system.

Elsewhere (Child, '21 a) I have pointed out that the organism represents a physiological pattern of a certain sort. This pattern is primarily the order and unity which constitutes the organism in its simplest terms. As the pattern of a house is different from, and on a larger scale than, the patterns of the various materials or parts which are integrated in the house, so the pattern of the organism is different from, and on a larger scale than, the patterns of its constituent parts. If the organism is a physico-chemical, and not, as the vitalists maintain, a metaphysical unity and order, its primary physiological pattern is the action system which constitutes the basis of this unity and order. Whatever the nature of this primary physiological pattern, it is evident that it must constitute the physiological basis of the behavior pattern of the organism and the investigation of the origins of behavior cannot stop short of this problem. Organismic pattern represents the first step in the origin of organismic behavior since it is the foundation of the order which appears in all such behavior. To interpret behavior we must know something of the nature and origin of organismic pattern, of the substratum or materials in which it arises and of the patterns of these materials. Such analysis carries us finally to the fundamental conceptions of chemistry and physics. This question of pattern and material has been more fully discussed elsewhere (Child, '21 a, Chap. I).

On the other hand, every organism as we know it is a product of evolution and bears in itself the records of its past history, if we could read them aright. Its behavior, as well as its structure depends upon this past history. The organismic mechanisms are characteristic and constant to a high degree for each particular species or kind of organism because of this history. Different kinds of organisms arise from different kinds of protoplasm and each such protoplasm must possess a specific constitution handed down from the past, *i. e.*, hereditary. Whatever the rôle of environmental factors in determining the characteristics of an individual organism, there can of course be no doubt that the organismic mechanisms arise on the basis of the hereditary substratum and that this determines that the organism shall be a certain species or variety of fern, elm, snail, fish, or ape. From this viewpoint the problem of behavior involves the whole problem of evolution as well as that of inheritance.

This consideration of the physiological and historical aspects of the organism presents of course nothing new, but is concerned with facts so familiar as to be almost truisms. It serves, however, as a basis for emphasizing the fact that biological problems are fundamentally indissociable. The different fields of biological investigation are merely the different aspects under which life appears and as investigation progresses their interrelation becomes more and more evident. Every biological problem involves finally all of life and the environment of life. The present purpose is the consideration of one aspect of this interrelation, viz., the significance of organismic pattern as a physiological factor in the origin and development of organismic behavior and its mechanisms. This consideration involves the questions of the nature and origin of organismic pattern, of its relations on the one hand, to the specific protoplasmic substratum in which it appears and on the other, to the external world, of the progressive modification and complication of the primary pattern in the course of development, and of the bearing of the data at hand in these various fields upon the problem of behavior. It is evident that the viewpoint in this consideration must be physiological, rather than historical. In other words, we are concerned primarily with factors and conditions in the development, maintenance and relation to environment of the individual organism in a protoplasm of specific hereditary constitution, rather than with the evolution of this specific constitution. As will appear in the following chapters, the recognition and maintenance of this distinction is important, particularly as regards the conception of organismic pattern to which experimental investigation leads us.

CHAPTER II

PROTOPLASMS, ORGANISMS AND ENVIRONMENT

PROTOPLASMS

We are accustomed to speak of protoplasm as the substratum
or seat of life and as if it were fundamentally the same substance in
all organisms and all organs. At present this is little more than a
manner of speech, but in earlier times, following recognition of the
fact that the phenomena of life take place in the more or less fluid
gel to which the name protoplasm was given, there was a widespread
tendency, at least to speak of protoplasm, as Huxley, for example,
does repeatedly, as if it were identical in all organisms. This was
perhaps due in part to the fact that most of the earlier investigators
of the material substratum of life were morphologists rather than
chemists and were devoting their attention to the general physical
properties of protoplasms as they appeared under the miscroscope
and to the naked eye. As regards these properties, many different
protoplasms show a high degree of similarity and it is not difficult
to see how the conception of a fundamentally identical molecular
constitution arose. But we as have come to learn something of the
chemical and colloidal constitution of this material substratum of
life, it has become increasingly evident, as Ritter ('19, Chap. V) has
pointed out, that we have to do, not with a single substance, protoplasm, but with many different protoplasms, and that no protoplasm is a single chemical individual. At present, even though our
knowledge of the physico-chemical differences of different protoplasms represents little more than a beginning, no biologist doubts
that the protoplasms of different species are different in constitution and that even within the species many differences of constitution must exist. Already these differences are demonstrated by
many different lines of investigation. For example, the differences in
metabolism and its products such as cellulose, chitin, bone, starches,
sugar, fats, proteins, gland secretions, odoriferous substances, etc.,
show us clearly enough that the protoplasms of different organisms are doing different things. The remarkable specificities of relation brought to light in serological investigations and in allied fields
of work also demonstrate that different protoplasms are physiologi-

6

cally different. The work of Reichert and Brown ('09) showing that characteristic differences in crystal form of the hemoglobins and certain of their derivatives exist in different species and the later work of Reichert ('13) on the differentiation and specificity of starches have brought to light other aspects of specificity of protoplasmic constitution. Again, the experimental work of recent years on nutrition demonstrates that substances which are adequate for the synthesis and maintenance of the protoplasm of certain species are inadequate for other species. In various cases it has been possible to show that a particular chemical substance or group is necessary. What we know of the chemistry of digestion and the chemistry and metabolism of different tissues and organs in different organisms points to the same conclusion. In fact, it is possible that at present we are rather extreme in our belief in specificity and inclined to regard differences in protoplasm and organisms as specific or qualitative until the contrary is demonstrated. The hormones, so called, are usually regarded as specific in their action, though the work of certain investigators suggests that in certain cases the specificity is less marked than usually supposed.[1] But whatever the truth concerning this or that detail, differences and specificities of constitution of different protoplasms exist beyond all question, not only in different species but in different parts of the individual organism. Granting this, however, we need not lose sight of the fact that different protoplasms are physico-chemical systems of the same general sort and that certain resemblances or identities are recognizable as well as specific differences between them. Moreover, various factors in the differences of different protoplasms are non-specifically or quantitatively, rather than qualitatively, different. In fact, the distinction between quantitative and qualitative differences in protoplasms presents many difficulties. Differences which are quantitative from one viewpoint are qualitative from another. For example, purely quantitative differences in rate of respiration may be dependent upon qualitative differences in the substances concerned

---

[1] For example, more than ten years ago Meisenheimer ('12) suggested that the internal secretions of the sex organs are not specific for the organs of a particular sex, but are merely substances necessary for the development and maintenance of the body in general. Investigations of recent years have made it highly probable that secretin and gastrin, which may be regarded as foundation stones of the hormone theory, are not specific substances. For the present status of this question see a recent discussion by Carlson ('23, pp. 18–21) and for further literature, the following papers: Luckhardt, Keeton, Koch and LaMer, '20; Keeton, Koch and Luckhardt, '20; Keeton, Luckhardt and Koch, '20; Koch, Luckhardt and Keeton, '20; Luckhardt, Henn and Palmer, '22.

in the metabolic reactions, and again differences in the relative
amounts of substances entering reaction may determine qualitatively
different products.

In its fundamental features the specific constitution of a protoplasm is continuous from generation to generation, *i. e.*, hereditary,
though we believe that it has undergone change in one way or another
in the course of evolution. Each protoplasm apparently represents
in a broad sense a dynamic equilibrium, or more properly speaking
is always approaching a dynamic equilibrium which is always being
disturbed by external factors (see Chap. XIII). Within the usual
range of environmental conditions to which they are subjected living protoplasms possess in a high degree the capacity of equilibration. It is probable, however, that a protoplasm after action of an
external factor upon it never returns to exactly the condition which
existed before such action.

In nature protoplasms exist only in organisms and since we make
a distinction between protoplasms and organisms it is necessary to
consider the basis on which this distinction rests and this involves
the problem of organismic pattern and the differences between it
and protoplasmic pattern.

ORGANISMIC PATTERN

As pointed out elsewhere (Child '21 a, Chap. I), organismic pattern is an order, plan, unity or integration of which a protoplasm
constitutes the material substratum. Certain features of this pattern are highly significant in their relations to behavior. In the first
place, protoplasms are found in nature only as organisms or parts
of organisms. Nevertheless, it is evident that the organism represents a pattern of a higher order of magnitude, on a larger scale,
which arises in some way upon the substratum which constitutes
protoplasmic pattern. The organismic pattern involves molar regions or masses of living protoplasm, or whole cells or cell masses
as its constituent elements, while protoplasmic pattern is colloidal,
or perhaps as regards certain features crystalloidal, molecular and
submolecular. Organismic pattern determines in some way what
we call organization in protoplasm, that is, different regions or cells
become different in structure, constitution and function. This organization is orderly and definite in character for each organism and
functional relations exist between its constituent parts. The organism represents then certain sorts of ordering, differentiation and
physiological correlation of activities in different molar regions of

protoplasm or in different protoplasms. As the house represents a pattern and integration on a larger scale than the patterns of any of the materials entering into its construction, so the organism represents a pattern and an integration on a larger scale than protoplasmic patterns. In multicellular organisms the pattern is on a larger scale than that of the single cell and in colonial forms the pattern of the colony is on a larger scale than that of the single zooid or person of the colony. In short, it is evident that in an organism different regions of protoplasm, different cells, or cell masses, or even different individuals are in some way integrated into a definite and orderly whole.

If we say that a protoplasm is a physico-chemical system in which various dynamic changes of certain sorts occur, then an organism is a system of protoplasms. That is to say an organism is an integration of protoplasmic systems differing from each other in some way. If the changes in a protoplasm constitute life, the organism is an idtegration of different rates or kinds of living. It is of course true that we know life and protoplasms only as they occur in organisms, but it is also true that we can distinguish different protoplasms in an organism, that these different protoplasms are alive and that the changes which constitute life in them differ in some way. Even though we cannot define life nor protoplasm exactly, it is perfectly evident that an organism is not merely life nor merely a protoplasm, but an orderly and definite integration of different ways of living and different protoplasms. Second, organismic pattern has reference at every point to the relations between protoplasms and environment. The organism as a pattern, a mechanism, has no meaning except in relation to environment. It is in fact a pattern which makes it possible first of all for protoplasm to persist in the external world, and second to modify and control its environment to an increasing degree. In whatever aspect we regard the organism, it is obviously in relation to environment at every point. Its mechanisms are all concerned in some way with either the dynamic or the material factors of its environment. The mechanisms and therefore the relations to environment of different organisms are of course different, primarily because their protoplasms are different, but however these mechanisms differ, they are all concerned with reactions to environment.

The evolution of the organism has modified organismic pattern chiefly in two directions. First, the adjustment of certain mechanisms to external excitatory impacts has become more and more delicate and exact, and second, mechanisms making possible in one way or another the control and modification of environment have been increasingly effective. The physiological foundations of these modifications are found in the simplest organisms. In the light of our present knowledge it appears that the simplest possible organism consists of a mass of protoplasm with a plasma membrane at its surface. In such an organism the impact of external energy may alter the physico-chemical state of the membrane, inducing what we call excitation and so affecting the interior. Moreover, the semipermeability of the limiting membrane makes possible some degree of selection among material environmental factors.

Turning to axiate organisms, we see that the presence of an axiate pattern provides a basis for a differential axial relation to the external world which may express itself in position or direction of growth, as in plants and sessile animals, or in directed locomotion, as in motile animals (see Chap. VI). And the character of axiate response to environmental factors is still further differentiated by the symmetry relations of the pattern. A bilateral organism behaves differently from a radiate organism. The development of localized sensory, nervous and motor organs contributes to the definiteness and speed of response. Other features of the organism, the alimentary, respiratory, circulatory and excretory systems, are concerned with the material exchange between organism and external world, and their development is in the direction of greater efficiency in this relation to environment. The organism may, in fact, be defined as a pattern of relation to environment appearing in protoplasm.

From this viewpoint the life of an organism is actually, as Spencer put it, "the continuous adjustment of internal relations to external relations." The organismic pattern, on the one hand, and the specific hereditary constitutions of the protoplasms in which the pattern is expressed, on the other, determine the possibilities, the directions, the range and the complexity of this adjustment. Organismic pattern then appears to be a behavior pattern in a protoplasm. Different regions and cells come to behave differently instead of alike, and these different behaviors are integrated into an orderly whole. In as far as it is concerned with organismic pattern, the so-called organization of protoplasm originates in, and is the expression of, these regional differences in behavior.

It may appear at first glance that to call the organism a behavior pattern in protoplasm is little more than a fanciful figure of speech.

It may be objected, for example, that localization and morphological differentiation of organs in an embryo are processes very different from the use of these organs in behavior of the fully developed animal. Moreover, even if it be granted that such phenomena may in some sense be called behavior, it may be maintained that such behavior is, at least in considerable degree predetermined or inherent in the protoplasmic constitution. If this is true, it is not an adjustment of internal relations to external relations, but is independent of external relations, whether these are relations of one part of the organism to others or of the organism to its environment. So-called mosaic development, for example, in which parts of the organism are able to develop and differentiate up to a certain point independently of each other, has often been regarded as proving such predetermination. All the evidence indicates, however, that mosaic development and self-differentiation are, with certain exceptions, secondary conditions in development (see pp. 146, 244). On the other hand, we find that many developmental processes do stand in direct relation to environmental factors, either intra- or extra-organismic. When we alter these relations, e. g., by isolation of such parts, they respond to the change by altered development. In fact by far the greater part of what biologists call plant behavior consists of exactly such changes in development, growth and differentiation.

Motor reactions, which are not infrequently regarded as essential factors of animal behavior, are, properly speaking, only one aspect of the behavior of living things, viz., excito-motor behavior. They are singled out and emphasized as behavior because of their very direct relation to environmental factors and their value to the organism as means of adjustment. If Spencer's definition of life has any real meaning, it is that life is the behavior of protoplasmic systems in relation to an external world. From this viewpoint organisms as individuals must represent behavior patterns of protoplasms, the specific constitution of the protoplasm and the environmental factors determining the behavior in each case. In other words, the individual organism represents certain hereditary potentialities of the particular protoplasm or protoplasms concerned which are realized under certain conditions as individuals. Similarly, behavior in the ordinary sense of the organism as a whole, represents in each particular case a behavior pattern potentially present in the organism, but realized only through the action of an external factor.

This conception of the organism as a behavior pattern is really nothing more than a conception of the organism in dynamic terms. The biologist, particularly the zoölogist, has in the past been inclined to look at life from the morphological side and to attempt to conceive it in morphological terms, but it becomes increasingly evident that morphology must sooner or later be interpreted in dynamic terms, that is to say, in terms of the behavior of the system in which it appears. That the organism is primarily a behavior pattern in a protoplasm of specific constitution is the principal thesis of this book.

RELATIONS OF PROTOPLASMS AND ORGANISMS TO ENVIRONMENT

In general the relations of a protoplasm or an organism to its environment are, biologically speaking, of two sorts, the material, and the dynamic or energetic. The material relations include all material exchange between a protoplasm and the external world, that is, all relations which involve the transfer or transportation in mass of substance between the protoplasm and its environment. The intake of nutritive substance and water, the intake of oxygen and of CO_2 in photosynthesis in plants and, on the other hand, the outgo of water, of food residues, of excretory products of metabolism of all sorts, are all relations of material character. On the import side, relations of this sort provide the material for growth and maintenance as well as that used in the energy liberation involved in functional activity. On the export side, they serve for the removal of by-products and residues of metabolism which have no further part to play in the protoplasmic system. The by-products or the residues, or even the substance itself of one sort of protoplasmic system may represent nutrition for another system or play some other part in its activity. Such relations are the nutritive relations of animals to plants, of the carnivore to its prey, of the parasite to its host and the mutual relations between symbiotic forms.

These material relations are specific so far as the material factors of the external world on the one hand or the protoplasmic constitution on the other are specific. Undoubtedly the specific material relations between protoplasm and environment have been factors in the evolution of the specific constitutions of the different protoplasms. In fact, we must believe that such material relations between different physico-chemical systems or individuals were concerned in the origin of protoplasm.

The dynamic or energetic relations between protoplasms and environment are concerned, not with the transport in mass of substance, but with the transfer of energy in one form or another. These relations may be grouped under two heads: first, the direct purely mechanical or non-excitatory relations in which the effect is mechanical and proportional to the energy; second, the indirect or excitatory relations in which the energy transfer between the external world and protoplasm serves merely as the initiating factor in bringing about energy changes which themselves depend upon the configuration of the system acted upon.

There may be difficulty, as in the case of most abstractions, in drawing a hard and fast line between these two groups of relations. Practically it may be difficult to determine in a given case whether, or to what extent a particular relation is mechanical or excitatory.

As a matter of fact, some degree of excitation or inhibition probably occurs in living protoplasm in connection with most or all dynamic action of external factors upon it. In spite of such difficulties as regards particular cases, the difference between the two sorts of relation is sufficiently clear. In the one the system acted upon behaves as an inert system and the effect produced is brought about solely by the external energy. In the other the external energy merely serves to initiate changes in the energy relations between component parts of the system and energy liberated by such changes may produce effects immeasurably greater than the original external energy.

So far as protoplasms are concerned, the action of external factors in its purely mechanical aspects is in general of less importance than other dynamic relations in determining the condition of the protoplasmic system. It may bring about passive deformation and so be a factor in determining shape in some cases: gravity may determine the positions or distribution of substances of different weight and in this way determine other changes. Again, extreme mechanical action may produce death and disruption of protoplasm, but such relations are "accidental" rather than an essential feature of life. Of course mechanical factors may act on protoplasm as exciting or inhibiting factors, but in such case their effect is no longer purely mechanical, the mechanical energy of the external action undergoing transformation in the protoplasm. Such effects belong in the excitatory rather than in the purely mechanical group of relations.

Turning to the other aspect of the mechanical relations, it is evident that the mechanical action of protoplasm in the form of organisms upon the external world is a factor of fundamental importance in life. The locomotion of organisms, the taking of food, lung breathing and the propulsion of water over gills all depend very largely upon such action. A large part of the work of man in altering the configuration of his environment is accomplished through mechanical action either directly or with the aid of tools and machines, that is, contrivances for bringing about mechanical action more rapidly or on a larger scale than is possible with the mechanical energy of the human organism alone. Most organisms would cease to exist in a very short time if it were impossible for them to alter their environment by mechanical action upon it. In short, the purely mechanical action of external factors upon protoplasms is of relatively little significance in life, while the mechanical action of protoplasms in the form of organisms upon the external world is essential to the life of organisms.

As already pointed out, the second group of dynamic relations, the excitatory relations, involves the transformation of the energy of the factor acting into other forms in the systems acted upon. Such transformation usually or always determines changes which liberate energy from the system. In any case the course and character of excitation depend primarily on the configuration and state of this system. Here the factor acting merely initiates and the result depends on the system affected as in the relation of the spark to the explosion, or the forest fire.

Whatever the exact nature and relation of the processes concerned in protoplasmic excitation — or inhibition — may prove to be, the process in general is a complex dynamic change, probably involving both physical and chemical factors. Doubtless the component processes differ in different protoplasms and perhaps even with different degrees of excitation in the same protoplasms, but it is evident that excitation is more or less similar in all protoplasms. Even though we regard excitation merely as a more or less complex physico-chemical change, depending rather on the configuration of the system acted upon than upon the energy acting, the general conception of excitation has not lost its usefulness, as some physiologists have suggested.

In excitatory relations it is the action of the external factor upon protoplasms, which is of fundamental importance for life. We believe that irritability or excitability is a fundamental property of all living protoplasms, though it may vary widely in degree. In excitation the action of the external factor is, so far as the excitatory effect is concerned, non-specific, that is, essentially quantitative, though of course the process of excitation may differ in different protoplasms, and while some protoplasms are more readily excited by certain forms of energy, others by other forms, it is probably true that all forms of energy within certain limits of amount and intensity are capable of exciting most if not all protoplasms to some degree.

While the material relations between protoplasms and the external world are of course absolutely essential for the maintenance of life, since they supply fuel, *i. e.*, energy to the system and accomplish the removal of residues, the excitatory relations constitute the primary factor in the behavior of living things. The irritability of protoplasm, its sensitiveness to the impact of external energies and the change in state brought about by such impact, are the foundations of all that we call reaction or response in organisms. Many non-living systems are irritable or excitable in one way or another, *e. g.*, dynamite, dry wood, coal, but the excitability of protoplasms constitutes the physiological basis of those characteristics of living things which distinguish them most sharply from the non-living, viz., the ability to react or to respond to the impact of external energies by changes in state which include a reference to the external factor and therefore serve a purpose, or in the higher animals and man are consciously purposive or intelligent in character. The evolution of intelligent behavior from the relatively simple excitation and its transmission in a primitive protoplasm is of course associated with and dependent upon the development and integration of complex mechanisms of excitation, conduction and effect and involves the whole problem of the evolution of organisms, but it is nevertheless true that the excitability of protoplasms in general is the primary physiological factor concerned in the functioning of all these mechanisms (Herrick, 1924, Chap. XXI). Life as we see it, particularly in the higher animals, and man, is a series of excitations with the resulting equilibration of the organismic mechanisms to the exciting changes. We cannot conceive what life without excitation would be and it is a question of some importance, though perhaps largely academic, how long life can continue in the total absence of excitation. Many excitations are obviously only indirectly related to an external factor, but we have at present no evidence to indicate that protoplasm is fundamentally capable of self-excitation in the strict sense (see pp. 184–186) and the arguments of the vitalist in favor of such autonomy are in the present state of our knowledge far from conclusive.

It is unquestionably true that the excitability of protoplasm constitutes the primary physiological factor in the behavior of organisms in its broadest sense. At least in motile animals the material relations are determined and ordered to a large extent by the excitatory relations. Even in most of the simpler animals the reaction to food involves excitation and the excitatory factor is undoubtedly concerned in the growth orientation of the roots and of other parts of plants with respect to chemical and photic conditions. In the case of internal parasites which live in a nutritive medium and in plants which also may be said to live in a nutritive medium the material relations may be to a considerable extent independent of excitation, but even in such forms the intake must depend to some degree upon the rate of transformation in the body and in this excitation is concerned. Even on the basis of this general discussion it is not going too far to say that the excitability of protoplasms has been a fundamental factor in making organisms what they are. It has been effective in two ways, physiologically, through the changes in protoplasm determined by excitation in the individual, and indirectly through the evolution of excitability, the process and mechanisms of excitation and transmission, and the integration of such mechanisms.

The ability of protoplasms to bring about excitation in their environment is biologically significant chiefly in relation to other organisms. Man of course is able with the aid of various tools to make fire, to bring about explosions, electrical excitation and various other excitatory changes in non-living systems, and these are of great though not of fundamental significance for human life. But in the relations of organisms to each other the excitatory factor has become always more significant during the course of evolution. In the higher animals and man the excitatory factor is unquestionably the primary factor in relations between individuals, the material factor being significant only as it is excitatory in effect. In fact all social integration is based upon the excitatory relation. By this is meant merely that the actions concerned in such integration are primarily determined and ordered by the energy impacts upon the sense organs of the individual. In the case of man speech and the written word are the most important means of communication and integration, but their action on the individual is accomplished through the excitability of his protoplasm. All his relations with other individuals, whether they involve material exchange, i. e., in social terms, commerce, or communication by speech, writing, signal, or symbol of any kind, are based upon the excitatory relation. The significance of this fact in social integration will be considered in later chapters (Chaps. XVI, XVII).

It has already been noted that the material relations between protoplasm and the external world are in general specific and qualitative in character, involving different substances, though of course different quantities, *i. e.*, rates, degrees, amounts of material exchange, are possible. The dynamic or excitatory relations are, however, fundamentally non-specific or quantitative, involving energy transfer as the primary factor rather than mass exchange of substances. This difference is, as will appear, of fundamental significance for the conception of the individual organism as a physiological order and integration. Protoplasm must have originated in specific material relations between different physico-chemical systems and unquestionably the present specific hereditary constitution of any particular protoplasm must be primarily dependent upon the whole history of its material relations with the external world.

On the other hand, all protoplasms exist as individual organisms and as regards the more general features the pattern of the organism shows no relation to specific protoplasmic constitution. For example, cells composed of very different protoplasms are almost or quite indistinguishably alike in form and general structure and the organismic axial relations, polarity and symmetry are very similar in many different protoplasms. When we regard the individual organism from this viewpoint it appears as primarily a non-specific or quantitative dynamic order in a specific protoplasm. In other words, organismic pattern is primarily a non-specific dynamic pattern in a specific protoplasm. Apparently such a pattern can originate only in the non-specific dynamic relations between protoplasms and environment. To what extent this conclusion is supported by facts, later chapters will show.

CHAPTER III

THE ORGANISM AS A WHOLE: HISTORICAL AND CRITICAL

That the organism represents a unity and order of some sort is believed by most biologists, but widely different conceptions and interpretations of this unity and order have been advanced and their existence has sometimes been ignored. Much of the discussion of the organism as a whole has suffered from a lack of clearness concerning the nature of the "wholeness." It seems to be clear enough, however, that this wholeness is the unity and order evident in the individual organism from the beginning of development through all its life in all its various aspects. This unity and order are associated with the specialization and differentiation of parts in definite and orderly ways and with the resulting physiological relations between them (see Chap. V), but in all these processes unity and order are clearly apparent. The problem of the wholeness of the organism is then the problem of the origin and nature of the unity and order of the individual. (*Cf.* Ritter, '19.)

The various conceptions of the organism fall naturally into several groups and the brief consideration of these in the present chapter will serve not only to indicate the position of this problem in biological theory but also to clear the ground for the presentation of evidence in following chapters.

THE RÔLE OF THE ELEMENTARY ORGANISM

The idea has been widespread among biologists that an elementary or fundamental organism of some sort exists and that all more complex organisms consist of groupings or associations according to some plan of these elementary organisms. But opinions differ widely as to what constitutes the elementary organisms. From the physiological viewpoint the cell or protoplast is commonly regarded as the elementary organism (Verworn, O. Hertwig), but the morphological theorists of the descriptive period in zoölogy have postulated elementary organisms of various sorts. Such for example are the microscopic granules of Altmann and the hypothetical en-

18

tities conceived by the corpuscular theories of inheritance and development, *e. g.*, the determinants of Weismann.

From this conception of an elementary organism, whether it be a cell, a granule or determinant, has developed very naturally the belief held by many biologists that the solution of all the problems of the organism must be sought in the elementary organism. In other words, the grouping of determinants into systems of higher order (ids, idants of Weismann) or of cells into a multicellular organism must be determined solely by the nature of the individual determinants or cells. Because of its nature each elementary organism fits, so to speak, into a certain place in the whole, as a particular piece fits into a certain place in a mosaic. According to this, the preformistic or predeterministic viewpoint, each part or characteristic of the organism is predetermined in the elementary organism or organisms constituting that part. Development is then primarily the realization of these predetermined characteristics quite independently of each other and only after a certain stage is attained do the parts enter into functional relation to each other (Roux, Weismann). So far as the normal individual is concerned, environmental factors are important only in that certain factors are essential to the continuance of life and the progress of the predetermined development.

In epigenetic theory the rôle of the elementary organism is very different from this. The individual elementary organisms composing a complex organism, *e. g.*, the cells of a blastula, are not necessarily predetermined as different parts, but may be primarily all alike in constitution, the differences which arise being determined by the action of environmental factors upon the whole group and upon each member of it. In the latter case of course relations to other members constitute environmental factors. In short, epigenetic theory conceives the organism as it exists as a product of the reaction between a particular kind of protoplasm, whether in the form of a single cell or of many cells, and environmental factors. The elementary organism itself represents the product of such reaction and its grouping with others to form complex organisms involves further reactions of the same sort and their results. From the epigenetic viewpoint then, a particular organism, whether elementary or complex, represents the behavior of a particular protoplasm in a particular environment.

To the vitalist it makes little difference whether the elementary organisms are conceived as primarily alike or different or whether they exist at all. For him the organism is essentially a metaphysical, a "supernatural" phenomenon and its pattern is not primarily a matter of physico-chemical factors of any kind but usually results from the control of physico-chemical factors by the non-mechanistic integrating principle, "entelechy," "dominant," "soul" or whatever he may prefer to call it. The question whether organismic pattern is predetermined in the germ or whether it is in each case a reaction of a specific protoplasm to environmental factors is of minor importance to the vitalist, for in the one case the structural pattern, in the other the behavior pattern is metaphysical in origin.

For present purposes it seems unnecessary to distinguish the cell or any other organismic entity as elementary organism. It may merely be pointed out that organisms range in complexity and scale of integration from simple cells or protoplasts, or probably from forms simpler than the ordinary cell, to individuals consisting of thousands or millions of cells, and that even multicellular individuals may be integrated into individualities of still higher order, such as colonies. The cell, it is true, represents a relatively simple form of organism and as such enters into the constitution of more complex forms, but there seems to be no good reason for believing or assuming that it is fundamentally different in origin or pattern from other organisms, whether of a higher or lower degree of integration.

PREDETERMINATION VERSUS EPIGENESIS

The problem which at present we formulate in terms of heredity versus environment has, in one form or another, occupied the attention of biologists since the time of Aristotle. In earlier times commonly the question whether the organism is wholly preformed or predetermined, it has undergone various changes as regards its terms and the meanings assigned to them. Nearly thirty years ago Whitman ('95) pointed out that it was no longer a question of preformation versus epigenesis, but rather one of the part played by each factor in determining the individual. Even then Weismann, the chief exponent of preformation was forced to admit the effect of environment, as is evident at various points in his writings, and Oscar Hertwig, perhaps his most notable opponent, postulated as necessary for the development of the different species of organisms, "different sorts of primordial substances which possess an extremely complex organization" (Hertwig, '94, p. 131) and which, because of this organization are capable of reacting specifically and with the greatest exactness to all external and internal stimuli to which they are subjected. With the development of experimental biology during the last thirty years, the chief difficulty of predeterministic theory has been to account for the variations and modifications in individual development with change in environment, while epigenetic theory has found it difficult to account for the constancy of development and individual pattern, but on the whole there has been still further approach to common ground.

Predeterministic conceptions of the organism have developed in large part on the basis of zoölogical data and have been perhaps more widely accepted by zoölogists than by other biologists. They attained their highest development during what may be called the morphological period in zoölogy in the latter half of the nineteenth century. In fact, they are essentially morphological theories of the organism and attempt to interpret development as a process of construction of a morphological machine by agents or factors inherent in the germ and usually conceived as distinct physico-chemical entities capable of growth and reproduction. According to the Weismannian theory, the most completely developed and most widely accepted of the predeterministic conceptions, each such entity or determinant represents or determines some character of the organism. More recent conceptions call the predetermined entities factors, genes, etc., and hold that, on the one hand, many such factors may be concerned in the development of any particular character, and on the other, that each factor may play a part in the development of more than one character.

In the minds of the earlier preformists there was no doubt that the pattern and course of individual development are predetermined and hereditary. The problem of the individual was not for them a physiological problem, but rather an evolutionary problem and therefore veiled in the mists of the past and belonging to the field of speculation rather than to that of experiment. Most predeterministic theories simply assume the existence of organismic pattern or integration in some terms. Weismann, for example, assumes that the determinants are integrated into groups of higher orders of magnitude, corresponding perhaps to organs, individuals, etc. Roux advanced the hypothesis of qualitative nuclear division as a basis for the orderly and harmonious differentiation of parts and Weismann adopted the idea. Later, however, the experimental investigations of Driesch and many others led Roux himself to abandon the hypothesis.

Current theories have advanced far beyond the predeterministic conceptions of Roux and Weismann, but they are still largely concerned with hypothetical hereditary entities of some sort and have little or nothing to say about the integration of these into an organism in development. The accepted view at present maintains on the basis of chromosome behavior in cell division, as well as of experimental embryology, that no sorting out or distribution of genes factors, hereditary potentialities occurs during development. Each cell is regarded as possessing the entire chromosomal mechanism and therefore, as Morgan puts it, "each cell *inherits* the whole germ plasm" (Morgan, '19, p. 241). In short, current theories of heredity provide no mechanism for individual development and differentiation. Morgan's discussion of "The Organism as a Whole, or the Collective Action of the Genes" (Morgan; '19, pp. 241–246) does not provide us with any theory of development. The chromosome theory of heredity tells us that each cell inherits the whole germ plasm but as to the manner in which different cells and cell groups become different, it has nothing to say.

Morgan's discussion of "The Organism as a Whole" is little else than a restatement of the particulate theory of heredity: it does not even define the organism as a whole and the author seems inclined to the view that the wholeness does not exist. The particulate theory of heredity certainly provides no basis for the origin of differences in different cells and cell groups and of physiological correlation between the different parts. But we know that such differences and correlative factors do arise, and if we accept Morgan's conception of heredity, it is evident that they must originate, either in the reactions of the protoplasm to differences in environment which determine the realization of different hereditary potentialities in different cells or cell groups, or in some ordering metaphysical principle, such as Driesch's entelechy. In fact, if Morgan is correct in saying that each cell inherits the whole germ plasm, and there is at present no good reason for doubting that this is essentially true, the individual organism, "the organism as a whole" cannot be accounted for in terms of heredity alone, but only in terms of heredity plus behavior, or in terms of metaphysics. Morgan apparently fails to distinguish clearly between the hereditary potentialities, the genes or factors of the germ plasm, and the realization of certain of them in the individual organism. No individual represents in its structure and function all the hereditary potentialities of its protoplasm. Each of its parts and each function represents, so to speak, a particular selection among the hereditary potentialities, and Morgan's statement provides no basis for such a selection. Morgan's difficulty appears to be in his belief that the organism as a whole represents in some way "the collective action of the genes." As a matter of fact, such collective action must be the same in all cells since all cells contain the same genes, therefore this collective action alone cannot give rise to local differentiation or to physiological correlation. The individual organism is not the collective action of the genes alone, but originates in some factor which determines what genes shall be concerned in determining the characteristics of each cell or cell group: it is in fact a matter of the action of different genes in different cells, and such differences must be determined, either by environment or by some metaphysical factor. This is equivalent to saying that the individual organism must be a behavior pattern arising in some way in the germ plasm of the species.

In an earlier discussion (Morgan, Sturtevant, etc., '15, pp. 43–44) this distinction between the hereditary potentialities and the realization of different potentialities in different cells seems to be more clearly recognized. There it is stated that we must suppose:

"that the Mendelian factors are not sorted out . . . but that differentiation is due to the cumulative effect of regional differences in the egg and embryo reacting with a complex factorial background that is the same in every cell. These regional peculiarities of different parts of the egg and embryo may, like the age of the individual, also be considered as influences external to the hereditary factors which affect the development of characters. And not only do regional peculiarities influence characters, but special regions are usually required for a given factor difference to manifest itself, just as certain temperatures or ages may be necessary."

If I understand this statement correctly, it is to the effect that development of the individual represents the reaction of the factorial complex to environmental factors. This seems to be Conklin's viewpoint ('22) and it is essentially the viewpoint of the present book, according to which the physiological gradient constitutes the primary regional differential, to which the factorial complex reacts. This view, however, seems to be very different from that advanced in Morgan's later book, according to which the organism as a whole represents the collective action of the genes. In this later discussion Morgan appears to leave little or no room for action of the environmental factor, nevertheless the statement quoted above appears without change in the revised edition of his earlier book (1923).

Whether or not one accepts all the details of the chromosome hypothesis, there is of course no necessary conflict between the particulate theory of heredity and the physiological conception of the organism as a whole. They are simply ideas concerning different matters, the one being concerned with the hereditary constitution of the protoplasm of the species, the other with the behavior of this protoplasm in certain environmental relations. It is this behavior which determines the actual individual. The wholeness of the individual organism lies, not in the relations between genes or factors, but in the relations between different regions, cells or cell groups, in which the potentialities of different genes or groups of genes or factors have been realized.

By way of illustration let us consider a very simple, perhaps one of the simplest cases of organization of protoplasm, viz., a mass of protoplasm bounded by a plasma membrane. Some of the micro-organisms are very probably little or nothing more than this. Our knowledge of plasma membranes in protozoa and other cells leads us to believe that any portion of such a protoplasmic mass is capable of giving rise to a plasma membrane, but as a matter of fact, only in those regions which are in contact with the external medium do the conditions arise which make possible the realization of the potentiality of membrane formation. We say that the plasma membrane results from the exposure of the surface to a medium of a certain physico-chemical constitution and we describe its formation in terms of physical chemistry. But as soon as such a membrane is present, the organism as a whole exists, that is, regional differences which make possible physiological relations between surface and interior exist. All regions of the protoplasm unquestionably possess the hereditary potentiality of membrane formation, but the membrane appears only under certain conditions and in certain regions. In this case the action of environmental factors is obviously necessary to make an organism out of the hereditary potentialities of the protoplasm. Attention may also be called to the fact that the formation of a plasma membrane is non-specific, i. e., it is not dependent upon the specific constitution of any particular protoplasm, but all protoplasms give rise under proper conditions to membranes. Undoubtedly the plasma membranes of different protoplasms differ in their constitution and properties, but the act of formation of a plasma membrane is a non-specific protoplasmic reaction to environmental factors.

In this, the simplest sort of organism, the specific hereditary constitution of each protoplasm concerned is predetermined as regards the individual, though in the course of evolution it too may have been determined in relation to external factors. The actual individual organism, however, as an order and unity of a certain sort and of a certain order of magnitude, is the product of a non-specific, a fundamentally quantitative reaction of that protoplasm to external factors. In short, as regards the individual organism the predeterministic conception fails at the outset.

Turning to a more complex case of a multicellular organism with physiological polarity and symmetry, e. g., *Planaria*, according to current theory as stated by Morgan, all the cells of this animal, as of others, inherit all the genes or factors, including those for head formation, and we know from experiments with pieces that at least certain cells at all levels are capable of giving rise to a head. In the development of the normal animal, however, only certain cells develop as a head while others develop into other parts. Something must determine these differences in behavior of the different cells and parts of the organism, for they occur in spite of the similar nuclear constitution. If we say that these differences between surface and interior in the simplest organisms and in relation to the axes in axiate forms, together with the physiological relations arising from them, are dependent upon physiological polarity and symmetry, it becomes evident at once that polarity and symmetry of some sort, spherical, radial, or bilateral, constitute the spatial basis of the organism as a whole and the question of their nature and of the physiological processes involved in the determination of the regional differences becomes of fundamental importance in the physiology of development. For the particulate theory of heredity then the question as regards such a form as *Planaria* becomes the question whether polarity and symmetry are represented by genes or factors.

In the past polarity and symmetry have very generally been supposed to result in some way from molecular or other characteristics of the intimate inherent structure of protoplasm in general. This conception has been stated in terms of crystalline or other stereochemical structure, or sometimes simply in terms of "intimate structure." If this intimate structure is characteristic of the nucleus as well as of the cytoplasm, polarity and symmetry must represent an even more fundamental feature of protoplasmic constitution than the genes or factors. If on the other hand, polarity and symmetry exist not in the nucleus but in the cytoplasm alone, genes for polarity and symmetry might be assumed to exist. Such genes, however, must behave very differently from others in that they give rise to a general substratum or framework underlying the features determined by the other genes. Moreover, the difficulty of accounting in such terms for the different polarities and symmetries of different regions and parts of the organism is just as great as for regional differences of other sorts, since the cell inherits the whole germ plasm.

In general predeterministic conceptions of polarity and symmetry have usually assumed a molecular or "micellar" structure and orientation, either similar or analogous to that of the crystal or that of the magnet, or of purely hypothetical character, as the basis of polarity and symmetry. Such theories of organismic form have been the subject of much discussion and the analogies between crystals and organisms have been stated repeatedly.[1] But even though the crystal does possess a characteristic form and is able to grow, regenerate and undergo "form regulation," the hypothesis that polarity and symmetry and organismic form are fundamentally similar to that of the crystal meets with various difficulties. Some of these difficulties are briefly pointed out. First, according to stereochemical theory, we should expect organisms to show at least as great a diversity of fundamental axial relations as we find of crystal forms, but as a matter of fact we find only three fundamental morphological patterns among all organisms, viz., radial, polar and polar bilateral, and various modifications and combinations of them (see p. 37). If such patterns were a matter of the molecular constitution, we should expect far greater diversity than this. The varieties of crystalline form in the hemoglobins as described by Reichert and Brown ('09) and the differentiation of the starches (Reichert, '13) show how pattern dependent on molecular constitution varies with that constitution. If polarity and symmetry are patterns of this sort, we ought to expect similar ranges of variation.

Second, the crystal is fundamentally a homogeneous system and the occurrence of chemical change in it is accompanied by the disappearance of crystalline structure. In protoplasm, on the other hand, an extreme degree of heterogeneity exists and growth, maintenance, structure, differentiation and function are all associated with, and dependent upon, chemical reactions. Is not the assumption of an inherent molecular or micellar structure and orientation as the basis of organismic pattern in such as system *a priori* a highly improbable one? Such pattern is built up by the metabolic reactions;

---

[1] See for example Przibram, '06, 21, for bibliography and for arguments in support of the essential similarity between crystalline and organismic form. The latter paper is concerned to a considerable extent with a hypothetical space lattice.

by altering metabolic relations in different regions or cells we can alter it; when the reactions cease only the formal, not the functional pattern remains.

Third, from what we know of the constancy of the specific constitution of protoplasm, we should expect a pattern dependent upon specific molecular structure and orientation to be exceedingly stable and but little susceptible to experimental modification. This, however, is far from being the case, as everyone knows. In at least many of the simpler organisms it is possible to obliterate or reverse polarity and to determine new polarities by various experimental conditions (see Chaps. VII–IX), and experimental conditions may also determine whether a particular protoplasm shall give rise to radial or bilateral structures, or both (Chaps. VIII, IX). Moreover, polarity and symmetry are less evident in small pieces of the bodies of the simpler animals than in large pieces, and in sufficiently small pieces the original polarity disappears or becomes ineffective, the further development being determined by one or more new polarities dependent upon experimental conditions (Child,' 07 a, '15 c, pp. 98, 99). And finally, there are cases such as the alga *Fucus*, in which the polarity of the individual plant is directly determined in the egg or spore by the differential action of incident light (see pp. 58–61).

Fourth, if such a molecular system does exist as the basis of polarity and symmetry and so of organismic pattern, it ought to be possible to obtain some evidence of its existence with the aid of polarized light. Unless the structure of such systems is the same in all directions, and this would be impossible in heteropolar organisms, they must possess optical axes and under proper conditions show some indications of optical anisotropy. During the nineteenth century extensive studies of many animal and plant tissues were made with polarized light,[1] and it was demonstrated beyond question that many structures of both animals and plants are optically anisotropic. But such structures are predominantly cuticular, non-protoplasmic membranes, shells, skeletal structures, starch grains, crystalloids and fibrillar differentiations, such as muscle, connective tissue, etc. The investigators agree that protoplasm in general, eggs and early developmental stages show no indications of anisotropy. The structure underlying anisotropy evidently arises secondarily in the course of development and, except as regards muscle and

---

[1] See for example, Valentin, '61, '71 a, b; Engelmann, '75, and references given by these authors. Pfeffer, '97, p. 70, gives references to the more important botanical work along this line.

some other fibrillar structures, it appears predominantly in dead secretions and inclosures rather than in the living protoplasm. It has been pointed out repeatedly that the appearance of anisotropy, particularly in various fibrillar structures, may be the result of mechanical tension. Very generally the axes indicated by such anisotropy have reference to local conditions, single cells, fibrils, etc., but in some of the unicellular organisms the anisotropy of the ectoplasm of its outer layers indicates a close relation between the axis of the organism and the structural system underlying anisotropy. In all the evidence, however, there is nothing to justify the assumption that anisotropy is a primary, inherent property of protoplasm. Apparently it arises secondarily, either because of the crystalline character of the substance in which it appears, in consequence of mechanical tension, or possibly of other local conditions. These investigations then afford no support to the theory of molecular or micellar polarity and symmetry.

And finally, the supporters of the stereochemical theories have not been able to show in any convincing way how the molecular structure and orientation determine the differences in rate of metabolism and of growth and the course of differentiation in different cells or cell groups. Harrison's recent stereochemical interpretation of the symmetry relations of amphibian appendages in his transplantation experiments (Harrison, '21) may be cited as a case in point. Here, as in so many other cases, the stereochemical structure is simply assumed, apparently without evidence and without consideration of the difficulties involved in the assumptions (see pp. 126–129).

As a matter of fact polarity and symmetry appear to be largely if not wholly independent of the specific constitution, whether molecular or molar, of different protoplasms. Different axes, different axial combinations and different symmetries may appear in nature or be experimentally determined in a particular protoplasm and similar polarities and symmetries may exist in very different protoplasms (see pp. 33, 41). In axiate organisms, then, as in simpler forms, the factor which determines the order and unity of the individual is apparently a non-specific factor, while the specific hereditary constitution of the particular protoplasm determines the specific characteristics of the individual.

It may also be noted in passing that the conception of formative substances advanced by Sachs and its various modifications in the hands of Loeb, Conklin, Morgan and others, do not afford a solution of the problem of polarity and symmetry, for the movement of the formative substances to the proper regions or their gradation or seg-regation in the proper order, must depend either upon a preëxistent underlying polarity or be in some way directly determined by external factors. In either case the nature of polarity and symmetry remains to be determined. Moreover, it seems to be true that thus far no one has really demonstrated the existence of a formative substance in organisms, or has even shown how any particular substance may exert a really formative action.

The fundamental difficulty of the predeterministic conception as regards the organism as a whole lies in the assumption that the unity and order, the "wholeness" of the individual organism, as well as the hereditary potentialities of the individual, are inherent in the protoplasm. No theory of heredity can account wholly for the individual organism. The individual represents heredity plus environment, in other words, behavior of a particular kind of protoplasm with certain hereditary potentialities, genes, or factors, in a particular environment. This behavior is the factor which orders and unifies the hereditary machinery and constitutes the starting point of the organism as a whole. The problem of the individual is then the problem of the environmental factors initiating this behavior, the nature of the behavior itself and of its action in realizing the hereditary potentialities.

This conception falls of course into the category epigenesis, but it differs somewhat from the earlier epigenetic theories. It does not necessarily conflict with, nor replace modern theories of heredity, except as they attempt to interpret the individual as "the collective action of the genes" alone, but merely supplements them by providing a physiological basis for the orderly realization of the hereditary potentialities in the form of an individual organism. The interpretation of the order and control of hereditary potentialities in the individual organism has alway constituted a stumbling block for predeterministic theories of heredity. They must either deny it or ignore it, or they must postulate a supergene which controls and orders all the others, or a predetermined harmony among the genes. There is no evidence for a supergene, and predetermined harmony among the genes can scarcely be accounted for in other than dualistic or vitalistic terms. If, however, it can be shown that simple reactions to environment, to which every germ is exposed, are concerned in the orderly and harmonious realization of the hereditary potentialities, all the difficulties concerning the organism as a whole disappear. Then the organism as a whole represents, not heredity alone, but heredity plus environment, in other words, it is primarily the reaction to environmental factors of a protoplasm with a certain hereditary constitution.

The organism is inexplicable without environment. Every characteristic of it has some relation to environmental factors. And particularly the organism as a whole, *i. e.*, the unity and order, the physiological differences, relations and harmonies between its parts, are entirely meaningless except in relation to an external world. Nevertheless predeterministic theories have maintained that the organism as a unity and order is primarily independent of an external world and enters into relation with it only secondarily. This viewpoint has resulted in confusion and sterility in various fields of biological thought, and, as Dewey has pointed out, a similar viewpoint has had much the same effect in philosophy (Dewey and others, '17).

It may be pointed out that the recognition of the significance of environmental factors in determining the unity and order of the organism does not, as often wrongly assumed, involve us in Lamarckian assumptions, or hypotheses. The action of environment is primarily a matter of the developmental physiology of the individual. If the effect of such action persists through more than one cell generation this persistence involves no transmission of effects from body to germ cell, but the effect persists merely as a physiological condition in the protoplasm which arises by cell division and growth from the protoplasm originally affected. In pieces isolated by section from the stems of certain hydroids the polarity of the original individual may persist in the piece and the new individual, therefore, inherits its polarity. On the other hand, it is possible to determine experimentally a new polarity in pieces and such pieces may give rise to new individuals and these may again be cut into pieces which inherit their polarity. Similarly an egg may conceivably inherit its polarity from earlier cell generations and somewhere in the course of these generations this polarity may have been determined by environmental factors. It is obvious, however, that such cases involve no Lamarckian assumptions concerning inheritance of "acquired" or somatic characters, but represent simply the persistence of direct physiological effect of environment upon the germ cell or other reproductive unit. Moreover, the general conception illustrated by such cases may provide a simple physiological interpretation of certain facts which have seemed to favor Lamarckian hypotheses.

VITALISM

Vitalism as a biological form of dualistic theory is simply the assumption of a metaphysical ordering and controlling principle of some sort as the basis of unity and order in the individual organism. The older vitalism was essentially the inference drawn from the uncritical observation of the behavior of living, as contrasted with non-living things and from introspection, and needs no comment here. The so-called neo-vitalism, however, is based to a considerable extent on the data of modern experimental biology, and is concerned primarily with the question of order and unity in the organism, i. e., the question of the organism as a whole. Driesch's entelechy, for example, is the ordering and controlling principle which brings order and unity out of the physico-chemical complex (Driesch '08, and earlier papers).

This neo-vitalism unquestionably represents in some degree a reaction from the predeterministic conception of the organism. The neo-vitalist sees clearly the difficulties involved in the conception of organismic unity and order in predeterministic physico-chemical terms, but at the same time he fails to recognize the significance of environmental factors in relation to unity and order. Consequently the only way out for him is the assumption of a metaphysical ordering and unifying principle to which he gives a name. The chief service of neo-vitalistic theory to biological thought is perhaps its clear recognition of the difficulties involved in physico-chemical predeterministic conceptions of the organism, but it fails to take account of environment. Driesch's arguments against the "machine theory" of the organism are valid only against predeterministic conceptions of the "machine" as consisting of specific or qualitatively different localized parts, and fall to the ground at once when it is conceived as a quantitative dynamic machine related in its action to environmental factors. Driesch used for example, the argument that "a machine cannot remain whole when separated into its parts" to prove, as he says, that a mechanistic interpretation of the reconstitution of new individuals from the various isolated parts of a pre-existing individual is impossible. The argument holds only of the "machine" as specifically or qualitatively different in its different parts. If it is fundamentally a dynamic "machine," e. g., an excitation-transmission process, or the record in protoplasm of such a process, it may remain whole when separated into parts just as truly as two flowing streams resulting from the division of one are wholes to the same extent as the original stream. In short, the physiological gradient (Child, '15 b, '21 a) is a "machine" for which Driesch's arguments do not hold.

In general, the vitalistic or dualistic viewpoint with its negation, explicit or implicit, of the value of scientific method, does not provide a solution of the problem of the organism which is intellectually satisfying to the inquiring mind, and real "proofs of the autonomy of vital processes" are at present non-existent. Only when all physico-chemical possibilities of experiment and interpretation shall have been exhausted without providing a satisfactory solution will a vitalistic formulation of the problem be scientifically justified.

CONCLUSION

If we admit that environmental factors play some part in ordering and unifying the process of realization of hereditary potentialities in the development of the individual organism we avoid the difficulties of predeterminism and do not require vitalism. We do not hesitate to say that certain potentialities given in the hereditary constitution of the protoplasm are realized only in relation to the action of an external factor. The pecking reaction of the newly hatched chick, for example, represents a high degree of integration of behavior, but although the machinery for it is present, the integration itself occurs in relation to an environmental factor. Similarly the hereditary constitution of the particular protoplasm, the genes, factors or whatever we may call the hereditary potentialities, constitutes, so to speak, the machinery for the development of the organism as a whole. The integration of this machinery into an orderly working unit, however, does not occur autonomously any more than the integration of motor behavior in later stages of development, but in the first instance only in response to the action of an environmental factor. From this viewpoint the organism as a whole represents an integration of behavior just as truly as do the complex motor reactions of later stages. Moreover, the organism as an order and unity in protoplasm is the primary behavior integration on an organismic scale, and on it all others are based. Following chapters are devoted to the further development of this conception.

CHAPTER IV

THE GENERAL CHARACTERISTICS OF ORGANISMIC PATTERN

In Chapter II it was pointed out that the organism stands in relation to environment at all points and that all of its characteristics are referable in one way or another to this relation. If this is true, it follows that the pattern of the organism in its more general features must constitute a physiological basis underlying the whole complex of reaction patterns and mechanisms, *i. e.*, the behavior in the broadest sense of the individual. As we pass from the general to the special features, the details of organismic pattern, we find that the more highly specialized and specific these features, the more directly are they concerned in some particular reaction pattern or mechanism of a particular species or group. We may say then that the general features of organismic pattern constitute the basis of physiological integration of the organism and so make it possible for it to react in one way or another as a whole, while the special mechanisms of reaction depend not merely upon the presence of an organismic pattern but upon the material, the kind of protoplasm in which the pattern exists.

When we compare different organisms we find that the most general features of organismic pattern are much alike for many different forms. For example, the same general plan of polarity and symmetry may appear in protoplasms of very different constitution but as we progress from the general to the special in organismic

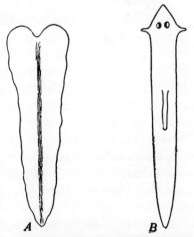

Fig. 1.—Diagrammatic outlines of polar-bilateral plant and animal: (*A*) a liverwort; (*B*) *Planaria*, a flatworm. The dominant region is the growing tip in the plant, the head in the flatworm (from Child, '15 c).

pattern the part played by the specific constitution of the protoplasm becomes more and more conspicuous. The special mechanisms and structures which arise along a polar axis or a plane of symmetry in

33

different species and groups depend not merely upon the existence of a polarity but upon the nature of the protoplasm in which the polarity or symmetry exists. For example, the liverwort *Marchantia*, the flatworm *Planaria* (Fig. 1) show certain resemblances as regards the general plan of organization, but differ as regards the particular reaction mechanisms. Both forms possess polarity and bilaterality, that is, a longitudinal and a ventrodorsal direction of order: the planarian possesses a head region, the *Marchantia* a growing tip and these regions dominate or control in some way and to some degree other regions of the body within a certain range. But in spite of these general resemblances the two organisms are very different in structure and behavior because the protoplasms are different in constitution. The general organismic pattern merely determines a general plan or order of integration, but the sorts of parts, organs, mechanisms, etc., which are integrated depend upon the constitution of the protoplasmic material. As a preliminary to further analysis along these lines it is necessary to determine if possible what the most general characteristics of organismic pattern are.

THE RELATION OF DOMINANCE AND SUBORDINATION

So far as the actual physiological relations which integrate the regions, parts or organs of an organism into an orderly whole are concerned, the fundamental characteristic of organismic pattern appears to be a relation of dominance and subordination of control and being controlled. The physiological relations between different regions or parts of an organism may be collectively called physiological or organismic correlation. Like the relations between organisms and the external world, they may be, on the one hand, material, *i. e.*, chemical or transportative, consisting in the mass transportation of substance, or, on the other, dynamic, consisting in energy transfer, and the dynamic relations may be either mechanical or excitatory (see Chap. V).

In material or chemical correlation between parts, the part producing a substance which influences another part controls the latter to some extent. This is also true in cases in which chemical relations between the two parts are more or less mutual. Such cases are in some degree analogous to the social reaction system consisting of two groups of human beings between which mutual commercial relations exist. To take a rather primitive social system of this sort, one group for example inhabits the coast, the other an inland region. The first group exchanges fish, shell, salt, for skins, game, or perhaps for metal articles. The articles received constitute a factor in determining the further activities of the group in each case.

In purely mechanical correlation the part in which the mechanical change is initiated dominates other parts, e. g., in the muscle-skeleton correlation, the muscle is dominant. In the mechanical correlation involved in circulation of the blood the heart is dominant, but as regards particular regions vaso-motor factors exercise a certain degree of control. In other forms of mechanical correlation dominance and subordination are also concerned in some way.

The relation of dominance and subordination appears most clearly, and is most important in excitation and its transmission. The point of primary excitation is the region of primary dominance, and as each adjoining region is excited in the course of transmission it becomes dominant over regions still unexcited. If a decrement occurs in transmission so that an excitation-transmission gradient appears (see pp. 186, 195) the region of primary excitation dominates the whole gradient because it is the chief factor in determining its existence. This sort of dominance and subordination is most highly developed in the nervous system of higher animals and its relations to other parts, but is a general feature of organismic pattern, since all protoplasm is excitable and to some degree capable of transmission.

The harmonious activity of different parts or organs, particularly in the motor reactions of organisms, we call coördination. It is this coördination which gives organismic behavior its orderly and definite character. The complexity of coördination increases with the complexity of mechanism and in the higher animals and man muscular coördination, for example, is almost inconceivably complex. We know that the acts of walking, flying, swimming, necessitate the harmonious activity of many different muscles and muscle groups and that the acquirement of skill in highly specialized motor reactions, such as writing with pen or typewriter, or playing the piano or violin, really consists in the development of a greater delicacy and refinement in coördination.

The conspicuous character and importance of this harmony or coördination in reaction has perhaps tended to obscure the fact that the coördination pattern represents physiologically a system of relations of dominance and subordination. In playing the piano, for example, a relation of dominance and subordination exists, first between the sensory cells, the receptors of the eye which receive the elements of the sense impression of the notes on the printed page, and their nerve fibers which transmit the excitation; second, between the ends of these fibers and other nerve cells stimulated by them, and so on, through various parts of the central nervous system until the motor neurons, leading to the effectors, in this case the muscles, and dominating them are reached.   The coördination of parts in the reaction actually consists of relations of dominance and subordination, of control and being controlled.   The order of these relations depends in any case upon the mechanisms concerned, that is, upon the manner in which the series of relations of dominance work out in that particular organism at that particular time.   Differences in physiological state of different neurons resulting from previous relations may determine that one is dominated by a certain nerve impulse reaching it, while another is not so dominated.   In this way the

FIG. 2.—Diagram of a simple reflex arc: (*R*) receptor; (*C*) center (adjustor); (*E*) effector; (*1*) afferent neuron; (*2*) efferent neuron (from Herrick, '22).

further path of the impulse is determined. In fact it is evident that the whole reflex arc (Fig. 2) consists fundamentally in a series of relations of physiological dominance and subordination, from the receptor, the sense organ, through the conductor to the central organ the adjustor, from this again through the efferent neuron to the effector, *e. g.*, the muscle.

According to this brief analysis, the physiological factor primarily concerned in the integration of the regions or parts of an organism in organismic reaction is a relation of dominance and subordination. This dominance and subordination may be determined in one of three possible ways, *i. e.*, by mechanical correlation, by material, chemical or transportative correlation, or by excitation and its transmission.   The question of the rôle which these different sorts of dominance and subordination play in the origin of organismic pattern is considered in later chapters.

THE SPATIAL AND MORPHOLOGICAL FACTORS IN ORGANISMIC PATTERN

The fundamental spatial factors in organismic pattern are those which determine the localization and arrangement of organs and parts, and so the form of the whole.   Whatever their nature, they constitute the general spatial plan of organization which underlies development and differentiation.   The most general characteristics of spatial pattern in organisms are physiological polarity and symmetry.

Since polarity and symmetry of some sort are of wide, if not of universal occurrence among anisorgms, they must be in large measure independent of the differences in specific constitution of the different protoplasms, or else they must differ in nature in different protoplasms. In relation to polarity and symmetry there are in fact only three components of pattern in all organisms (see p. 26, Chap. VI). These are the radiate, the polar or longitudinal and the bilateral or dorsoventral. In the radiate pattern the arrangement of parts is geometrically about a point, in the polar pattern it is referable to a line and in the bilateral pattern to a plane, the so-called plane of symmetry. It is important, however, to note that physiologically a bilateral pattern may result from ventrodorsality or dorsoventrality, that is, the general direction of the order or pattern may be either ventrodorsal or dorsoventral, in other words neurohaemal, so far as animals are concerned, but since the organism is tridimensional, dorsoventral difference involves also a difference between median and lateral, and right and left sides are mirror images of each other, hence the term "bilaterality." In other words, as regards the right and left sides of the body, the primarily ventrodorsal or dorsoventral order consists of two similar components in opposite directions from the median plane, but viewed as a whole it represents only the one order.

The botanists have apparently recognized this fact more clearly than the zoölogists, perhaps because of the direct relation of the dorsoventral order in many plants to an environmental differential in one direction. In the present book the terms "bilaterality" and "bilateral symmetry" are employed in conformity with general zoölogical usage, but it is important from the physiological viewpoint to recognize the fact that bilateral pattern may be an incidental feature of a single order at right angles to the polar axis and determining primarily ventrodorsality or dorsoventrality. We very commonly refer bilateral symmetry to both a transverse and a dorsoventral axis, but though our knowledge of the physiological conditions underlying bilaterality is still far from complete, it seems to be true that the bilaterality of whole organisms is usually the result of a physiological order in one direction, a direction different from that determining the polar pattern. Obviously, however, the origin of bilaterality is possible by a direct determination of a physiological order in two opposite directions independently of, and preceding determination of a dorsoventral order. This possibility may be realized in various cases. And finally the asymmetric modifications of bilaterality result from differences in the two sides which must be determined by special conditions. These conditions may be different in different cases, but concerning them we know as yet practically nothing.

Polarity and symmetry constitute in some way the basis of the geometric order or plan of the organism. They represent, so to speak,

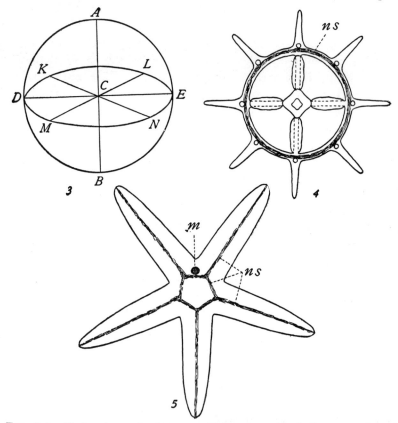

Figs. 3–5.—Various types of radiate organismic pattern: Fig. 3, diagram representing surface-interior pattern. All radii (AC), (EC), (KC), etc., are alike and the only regional differences are along the radii from surface to interior; Fig. 4, diagrammatic outline of a hydromedusa. The two radii of each diameter represent similar orders, but in opposite directions; Fig. 5, diagrammatic outline of a starfish. The two radii of each diameter represent dissimilar orders and indications of bilaterality are present in the position of the madreporite (m), and of certain internal organs. In Figs. 4 and 5 general plan of central nervous system, (ns) is indicated.

a system of coördinates to which we refer organismic pattern. The simplest conceivable organisms are those in which differences exist merely between surface and interior (Fig. 3). Such organisms are completely or spherically symmetrical, that is to say, the geometric plan of the pattern is represented by the radii of a sphere. Most organisms, however, show some degree and kind of axiate pattern

(Figs. 4–9), *i. e.*, some combination of polarity and symmetry. As regards the chief axis, axiate organisms are heteropolar, *i. e.*, the polar axis represents the direction of an order, arrangement and relation in which each level differs from all others (Figs. 4–9). The

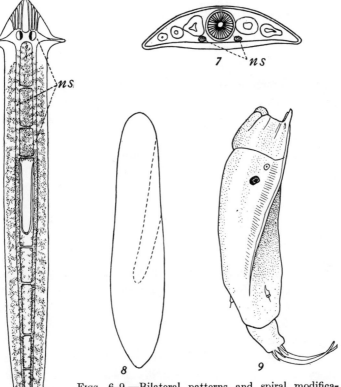

FIGS. 6–9.—Bilateral patterns and spiral modifications: Fig. 6, diagrammatic figure of *Planaria* as example of bilateral pattern, (*ns*) central nervous system (from Child, '15 c); Fig. 7, diagrammatic transverse section of *Planaria* (*ns*), longitudinal nerve cords; Fig. 8, *Paramecium* showing spiral course of oral groove; Fig. 9, a rotifer, *Diurella tigris*, showing the spiral ridge along body (from Jennings, '03).

axes of symmetry, *i. e.*, the directions in which the order constituting symmetry appears, may be either homopolar or heteropolar. They are homopolar in certain radiate forms (Fig. 4) in which the two radii of a diameter represent similar orders, but in opposite directions, *i. e.*, are mirror images of each other, and in bilateral forms in which the medio-lateral orders are likewise in mirrored relation, *i. e.*, similar, but in opposite directions (Figs. 6, 7). In certain other radiate forms the symmetry axes are heteropolar, *e. g.*, in starfish and sea urchin (Fig. 5), and the two radii of a diameter represent more or less dissimilar orders, opposite in direction. Again, the dorsoventral axis in bilateral forms is heteropolar, *i. e.*, a single order, each level differing from others (Fig. 7). And finally, there are spiral modifications of radial and bilateral pattern (Figs. 8, 9) and left and right lateral asymmetries of many different parts occur in many forms, *e. g.*, the visceral asymmetry in mammals and man.

Even if it is true that these different forms of spatial pattern are independent or largely so of the specific differences of different protoplasms, the kinds of organs and parts which appear in the pattern must depend more or less upon the specific differences. The apical end of a plant axis, for example, develops as a growing tip, the apical end of a hydra as a mouth region surrounded by a ring of tentacles. Again, in bilateral forms the anterior end may be a growing tip, as in *Marchantia*, a head, as in bilateral animals (Fig. 1). In other axes also, the working out of the pattern differs in different protoplasms. Evidently then, organisms with the same general plan may be very different in actual structure because the materials, the protoplasms, are different.

The general spatial pattern also constitutes the basis on which the relations of dominance and subordination characteristic of the particular organism develop. In the spherically symmetrical pattern there is no fixed dominance, except in so far as such a relation may arise between surface and interior. In the cell, for example, the nucleus appears to dominate the cytoplasm in certain respects, while in others it is probable that the cytoplasm, or some part of it, dominates the nucleus. Undoubtedly these relations are, in part at least, transportative or chemical, but whether a transmissive factor is concerned, we do not know. As regards the different parts of the surface there is no fixed dominance. Differential excitation may determine the dominance, now of one part, now of another.

The axiate pattern differs from this in constituting a basis for definite and fixed relations of dominance and subordination, though their range and degree may vary widely according to conditions. In the axiate plant the growing tip dominates the axis, and in the animal an apical region or head, containing the chief aggregation of nervous tissue represents the primary dominant region. The symmetry pattern also determines certain minor relations of dominance and subordination, *e. g.*, between peripheral and central in radiate forms, and between dorsal, lateral and ventral in bilateral forms. The complication of axiate pattern in the symmetrical animals, and particularly in the vertebrates, brings with it complications in the relations of dominance and subordination, and in higher vertebrates and man the nervous relations have become almost inconceivably complex. But whatever the differences in the working out of the details of pattern in different protoplasms, the general spatial pattern as expressed in polarity and symmetry, and the pattern of physiological relation, as expressed in the relation of dominance and subordination, are indissociable. In fact, as will appear, the evidence indicates that they are different aspects of the same general factor which constitutes the basis of organismic pattern in protoplasm.

ORGANISMIC PATTERN AND INDIVIDUAL ORGANISMS

From the viewpoint of this chapter, the general features of organismic pattern must be clearly distinguished from the specific morphological and physiological characteristics of individual organisms. These latter represent the working out of an organismic pattern in a specific protoplasm as material. Organismic pattern in general stands in somewhat the same relation to the individual organism as the plan of a house does to a particular house. The individual house represents the plan worked out in certain materials. Organismic pattern is what distinguishes an organism from other things. But the particular kind of organism depends not merely upon the presence of an organismic pattern but upon the specific protoplasm in which the pattern is worked out.

In the case of physiological polarity, for example, whatever we may conceive its nature to be, we believe that it is essentially similar in different organisms. If then we discover what polarity is in one sort of organisms we are justified in concluding that polarity in other organisms is similar in nature. But in each kind of organism the polarity exists in a specific protoplasm and this protoplasm determines how the polarity pattern shall work out in each particular case. The polarity does not determine whether an axiate plant or an axiate animal, or whether a particular species of plant or animal, shall arise: it merely determines a physiological axis along which the differentiations determined by the hereditary potentialities of the particular protoplasm occur.

The pattern is first of all a factor in the physiology of development, i. e., in the realization of hereditary potentialities of the particular protoplasm in which it exists. Something determines which potentialities shall be realized in each particular region of the developing organism and this something is the organismic pattern. For example, in certain liverworts, as well as various other plants, every cell is potentially able to give rise to a new growing tip and so to a whole new individual, but normally only a certain cell develops as a growing tip and the others perform other functions in an orderly way. Again in *Planaria* and various other animals, every level of the body is potentially capable of giving rise to a head, but in the normal animal the head arises only from certain cells at one end of the axis. The potentialities are given in the hereditary constitution of the protoplasm and are realized as the organismic pattern determines.

In short, the facts indicate that the specific constitutions of particular protoplasms are not the only nor the primary factors in determining the origin of the individual organism as a physiological order and integration appearing in a protoplasmic substratum. Unquestionably the constitution of the particular protoplasm determines the kind or species of individual which develops, but the real question is whether this constitution alone does or can determine that an organism shall arise. In other words, is not an organism the result of a reaction of a protoplasm to environment, and since all protoplasms give rise to organisms is not this reaction fundamentally non-specific with respect to the constitutions of particular protoplasms? An attempt to answer this question is reserved for later chapters.

CHAPTER V

THE MECHANISMS OF PHYSIOLOGICAL CORRELATION
AND THE ORGANISM AS A WHOLE

In the preceding chapter it was pointed out that the fundamental physiological characteristic of organismic pattern is a relation of dominance and subordination established by physiological correlation between parts. Physiological integration takes place on a basis of dominance and subordination or control and being controlled. Some further consideration of the various mechanisms of integration and of the part played by each is necessary.

THE FACTORS OF PHYSIOLOGICAL INTEGRATION

In physiological integration of the organism two sorts of factors are evidently concerned: differences in physiological condition or constitution in different regions or parts, *i. e.*, specialization or differentiation, and physiological correlation of one sort or another between parts. The existence of definite and orderly physiological correlation between parts depends of course on the existence of definite and orderly physiological differences in the parts concerned, however such differences may have arisen. These two factors, then, physiological differences in and physiological correlation between parts constitute "the organism as a whole." Given the pattern of the individual organism, the mechanisms which make it behave as a whole are the mechanisms of physiological correlation. The problem of the organism as a whole is the problem of the origin, development and maintenance of the mechanisms of integration in their relation to origin, development and maintenance of the individual. This is first of all a problem of physiology, not of heredity, because as we have seen, heredity does not account for the individual, but merely for the potentialities some of which are realized in the individual.

PROTOPLASMIC AND ORGANISMIC MECHANISMS OF INTEGRATION

At the risk of some repetition it seems necessary to emphasize once more the point developed in Chap. II (pp. 8–10), that the organism represents, not simply the integration which constitutes life, but an integration of living systems which differ in some way from each other, *i. e.*, an integration of different rates or kinds of living. To determine how these different sorts of life differ from each other, how the differences arise, how they are localized as different regions or parts of the organism and how they determine physiological correlation, this is to determine what the organism as a whole is.

The assertion that organismic pattern is a pattern on a larger scale than that of protoplasm (pp. 4, 8-12) is simply an assertion of this fact, that the organism is an integration of living protoplasms rather than merely the sort of integration which constitutes life. Physiological correlation in the proper sense then comprises all the physiological relations between the different living protoplasms and their products which make up the parts, organs, tissues, etc., of an organism. It obviously constitutes relation of higher order of magnitude than the relations between the components of a single protoplasmic system.

However we define life and wherever we draw the line between living and non-living, it remains true that an organism as an individual represents an integration into an orderly whole of ways of living, differing either quantitatively or qualitatively from each other. These different ways of living are given as hereditary potentialities in the so-called germ plasm out of which the individual develops, and each organism represents in its various parts the realization of certain of them. As soon as differences or parts appear, physiological correlation between them becomes possible and constitutes the mechanism of integration.

Like the relations between living protoplasm and its external environment (see pp. 12–17) the physiological relations between the different protoplasmic systems, parts, organs, etc., of an organism are either material, involving primarily the mass transportation of substance, or dynamic, involving primarily the transfer of energy. We must learn something of the forms in which these two groups of correlative factors appear in the organism and of their rôles in the process of organismic integration.

MATERIAL OR TRANSPORTATIVE CORRELATION

Material correlation includes all those relations between parts in which the essential feature is the transportation in mass of a substance or substances from one to the other or others. The manner in which the transportation occurs may differ widely in different cases, but this is a matter of detail. For example, a substance may be transported passively in solution or in suspension in a moving fluid within the body as in the case of salts, sugar, fats, etc., in the blood of animals and to some extent salts and sugar in the sap of plants. Again simple osmotic factors or more commonly the more complex condition commonly known as semi-permeability may be concerned in transportation. It is by no means necessary to assume that the substance always remains unchanged during transport. It may undergo electrolytic, dissociation or association, or it may enter chemical reaction, in fact, transportation in many cases may consist in the passage of a chemical group from molecule to molecule in a certain direction. But whatever the method of transport the essential characteristic of material correlation is that the effect produced is in some way associated with the physico-chemical constitution of the substance transferred. Certain substances may produce at least some of their correlative effects through certain generic characteristics which they share with many other substances: for example, electrolytes and their ions may produce correlative effects of electrolytic or ionic character quite apart from their chemical constitution; CO_2 as well as many other substances may produce effects through change in the hydrogen-ion concentration. Various substances may alter surface tension, water content, colloidal dispersion, etc., and so bring about correlative effects in a generic rather than in a specific way.

In many other cases there is a greater degree of specificity in material or transportative correlation, and the effect produced is apparently in some way related to the chemical constitution of the substance transported. The products of the glands of internal secretion, e. g., the thyroid, the adrenals, etc., are commonly regarded as examples of this sort of transportative correlation, i. e., so-called chemical correlation. Such substances known or postulated are now often called hormones, i. e., substances which arouse, activate, or set in motion something, viz., a physiological process. The researches of recent years have shown that chemical correlation of this specific sort is of very great importance and complexity in the higher animals and man, and some physiologists have been inclined to regard it as the fundamental factor in physiological integration. Sach's theory of formative substances and its later modifications in the hands of Loeb, Morgan, Conklin and others are essentially theories of physiological integration which either assert or imply the fundamental importance of chemical correlation in embryonic or regulatory development. Ritter ('19, Chaps. XVIII–XX) is also inclined to regard material correlation as the primary factor in organismic integration.

Concerning the importance in physiological integration of material or transportative correlation in general and of those forms of it commonly called chemical correlation there can be no possible doubt. In general the specificity and complexity of this sort of correlation undoubtedly increase with the increase in number and specialization of different organs and tissues, and are therefore greatest in the higher animals and man. Many facts also indicate that the specificity and complexity of chemical correlation increase in the course of individual development. It is not difficult to understand how this comes about: increase in degree and complexity of specialization of organs and tissues means a more highly specific chemical constitution of each; with this is associated more highly specific metabolic reactions and products; and finally these factors must be concerned in determining a higher degree of specificity of chemical correlation between organs and parts of the highly specialized species or stages.

These facts in themselves are highly significant with respect to the rôle of transportative correlation in physiological integration.

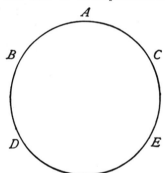

They show clearly enough that transportative correlation depends first of all upon the existence of differences of some sort in the parts concerned. If we conceive the organism as a physico-chemical system we cannot doubt that specific chemical correlation between certain parts depends upon the existence of specific differences in those parts. The specific substance transported must be produced in one or certain of them and produce certain effects in others. Moreover, if this sort of correlation is orderly and definite in character as it is in organisms, the differences on which it depends must be orderly and definite. Such differences cannot originate through transportation of a substance because if all parts are alike all will produce the same substances in the same amounts. To illustrate by a simple diagram (Fig. 10), transportative correlation exists between A on the one hand and B and C on the other. A must be different from B and C: it must represent to some extent a different organ or tissue. Simi-

Fig. 10.—Diagram illustrating the basis of transportative correlation. Specific transportative correlation between the different regions (A–E) or between any two of them, is possible only after specific differences have arisen between the regions concerned.

larly if transportative correlations exist between B and E and between C and D all four of these regions must be different from each other in some way, otherwise definite relations would be impossible. Moreover, as noted above, transportative correlation as we find it in the organism differs in order of magnitude from the physico-chemical relations between molecules or chemical groups which constitute life in a protoplasmic system. It is not merely the process of living in such a system but it is a material relation between different protoplasmic, cellular or multicellular systems in which the process of living is different in some way (pp. 8–12).

It is clear then that transportative correlation cannot exist until the different systems are present, that is to say until the organismic pattern has appeared, therefore it cannot originate such pattern. The flow in opposite directions of stem-forming and root-forming substances postulated by Sachs for plants cannot occur autonomously, but becomes possible only when regional differences of some sort are present which determine such flow. Such differences may conceivably be either inherent, or determined by external conditions, but in any case they are more fundamental factors than the hypothetical substances in determining the pattern of the plant. The segregation of substances in the animal egg, or along the axis of the animal organism must be determined by preëxisting differences of some sort in the different regions. Hormone relations between parts are possible only when the parts are already different. There is in fact no escape from the conclusion that transportative correlation as a material correlation between living systems cannot of itself originate organismic pattern, but is itself a consequence of the existence of such pattern. The basis of that pattern must be some factor, either inherent or external, which is able to determine in an orderly and definite way in a protoplasm, a cell, or a cell mass the regional differences in the rate or kind of the processes of living on which material correlation depends. Only through the origin of such regional quantitative or qualitative differences can an actual organism arise, and transportative correlation in the organism is an incident and consequence of the fundamental organismic pattern.

DYNAMIC CORRELATION

Dynamic correlation involves primarily the transfer or transmission of energy rather than the mass transport of material. Transport of ions or of electrons from one molecule or atom to another must of course occur in various forms of dynamic correlation, but such transport differs in process and effect from the mass transport of substances. In dynamic correlation the essential factor is the energy, while in material correlation it is the particular substance. Of course various substances transported in the body serve as sources of energy, but the energy is liberated in these cases through chemical reaction after they have been transported to certain parts of the body, while dynamic correlation is initiated by an energy change and this change is then transmitted in one way or another.

Dynamic correlation in the organism is accomplished chiefly in two ways: through the direct mechanical transmission by pressure or tension of mechanical changes; and through the transmission of excitation. Of course transmission or conduction of other forms of energy, heat, light, electricity, may occur in living protoplasms, and be of some correlative significance. The conduction of heat, for example, is important in maintaining and regulating body-temperature. The transmission of light through the refractive apparatus of the eye makes vision possible. Conduction of electricity is probably occurring in all living organisms at all times. But the chief importance of these forms of energy as correlative factors lies in their relation to excitation and its transmission. All forms of energy may bring about excitation in living protoplasm and the chief significance to the organism of all except mechanical energy is as excitatory agents, *i. e.*, as factors initiating energy changes of definite character in the living system. It is true, therefore, even though transmission or conduction of any form of energy may occur in protoplasms, that dynamic correlation in the organism is chiefly either mechanical or excitatory and transmissive in character.

Mechanical and transmissive correlation.—Purely mechanical correlation consists in pressure and tension. In such correlation the source of the energy involved is wholly external to the part affected. This behaves as inert body in accordance with the laws of mechanics. For example, in development change of shape of a part may be brought about mechanically by the pressure of other parts upon it, or by tension of growth. Again, movements of parts by means of muscles represent primarily mechanical correlation. Mechanical correlation, as the term is used here, means merely the mechanical factor in physiological correlation. Any mechanical correlation may have nonmechanical, as well as mechanical effects. The effects of pressure and tension on living parts are not purely mechanical, but may include changes in the protoplasmic system itself. Nevertheless, the purely mechanical factors constitute so definite a feature of correlation and are so widely different from the factors of excitation and transmission that the distinction is useful.

Excitation and transmission differ from mechanical correlation in that they involve reversible or partly reversible changes in the energy relations between components of the protoplasmic system. Since all protoplasms are highly complex physico-chemical systems in which the various changes are closely interrelated, alteration of the energy relations of the system results in general, either in excitation, an acceleration, or in inhibition, a retardation of living. In these changes the external factor merely initiates and the result is determined primarily by the energy relations within the protoplasm, not by the energy of the external factor. For present purposes excitation rather than inhibition is of primary importance.

All living protoplasms are irritable or excitable to some degree, both by various extra-protoplasmic dynamic factors and by the dynamic factor concerned in excitation of an adjoining protoplasmic region. The excitation of one protoplasmic region by another in continuity with it constitutes physiological transmission of excitation. Undoubtedly the changes which constitute excitation differ to some extent in different protoplasms and perhaps in the same protoplasm under different conditions. The relations between chemical reactions, e. g., the oxidations, and physical changes in excitation may differ widely in different protoplasms, and it is not at all improbable that the primary change which brings about excitation differs in different protoplasms or even in the same protoplasm with different exciting factors. But in spite of such differences it is clear that excitation in general involves acceleration in certain changes which liberate energy in living systems, and in a broad sense it may be regarded as an accelleration of livnig. Excitation rather than inhibition is important in correlation because from what has been said it appears that so far as known inhibition is not transmitted as such. The existence of inhibitory nervous correlation is of course a familiar fact, but in such cases the inhibitory effect is apparently produced, not by transmission of an inhibitory change, but by transmission of an excitation and the mechanism of the final inhibitory effect is still obscure.

Dynamic correlation in relation to organismic pattern. — As regards the part played by dynamic correlation in physiological integration, it is evident at once that transmission of excitation is far more important than purely mechanical correlation. Mechanical correlation may be a factor in determining shape and position of various parts, and as already pointed out, it is an essential feature in motor reactions, but it is evident that a definite and orderly mechanical correlation, such as we find in organisms, is dependent upon the existence of definite and orderly organismic pattern in which differences of mechanical condition exist at different points. In the function of motor organs generally, from cilia and flagella to the complex musculoskeletal systems of the higher animals, mechanical correlation is an essential factor, but the correlation is a result of the pattern and has nothing to do with its origin. Again, mechanical relations of pressure and tension may affect growth and differentiation, though their action in such cases is not directly mechanical, but rather a matter of excitation or inhibition. The internal structure of bone, the direction of connective tissue fibers in tendons, apparently also the differentiation of muscle, if Carey's conclusions are correct (Carey, '20, '21), are determined by reactions of living protoplasm to relations of pressure and tension and similar reactions are undoubtedly concerned in many other differentiations. In these cases, as in purely mechanical correlation, the mechanical relations which determine the growth and differentiation are themselves determined by the organismic pattern. The mechanical relations of differential growth are possible only when different parts have been determined and are growing in an orderly way. In short, mechanical correlation though obviously a factor of great importance in motor behavior, and also concerned in growth and differentiation is, like material or transportative correlation, a secondary factor in organismic integration.

It remains to determine whether the other form of dynamic correlation, the transmission of excitation, will throw any further light upon the problem of physiological integration. In the first place attention was called above to the fact that all living protoplasms are to some extent excitable by external factors and capable of transmission of such excitation. Although the processes of excitation and transmission may differ in details in different protoplasms, excitation and transmission are, generically speaking, non-specific in the sense that they occur in some form in all protoplasms independently of their differences in constitution. Second, the only pattern necessary for the occurrence of excitation and transmission is the pattern of a protoplasm with a limiting surface in contact with environment. Preëxisting physiological axes and differentiation of different regions are entirely unessential. Excitation is primarily a reaction of a living protoplasm to an external dynamic factor and transmissive correlation is the excitation of one protoplasmic region by another. In other words, the regional physiological differences which make transmissive correlation possible arise through the local action of an external factor. If we imagine a living protoplasmic system without any regional pattern of organismic magnitude except a limiting surface, which is merely that part of the protoplasm in contact with the external world and completely reversible, it is evident that local excitation of such a system at any point such as *A* (Fig. 11) introduces a differential not previously present. The region *A* as an excited region excites adjoining regions and transmission occurs to *B* and *C*, and if the decrement is not too steep, to *D* and *E* or still further.

The presence or absence, or the steepness of decrement in the degree or the intensity of the excitatory change in the course of transmission depends upon the constitution of the particular protoplasm concerned. It is apparently true, however, that in most if not in all protoplasms in which specialized conducting paths are not present, such a decrement appears, so that the range of effectiveness of transmission is limited. In such a primitive transmission process points at different distances (*B* and *D*, or *C* and *E*, Fig. 11) from the point *A* of the origin of the excitation will show different degrees of excitatory change, decreasing from *A* to a point at a greater or less distance from *A* at which it ceases to be effective in producing further transmission. The result of the excitation at *A* is then an excitation-

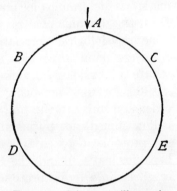

Fig. 11.—Diagram illustrating the basis of transmissive correlation. For the occurrence of transmissive correlation preëxistent differences between any of the regions (*A–E*) are not necessary. Excitation of some point (*A*) determines the differential which initiates transmission.

transmission gradient of greater or less length, the different levels of which represent different degrees or intensities of excitation.

Moreover, *A* being the region of primary excitation is to some degree physiologically dominant over other regions (*B*, *C*, etc.), to which the excitation is transmitted, because through this transmission it has more effect upon them than they upon it.

There is no escape from the conclusion that the excitation of *A* and the transmission of this excitation to a greater or less distance gives rise, at least momentarily, to a new organismic pattern. The region of primary excitation, *A*, becomes the dominant region and other regions B–E within the range of the transmissive correlation become subordinated to it. Before the excitation occurred at A such pattern was not present, nor represented in any way in the protoplasmic system. The potentiality of excitation and transmission was of course present, but this in itself could not determine the pattern which results from excitation at A. Here then the action of an external factor is necessary for the realization in the form of a definite physiological pattern of the potentialities of the protoplasmic system. Moreover, such a pattern cannot possibly arise in the first instance except through the local or differential action of an external factor.

Such an excitation-transmission pattern possesses all the fundamental characteristics of a new organismic pattern in the protoplasmic mass. It determines localized differences at different points, A, B, D, in the dynamic changes constituting life, these differences determine physiological correlation between the different regions with A as the dominant region and these differences and relations constitute a physiological axis with A as one pole. This pattern constitutes for the time being a new physiological integration, a new order and unity in the protoplasmic mass, and this new integration is determined, not by heredity, but arises as a reaction of the living protoplasm to environmental factors. In other words, it is a behavior pattern and the most primitive behavior pattern which can arise in a living protoplasmic system. Only the potentiality of excitation and transmission is determined by heredity in the protoplasm. The actual excitation-transmission pattern arising in any particular protoplasmic mass is a matter of the behavior of that mass in a particular environment.

There can be no question then that pattern of organismic character and magnitude can arise at least temporarily through excitatory reaction of a protoplasm to an environment. Such a pattern is obviously a behavior pattern, even though in the absence of specialized mechanisms it does not lead to movement or other directly visible reaction. If such an excitation-transmission gradient is able to bring about more or less persistent changes in the protoplasm it may become the starting point of a permanent physiological axis and so of the pattern of an axiate organism. In following chapters it will appear that the physiological axes in their simplest terms are very similar to, if not identical with such excitation-transmission gradients and that they may arise through the non-specific differential action of external factors.

THE PROBLEM OF THE ORIGIN OF DIFFERENTIATION

We have seen that physiological correlation and the integration which constitutes the organism as a whole are impossible without the existence of orderly and definite differences, either quantitative or qualitative, in different regions and parts of the organism. Such differences are characteristic features of organisms and individual development appears to consist in the localization and progressive specification of such differences and the progressive complication of mechanisms of correlation between the different parts. In Chapter III it was pointed out that current theories of heredity do not provide any basis for the process of differentiation in individual development. If we accept these theories, differentiation in the individual must apparently originate in the action of external factors upon the protoplasm. External factors may conceivably act directly and specifically, determining specific differentiations in the parts acted upon, or they may produce non-specific or quantitative effects. In the latter case specific or qualitative differentiations can result only indirectly from their action.

Examination of the specific material relations between protoplasm and the external world indicates that such relations do not play any considerable rôle, if any rôle at all, in directly localizing and initiating differentiation. For example, we do not usually find that a region of a cell or a cell of a group, into which a specific substance enters from the exterior, is thereby made specifically different from other regions or cells. If the specific substance is nutritive in character, it is either broken down and parts of it are synthesized into the protoplasm of the species, or it becomes a source of energy. In either case it loses its specific character without determining a persistent specific differentiation in the part entered by it. A specific substance may of course produce excitation, but this is not a specific effect for that substance: again, it may be toxic, but the action of toxic agents is certainly not of great importance in initiating differentiation of parts in the individual. There may be cases of the origin of specific differences in organismic pattern through specific differences in the material relations of different regions or cells with environment, but it is evident that organismic pattern in general does not originate in such manner. Even if specific differences do arise in this way in a protoplasmic region, a cell, or a cell group, we find in general that the specific substances are gradually distributed to other regions, cells, or cell groups. Certainly the localized entry of specific substances is not of fundamental importance as a direct factor in originating the specific regional differentiations of organismic pattern.

Gravity may conceivably be a factor in distributing and localizing specifically different substances on a basis of weight and so in initiating differentiation. The question of the relation of gravity to differentiation in organisms has been the subject of much investigation and discussion. It has long been known that in many plants the localization of regions of outgrowth of roots and stems may be determined in part by gravity. Loeb ('91) has maintained that localization of regions of outgrowth of stem-axes and of stolon-axes is determined by gravity in the hydroid *Antennularia*, but the later work of Morgan ('01) and Stevens ('02, '10) has shown at least that other factors than gravity may determine this localization. Moreover, a similar localizing action of gravity has not been observed in other animals.

The localizing action of gravity in plants appears to be a general predisposing rather than a definitely localizing action. It may favor or determine outgrowth of roots or rhizoids in a certain general region of the plant and of shoots in another region, but so far as is known it does not determine the localization or the polarity of individual root axes or bud axes. For example, in a piece of willow stem as well as various other plants in horizontal position gravity favors development of roots on the under side and of shoots on the upper side, but although the action of gravity on all the cells along the mid line of the lower side must be the same, not all these cells give arise to roots, nor do all the cells of the mid line of the upper side give rise to shoots. In *Bryophyllum* also gravity does not determine buds nor root-forming regions, but merely favors the growth of preformed buds on the upper side of a stem and the development of roots from predetermined root-forming regions on the lower side. In certain plants which normally lie flat on the earth, *e. g.* certain liverworts, and in certain branches growing horizontally, gravity may determine the normal dorsoventrality.

It is by no means clear how gravity brings about such localizing effects in plants. Loeb ('19, '20) postulates an action on the distribution of sap in the case of *Bryophyllum* and a distribution or segregation of substances of some sort is commonly regarded as underlying such action. It is, however, a question of some interest whether the effect of gravity is the direct determination of specific material differences representing, for example, shoot and root as Loeb apparently assumes, or a determination of non-specific dynamic condition. Segregation of inert substances in one region, for example, may determine a decrease in rate of dynamic change in the region in which the substances accumulate, and an increase in the region from which they are removed. If the distribution of the sap in the plant is directly influenced by gravity as Loeb assumes, the significance of the distribution may be dyanmic rather than material and specific. In fact there is no conclusive evidence that the effect of gravity on organismic pattern is exerted by localization of specific "formative" materials. So far as the facts go such distributing or segregating action of gravity may equally well be regarded as merely a physical basis for non-specific dynamic differences. The fact that light is far more effective than gravity in determining polarity and symmetry in plants is also significant in relation to the dynamic conception of organismic pattern.

In the light of these considerations it appears at least doubtful whether specific material differences in constitution of different protoplasmic regions are in any case primary factors in organic pattern. Moreover, if they were, we should expect to find axial relations even more diverse than in crystal forms, instead of only the three fundamental types of relation, radiate, polar, and bilateral as the basis of all spatial and regional organismic pattern.

Even more convincing than these general considerations are the data of reconstitution of new individuals from parts of others. Such processes as the development of whole embryos from one of the first two or four cells of the dividing egg, of whole animals from small fragments of the bodies of hydroids, flatworms, etc., are not readily accounted for in terms of specific material pattern. Either Driesch is right in turning to vitalism for an interpretation, or else these processes must be interpreted in terms of a dynamic pattern, primarily quantitative, rather than in terms of specific materials. That is to say, the pattern originates in the first instance as a dynamic differential of degree, rather than of kind, e. g., an excitation-transmission gradient resulting from the local or differential action of an external factor and the specific material differentiations result secondarily from the regional differences in relation of the specific constitution of the protoplasm to the dynamic pattern. To sum up, the evidence points clearly to a non-specific, dynamic factor as the most important factor in the origin of organismic pattern. Excitation is such a factor and I have already pointed out (pp. 50–52) that local or differential excitation gives rise, at least temporarily, to an organismic pattern. The question whether such an excitation-transmission pattern may become more or less permanent and constitute a physiological axis and a basis for differentiation is considered in later chapters.

CHAPTER VI

THE SIGNIFICANCE OF ORGANISMIC PATTERN IN THE BEHAVIOR OF INDIVIDUALS

It is of course evident that for any sort of behavior of the organism as a whole some kind of integrative pattern must be present. The behavior of the organism as a whole must result first from the pattern already present and second from the possibilities of further development and integration in response to particular external factors which the pattern presents. The excito-motor behavior pattern at any given moment may be only one of an indefinite number of such patterns possible on the basis of the general pattern of the organism, and its particular character may depend on many different factors besides the general pattern, *e. g.*, the localization, intensity, duration, form of energy, etc., of the external agent and the physiological condition or state of the organism as determined by the effects of preceding or simultaneous reactions. Before attempting to analyze organismic pattern in general it seems desirable to call attention to its relation to the behavior of the organism as a whole, particularly excito-motor behavior. In Chapter IV it was pointed out that the fundamental integrative relation of physiological character is a relation of dominance and subordination and that this relation may appear in three spatial patterns, the completely radiate or spherically symmetrical, the polar, and the bilateral, and in various combinations and modifications of these. The present chapter is a very brief and fragmentary consideration of the significance of these fundamental factors of organismic pattern as a basis of behavior patterns in the organism.

DOMINANCE AND SUBORDINATION IN REACTION

It scarcely need be repeated that the physiological relation of dominance and subordination between different parts of the organism lies at the very foundation of orderly and definite reaction of the organism as a whole to its environment. In its absence such reaction would be quite impossible, there would be no reflex arcs, no coördination, and any reaction of the organism as a whole could be referred only to some sort of preëstablished harmony or to some metaphysical integrating principle, such as Driesch's entelechy. This possibility of one molar region of a cell or a cell mass determining what shall occur in another region at a greater or less distance from it, underlies all except perhaps the simplest processes of reaction to environment, those in which reaction is apparently limited to the region directly affected by the external factor. Even in such cases, however, there is probably some transmission or transport from the region primarily concerned to others. In fact, as soon as regional differences in excitation or in chemical constitution arise in protoplasm the relation of dominance and subordination appears in some form. It is an essential physiological factor in making the organism an orderly and integrated whole capable of behaving as a unit with reference to its environment.

SURFACE-INTERIOR PATTERN

The spatial plan of the organism is obviously a factor in its behavior as an organism. The spherically symmetrical organism behaves in general differently from the axiate-radiate form and this again differently from the axiate-bilateral form and the spiral and asymmetric modifications also affect behavior in one way or another.

In the case of a spherically symmetrical organism, if an external factor acts locally on a part of the surface or differentially on different parts of the surface, the reaction of the organism must either be purely local on that part of the surface directly affected or else it must give rise to an axiate pattern, which may be either temporary or permanent. The purely local reaction, if it ever occurs, is not organismic in character and needs no consideration here. With the appearance of an axiate pattern, even if only temporarily, the organism, if motile, may move toward, or away from the external factor, or if not motile it may show a differential in growth rate or other processes with respect to the external factor.

The case of *Amœba* will serve for illustration. So far as we know, *Amœba* possesses no fixed, permanent axiate pattern, but as a whole is essentially a spherically symmetrical organism. Consequently all regions of the surface are primarily alike and any region may react like any other by giving rise to a pseudopod or by retracting pseudopods already present. Any region of the surface may become temporarily an "anterior" end, and when the animal reacts to an external factor by change in direction of movement the body does not turn about so that the same region is in advance in the new direction, but another region becomes the chief region of pseudopod extension, and so functionally anterior (Fig. 12). Hyman ('17) has found that each pseudopod of *Amœba* possesses for the time being the graded quantitative differences characteristic of a simple physiological axis. The pseudopod represents then a temporary axiate pattern. In the physiological condition or species often called *Amœba limax* in which the whole body is advancing in one direction and the anterior region is a single blunt pseudopod (Fig. 13), the whole body has acquired, for the time being, an axiate pattern. Such a pattern is also present to some degree, though less distinct and perhaps not involving the whole body, in many individuals advancing in a definite direction with pseudopod extension chiefly or only in the general direction of movement (Fig. 14). But even in such cases the protoplasm may change its position with respect to the pattern, so that the anterior end or any other level of the axis represents a physiological condition, not a definite region or portion of the protoplasm. In those forms which advance by means of a rolling movement, a particular region of the ectoplasm, as indicated by particles adhering to it, occupies successively every level from anterior to posterior and then from posterior to anterior (Fig. 15). In all these cases the axiate pattern persists for the time being, but the material changes position from moment to moment. In *Amœba*, however, even the axiate patterns are not permanent, but are merely reactions to differentials in certain environmental factors. They are in fact very evidently behavior patterns in the strict sense, excito-motor patterns, in protoplasm as material and as the action of the external factors changes they undergo change. An axis in a new direction may replace the earlier axis, or the axiate pattern may give place to radiate pattern. Apparently the only sort of organismic pattern that persists in *Amœba* is the surface-interior pattern, and all the other patterns are temporary functional modifications of this primary pattern. They represent, in short, the various possibilities of behavior on the basis of a surface-interior pattern in certain kinds of protoplasm.[1]

The egg or spore of the alga *Fucus* evidently consists of a very different kind of protoplasm from that of *Amœba*, for it gives rise to a multicellular plant, and its behavior when subjected to the differential action of an external factor, viz., light, is strikingly different from that of *Amœba*. Whether or not this egg possesses physiological polarity at the time of extrusion from the parent plant is uncertain. There is no structural or functional indication of such polarity and under the usual conditions in nature the axis of the thallus to which

[1] See Herrick's discussion of the behavior of *Amœba*, Herrick,' 24, Chap. VI.

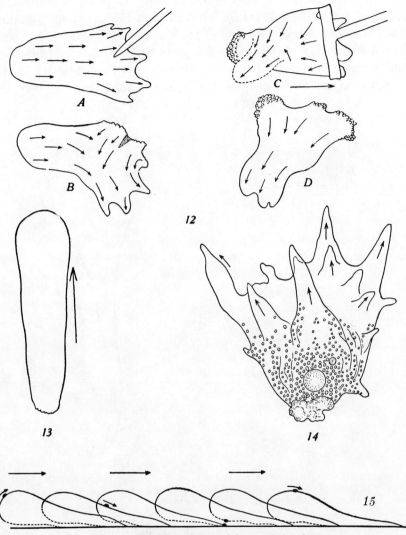

FIGS. 12–15.—Reactions and forms of *Amœba*.

FIG. 12A–D.—Negative reaction of *Amœba* to a mechanical stimulus: (*A*) and (*B*) reaction in which the change in direction is about ninety degrees; (*C*) and (*D*), reaction in which the change in direction is greater than ninety degrees (from Jennings, '04).

FIG. 13.—*Amœba limax*, a physiologically axiate form.

FIG. 14.—*Amœba angulata* advancing in general direction of the arrows. The body as a whole is temporarily axiate, but axiation is less highly developed than in *A. limax* shown in Fig. 13 (from Jennings, '04).

FIG. 15.—A rolling *Amœba, A. verrucosa*. The positions of the black dot indicate the movements of a particle attached to the surface (from Jennings, '04).

the egg gives rise has, at least in some species, no relation to any such polarity, but is determined by incident light (Farmer and Williams, '98; Winkler, '00 b; Küster, '06; Kniep, '07; Hurd, '19, '20). The first division of the egg, which gives rise to a larger thallus cell and a smaller rhizoid cell, occurs with cell wall perpendicular to the direction of incident light and the region toward the light becomes

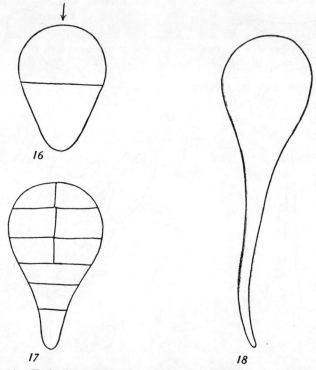

FIGS. 16–18.—Early development of the alga, *Fucus:* Fig. 16, outgrowth of rhizoid and first division of egg. Direction of light indicated by arrow; Fig. 17, stage of several cells; Fig. 18, many celled young thallus with rhizoid.

the apical pole, the region away from the light the basal, or rhizoid pole of the thallus (Figs. 16–18). In the absence of light development is delayed, but a polarity may appear sooner or later. Whether such polarity represents a polarity predetermined from the parent plant or a polarity determined by some other external factor than light is uncertain. Hurd ('19) has found that external factors other than light may determine the polarity of these eggs. When groups of eggs lie within 0.2 mm. of each other the apical poles of the members are determined on the side away from the center of the group, the rhizoid poles on the side toward the center. It is not known what factor is concerned in these cases.

This cell either possesses only a surface-interior pattern when it leaves the parent plant, or any polarity it may have is usually replaced by a new one. If the cell is exposed to light of a certain minimum intensity for a certain minimum time the action of light determines, not a transitory differential excitation with directed locomotion, as in *Amœba*, but a new axiate organismic pattern which persists and determines growth and form of the plant throughout its life. The appearance of this new axiate pattern and its consequences are just as truly behavior as is the directed locomotion of the *Amœba* in reaction to light. The *Fucus* egg possesses a certain organismic pattern when it leaves the parent plant, but it is subjected to the differential action, that is, it undergoes a new experience. To this experience it reacts by the development of an axiate pattern which persists and becomes an important physiological factor in the further behavior of the individual. Here then the later reactions of the plant are modified by the effect of its reaction when first exposed to light after extrusion from the parent plant. The change of pattern determined in the cell by its primary reaction to light becomes an essential physiological factor in determining its later behavior.

Something of the same sort must occur in every case of modification of behavior by a previous reaction. The earlier reaction must have determined changes of some sort in the pattern, which persist and so become a factor in determining the character of later reactions. Such determination of polarity by incident light in *Fucus*, or in any other plant (see for example Stahl, '85; Noll, '00; Winkler, '00 a), even though it does not result in locomotion and its effects are to a considerable extent morphological, represents the behavior of a certain kind of pattern in a certain kind of protoplasm, no less than the movement of *Amœba* away from the light. Both are reactions to an external factor and in both the kind of reaction depends primarily upon the constitution of the protoplasm and the pattern which it already possesses.

POLAR PATTERN

In organisms in which an axiate pattern is already present at the beginning of embryonic development, however it may have arisen, it becomes a factor in the later behavior. In general in sessile forms the apical end of the polar axis is the free end and the dominant region of the body. This is true both of the growing tip in plants and of the apical region in sessile animals, so far as data are at hand. In hydroids the relations of dominance and subordination between the different parts of the colony are apparently much the same as in plants (Child, '19 b). In both the plants and many sessile animals new axes may arise by budding and each axis becomes the basis of an axiate behavior pattern which is subject to more or less modification by the relation of any particular axis to the other axes of the system. In the conifer, for example, the growing tip of the lateral branch reacts differently from the tip of the main stem. It grows in a more or less horizontal direction and is in most forms more or less bilaterally sym-

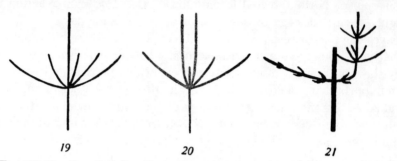

19   20   21

Figs. 19–21.—Reaction of conifer to removal of growing tip: Fig. 19, apical region of fir with young lateral branches forming a whorl about main axis; Fig. 20, main tip has been removed and two of young lateral branches have turned upward. One or both will replace main stem; Fig. 21, reaction in an older branch. Lower part of branch developed before removal of tip retains the bilateral form and the direction of a lateral branch, but later growth occurs in vertical direction and this part of branch is radially symmetrical and continues growth as the main axis while other branches which do not change direction of growth retain bilaterality.

metrical or dorsoventral, *i. e.*, secondary branches arise only laterally on it. If, however, the growing tip of the main stem is removed the action of the uppermost lateral branch or branches undergoes change. The direction of growth becomes vertical instead of horizontal and the branch becomes radially instead of bilaterally symmetrical (Figs. 19–21). Experimental data along this line for the hydroids are not yet at hand, but many facts indicate that the relations in the hydroid colony are essentially similar. As regards the corals, however, some facts are known. Wood-Jones ('12, pp. 82–83, 111–116) has shown that in the staghorn coral the relations are very similar to those in the plant axis. The apical zooid is dominant, radially symmetrical and gives rise by budding to the bilaterally symmetrical lateral zooids which do not bud at all under ordinary conditions. But if the apical zooid is removed or if the branch attains a certain length, one or more of the lateral zooids may transform into a dominant apical zooid and become the tip of a new branch, changing its symmetry in the process from bilateral to radial and beginning to bud.

In some forms the polar pattern of the earlier stages may disappear and give place to another. In many hydroids, for example, the apical end of the free swimming planula (Fig. 22) becomes the attached end of the hydroid and the new apical end develops as a bud from the original basal end (Figs. 23, 24). Discussion of the physiological factors concerned is postponed, but it may be noted that in both the planula and the later hydroid the polar pattern constitutes the basis of the behavior pattern, though the reaction complex is different in the two stages.

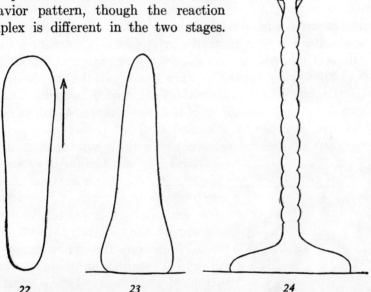

22 23 24

Figs. 22–24.—Development of hydroid from planula of *Phialidium:* Fig. 22, free swimming planula, locomotion in direction of arrow; Fig. 23, attachment of planula by original apical end; Fig. 24, development of hydranth as a bud from original basal end of planula.

The planula swims with apical end in advance and finally becomes attached by this end, while the hydranth which arises from the basal end of the planula reacts to external factors by movement, extension and contraction of tentacles and body.

Among animals the axiate radiate pattern appears in two chief modifications; the cœlenterate (Figs. 4, p. 38, 24) and the echinoderm types (Figs. 5, p. 38, 25–32, pp. 65–67). The apico-basal axis determines certain relations to external factors in position and locomotion and the radiate symmetry becomes the basis of other relations. In the sea anemone, the hydroid (Fig. 24), or the jellyfish (Fig. 4) any region of the circumference, *e. g.*, any tentacle, which is directly excited by an external factor, such as contact with food in the case of the tentacle, may become for the time being dominant over all other regions of the circumference and determine their behavior. Such a relation arises when food is caught by one or a few tentacles. The excitation of these tentacles brings about a coördinate reaction of adjoining or even of all tentacles, which assist in holding the food and in carrying it to the mouth which also reacts as a subordinate component of the system. At another time another tentacle or tentacle group may be the dominant component. In certain unattached sea anemones which are able to creep about (*e. g.*, the *Cerianthidæ*) there are indications of a bilateral differential in the radiate pattern. The creeping surface is in a particular radius and the structure shows indications of bilaterality with respect to this radius. Certain other traces of bilaterality appear in other forms. In the free-swimming jellyfish the apico-basal, polar pattern determines locomotion in the direction of the axis, but the chief radii are equivalent and, as in the sea anemone, any one may become temporarily dominant over all other regions of the circumference. In the scyphomedusæ *Aurelia* (Romanes, '93), *Cassiopea xamachana* (Mayer, '06, '08, '16) a nervous impulse may originate in any one of the marginal sense organs which is excited, and may pass around the umbrella in both directions. Moreover, the initiation of impulses from a sense organ is rhythmic and that particular organ which is most excited at a given time has the most rapid rhythm. Therefore it becomes for the time being the pacemaker for all the other marginal organs and so determines the rhythm of contraction of the whole umbrella. In this physiological equivalence of different radii the radiate component of cœlenterate pattern is somewhat similar to the *Amœba* pattern, in that different radii may be dominant at different times.

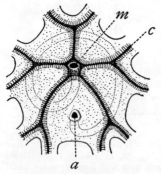

Fig. 25.—Oral area of a crinoid, *Antedon*, with bases of arms: (*m*), mouth; (*a*), anus; (*c*), ciliated grooves leading from arms to mouth (from Hertwig, '05).

Among the echinoderms various combinations of radiate and bilateral pattern exist and with these are associated interesting differences in behavior. In the crinoid (Fig. 25), for example, the disc shows a certain degree of structural bilaterality, but there is complete or practically complete physiological equivalence of the different arm radii in reaction. In the free crinoids locomotion may occur in the direction of any radius.

As regards the starfishes, both asteroids and ophiurids, most authors state that there is no preferential use of the rays related

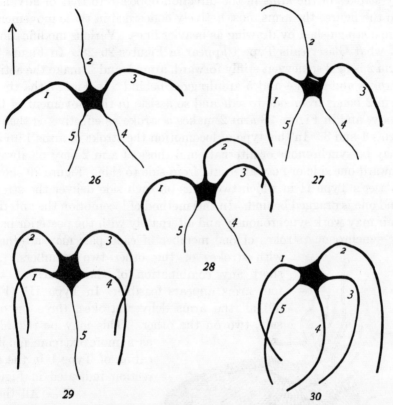

FIGS. 26–30.—Diagrams showing different patterns with respect to use of arms in locomotion of ophiurid starfish, *Ophiura brevispina*. The arms most active in locomotion in each case are indicated by heavier lines and direction of locomotion by arrow (from Glaser, '07).

definitely to the structural bilaterality, but Cole ('13) has found that in *Asterias forbesii* a certain ray is physiologically anterior. This ray corresponds to the anterior ambulacrum of the spatangoids in which structural bilaterality is more highly developed (see below). In general the preferential function of one arm as anterior appears to be absent or not very strongly marked in the starfishes and any one of the arms may precede in locomotion. The variability of behavior of the arms in locomotion determines different results in different individuals and in the same individual at different times.[1] The process of locomotion in the brittle star, as described by Glaser ('07), will serve as an illustration. The various ways in which the arms are used in locomotion are indicated in Figures 26–30 taken from Glaser's account. Locomotion over a surface is accomplished in these animals by strokes of the arms in the direction opposite to that of advance. In the figures the arms most actively concerned in these movements are distinguished by drawing as heavier lines. Various modifications of what Glaser calls Type I appear in Figures 26–28. In Figure 26 arm 2 is held somewhat stiffly forward, arms 1 and 3 make the active strokes and arms 4 and 5 are dragged behind. In Fig. 27 the tip of arm 2 bends from side to side and so assists in the movement of the body, and in Figure 28 arm 2 makes a stroke as effective as that of arms 1 and 3. In this type of locomotion the stroke of arms 1 and 3 may be synchronous or alternate and those of arm 2 may be always toward one side or may alternate from side to side. Figure 29 shows Glaser's Type II in which two arms on each side deliver the stroke and one is dragged behind. In this method of locomotion the anterior pair may work synchronously and alternately with the posterior pair, or synchronous strokes of one member of each pair may alternate with strokes of the other two members. In short any combination of the strokes of the four arms appears feasible. In Type III (Fig. 30) all the arms deliver strokes, three on one side, two on the other. This may be regarded as a more extreme modification of Type I in the direction indicated in Figure 28. All these various methods of locomotion may vary in details, such as the rate or strength of stroke of different arms or

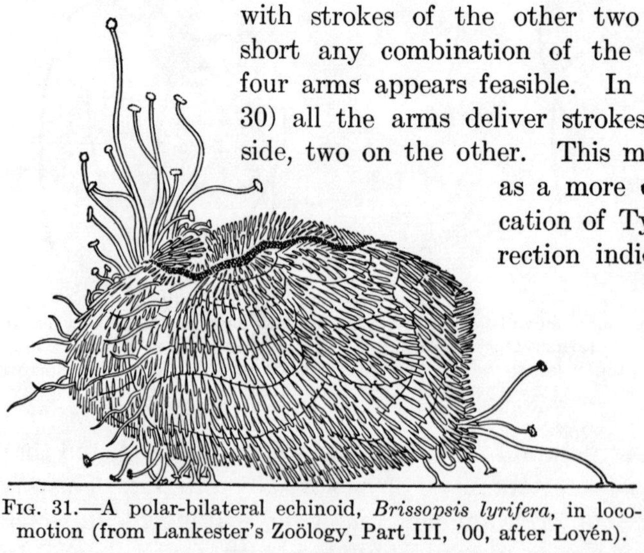

Fig. 31.—A polar-bilateral echinoid, *Brissopsis lyrifera*, in locomotion (from Lankester's Zoölogy, Part III, '00, after Lovén).

pairs or groups of arms. In the asteroid starfish locomotion is accomplished by means of the ambulacral feet, not by strokes of the

[1] See Romanes, '85; Preyer, '86; Grave, '00; Glaser, '07; Jennings, '07.

arms, but the versatility in the use of the arms is very similar to that in the ophiurid (Romanes, '85; Jennings, '07).

The echinoids (sea urchins, sand-dollars, etc.) show various degrees of development of bilateral pattern. In the common sea urchins fixed bilaterality is limited to the structural features common to all echinoderms: in these forms the radii are equivalent so far as determined physiologically and bilaterality in behavior is temporary and shifting. The other groups of echinoids, the sand-dollars (*Clypeastroidea*) and the heart urchins (*Spatangoidea*) both represent secondary polar and bilateral modifications superimposed on the radiate pattern and involving in the latter group general body form, position of mouth and arms, development and function of different radii and direction of locomotion (Fig. 31).

In the holothurian the axiate-bilateral pattern is developed in a different way. The original apico-basal axis becomes the longitudinal axis of the animal with one end anterior, the other posterior and the five radii of the radial pattern are represented by the five longitudinal zones of the body wall, but more or less dorso-ventrality appears among these radii, one radius being median ventral and an interradius median dorsal (Fig. 32). In some forms the ventral surface including three of the rows of ambulacral feet (the trivium) is distinctly flattened and the dorsal surface (bivium) is without true ambulacral feet. Motion in the holothurians is chiefly in the direction of the longitudinal axis, but the definiteness and degree of fixity of the dorsoventral differential differs in different forms corresponding in general to the structural differential.

This brief survey is sufficient to show that the echinoderms present extremely interesting combinations and modifications of radiate and bilateral patterns. While we know in general something of the relations between these various modifications

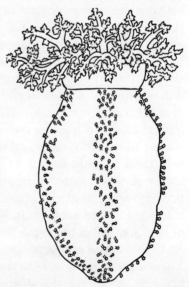

FIG. 32.—A holothurian, *Pentacta frondosa*, ventral aspect, illustrating another bilateral modification of pattern in echinoderms (from Kellogg, '01, after Emerton).

of pattern and the motor behavior, further comparative study along these lines would be of interest.

The versatility of the starfish to which Jennings ('07) calls particular attention must result from the physiological equivalence of the rays [1] and the fact that any one of two or three of them may be-become dominant. With different physiological states of the different rays the reaction of the animal as a whole to the same external factor will differ, as regards the relations and functions of the different rays. This versatility is very evident in Glaser's figures of the motor reactions of the brittle star (Figs. 26–30). All the radiate animals show more or less of this sort of versatility and the *Amœba* is perhaps the most versatile of all. With the increasing development of bilaterality in the echinoderms this versatility as regards the functional relations and combinations of different rays must more or less completely disappear and the processes of motor reaction become more definite and stereotyped in character.

BILATERALITY

Bilaterality involves physiological differentials in all three dimensions, *i. e.*, between median and lateral in opposite directions and between dorsal and ventral in one direction in addition to the longitudinal or polar differential (see pp. 36–40). These differentials are of course factors in increasing the definiteness of behavior patterns. In bilateral animals the only possiblity of physiological equivalence of motor organs is that of right and left, or in animals with reduplication of segments and appendages, that between the organs of neighboring segments. With respect to the use of such organs in reaction we often observe a versatility which, so far as it goes, is similar to that of radiate and surface-interior patterns. For example, in various animals organs of right and left sides may move alternately or synchronously according to conditions and in many arthropods movements of the appendages of successive segments may be combined in various ways in locomotion. But even the equivalence of right and left is by no means alway present. Many animals, bilateral in certain respects, show in other respects definite asymmetries. These may appear in behavior in the preferential use of organs of one side, as in righthandedness or lefthandedness, or general morphological asymmetry may be associated with special methods of locomotion.

In a bilateral pattern there is not only differentiation along the anterior and posterior axis, but differentiation of another sort in

[1] According to Cole ('13) the rays are not completely equivalent in *Asterias forbesii*.

two opposite directions between median and lateral, and still a third sort of differentiation dorsoventrally. Besides all this, differentiation between surface and interior occurs as in simpler organisms. Evidently the bilateral pattern makes possible more definite and more complex differentiation than the other patterns. In such a pattern each particular behavior mechanism is more definite and more fixed in structure and in relation than in the simpler patterns and must therefore possess a more definite and stereotyped function. This being the case it appears at first glance that the behavior of bilateral organisms must be less versatile and more rigid and stereotyped than that of other patterns. As regards the particular mechanism this is true, but as regards the behavior of the organism as a whole it is far from being true. The versatility of the *Amœba* results from the absence of fixed specialization of different regions. Similarly the versatility of the starfish with respect to the different rays depends on the fact that the rays are physiologically equivalent, although each may represent a complex system of more or less definite and specialized mechanisms. The behavior of each part of the surface of *Amœba* or each ray of the starfish varies from moment to moment according to external factors and physiological states.

The bilateral pattern, however, affords greater possibilities of specialization and differentiation of parts than the other patterns and in the higher animals the complexity of structure and function is very great. The more definitely structure and function become fixed the more does versatility in behavior consist in the combinations and relations of the different mechanisms, each of which is in itself highly specialized and relatively stable in character. This sort of versatility is particularly characteristic of the higher animals and man. The relation between a particular muscle of the arm or hand and the skeletal parts with which it is connected is definite and fixed. The versatility in function of the arm and hand results from the many possibilities of combination and relation of the different musculo-skeletal mechanisms. Moreover, versatility also appears in the processes of realization of these various possibilities. The specialization of different sense organs makes possible the combination of various sensory impressions and different combinations and relations may determine different use of the behavior mechanisms. But the most important factor in the versatility and modifiability of behavior in the higher animals and man is the central nervous system. In certain parts of the nervous system the path of an impulse is not fixedly predetermined but is determined by the combination of conditions, physiological states, excitations, etc., in the nervous system or in the parts concerned at the moment (Herrick, '24, Chap. XIX). There is then in these regions of the nervous system a certain physiological equivalence of path which is similar in a general way to the physiological equivalence of the starfish arms, the medusa sense organs, or the different parts of the *Amœba* surface. The physiological equivalence of path in the nervous system results, not from simplicity and absence of specialization, but from the complexity of structural mechanism and physiological relation.

In the higher invertebrates, notably the insects, this physiological equivalence of path in the nervous system is apparently but little developed as compared with the higher vertebrates and the behavior patterns of the insects are relatively fixed and stereotyped, and largely "instinctive" in character. For the present, these differences are merely noted without discussion of possible reasons for them. There can be no doubt that they both represent in some way the working out of bilateral pattern in different protoplasms.

ALTERATION OF ORGANISMIC PATTERN BY EXCITO-MOTOR BEHAVIOR

There can of course be no doubt that in general terms organismic pattern constitutes the basis on which the excito-motor behavior patterns of an organism are built up, in others words, organismic pattern is the general framework within which such behavior occurs. But behavior represents the results of action of external factors upon an organism and these may not only change from moment to moment, but some of their effects may persist for a time or permanently and modify further behavior. Because of this relation between behavior and external factors we find certain behavior patterns integrated on an organismic scale, but transcending the permanent organismic pattern of the individual in which they occur. In the ophiurid starfish, for example, the general pattern is radiate so far as the physiological equivalence of the rays is concerned, yet behavior patterns which are just as truly bilateral as the usual motor patterns of an insect appear in the correlated function of the arms (Figs. 26, 29). To my mind this bilateral behavior pattern is just as truly on organismic pattern as that of any bilateral animal. It differs from such pattern merely in that it is temporary and functional, and does not possess a permanent morphological basis. In such cases as this we can only conclude that the temporary bilateral pattern has been superimposed on the permanent radial pattern by the action of external factors. Because of their relation to present or preceding external factors two pairs of arms are in such physiological state that they react similarly. Again certain *Amœbæ* may temporarily assume the limax form, *i. e.*, an axiate pattern. In the case of the plant *Fucus* the reaction to light differential determines a new axiate organismic pattern which is permanent for the individual plant (pp. 58-61). In bilateral animals, on the other hand, we often see asymmetric behavior patterns in the different use of bilateral organs. A bird may stand on one leg and draw the other up beneath it, use it to scratch its head, etc. Many such asymmetric behavior patterns may bring about permanent modifications of the organismic pattern of the individual. Learning to write with one hand involves the establishment of permanent differences in pattern between the two sides of the body, chiefly or wholly in the nervous system. On the other hand, the muscular and skeletal asymmetry of the blacksmith involve the gross morphological features. In still other forms we find an excito-motor behavior pattern compensating asymmetry or other structure as in the spiral course of

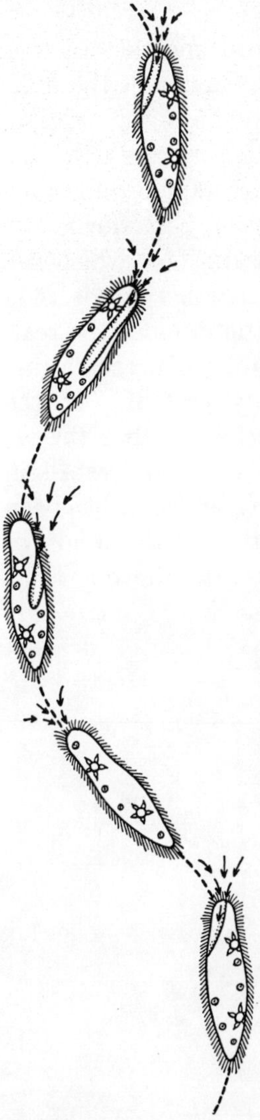

FIG. 33.—Spiral path of *Paramecium* (from Jennings, '06 © Columbia University Press).

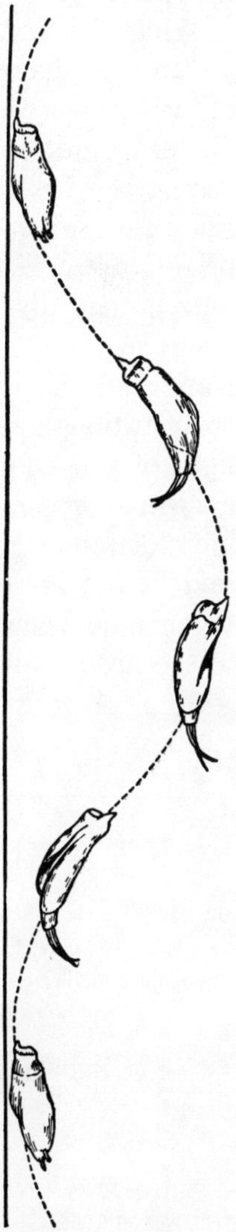

FIG. 34.—Spiral path of rotifer, *Diurella tigris*, showing that animal continually swerves toward dorso-dextral side (from Jennings, '03).

Paramecium (Fig. 33) and of certain rotifers (Fig. 34) with revolution of the body about a longitudinal axis (Jennings, '06 and earlier papers).

While it is perfectly true that the existing organismic pattern constitutes the general physiological basis for the behavior of the individual, it is also true that such behavior modifies the original pattern, determines new patterns within it or superimposes new patterns upon it. These changes may be either temporary or may persist. So far at least as the individual is concerned, behavior is the originator of new organismic patterns, new integrations, which are only potentially given in the original pattern. In other words, it is behavior, *i. e.*, the individual experience, which determines the realization in the individual of the potentialities of the protoplasmic constitution and the organismic pattern already present. In the light of these facts the statement in an earlier chapter that the organism represents a behavior pattern in protoplasm acquires a still more definite significance. At any rate it is clear from what has been said in the present chapter that any consideration of the origin of organismic behavior must deal sooner or later with the questions of the nature and orgin of organismic pattern itself.

CHAPTER VII

THE PHYSIOLOGICAL GRADIENTS

Physiological polarity and symmetry, either radial or bilateral, are commonly thought of as conditions of some sort underlying and determining the localization and arrangement of parts and organs of the individual, *i. e.*, its spatial, morphological pattern. Actually, however, polarity and symmetry have to do not only with morphological pattern but with physiological relations of parts. The relation of dominance and subordination to which attention has already been called (pp. 34–36) is very intimately associated with physiological polarity and symmetry. Again, differences in rate of cell-divison, growth and differentiation are associated with polarity and symmetry, and the relations between the behavior patterns of the individual and polarity and symmetry have been indicated in Chapter VI.

Polarity and symmetry are really only terms to designate the directions, the axes or radii, in which a spatial morphological and physiological order is perceptible. As already noted, the simplest conceivable organisms are spherically symmetrical forms with surface-interior pattern. In these the order appears along the radii of a sphere. Whether such organisms actually exist, we do not certainly know, though some of the microörganisms appear to be of this sort and the simple cell or protoplast is probably little or nothing more than a surface-interior organism.

Most organisms, however, are axiate, the axes constituting a sort of physiological coördinate system to which the order is referable, and the questions of the nature and origin of physiological axes are obviously of fundamental importance for any physiological interpretation of organismic pattern. When we examine a physiological axis, or more strictly speaking an axial direction in an organism we find that it is indicated in many of the simpler organisms throughout life and in the earlier developmental stages of the more complex forms by gradations of various sorts, rather than by clear-cut qualitative differences. We find, for example, axial gradations in protoplasmic structure, in rate of growth and differentiation, in rate of, or capacity for, regeneration, and in various other physiological char-

73

acteristics. Some of these gradations in condition, for example, the apico-basal gradation in yolk in many animal eggs, the apico-basal or antero-posterior gradation in rate of cell division, growth and differentiation in many embryos, have long been familiar to biologists. In various publications Morgan (e. g., '05) has advanced the hypothesis of a gradation of materials as a factor in physiological polarity. The results of experimental alteration of cleavage of the *Ascaris* egg led Boveri ('10) to the conclusion that polarity must be a gradation of some sort.

During recent years investigation along various lines has accumulated a large body of evidence in support of the conclusion that physiological axes are primarily quantitative dynamic gradients in living protoplasms, that they represent primarily differences in physiological state, rather than in molecular structure. Such gradients involve differences in rate of the fundamental metabolic reactions as well as differences in physical state of the protoplasmic substratum. They have been called for convenience, axial, metabolic, or physiological gradients. So far as the facts go, they are the primary indications of the existence of axiate pattern and there is at present no evidence to indicate that axiate pattern can arise in any other way than as a gradient in physiological state. It is not necessary to assume that these gradients consist primarily in metabolic differences alone. Protoplasm is a system in which the chemical reactions of metabolism are so intimately associated with other factors, e. g., colloid dispersion, active mass of enzymes, permeability of limiting surfaces, electrolyte content and dissociation, water content, etc., that to distinguish one particular factor rather than another as primary is at present impossible.

THE EVIDENCE FOR THE EXISTENCE OF PHYSIOLOGICAL GRADIENTS

The evidence demonstrating or indicating the existence of physiological axial gradients in organisms is varied and extensive and has been more or less fully presented in earlier publications. The evidence at hand eight years ago was briefly discussed in "Individuality in Organisms," 1915, but since that time further investigation, the results of which have been published in part, has added much to the evidence. More recent reviews of this evidence (Child, '20 c, '21 a, Chap. II) have presented the data at hand up to the beginning of 1920 with a practically complete bibliography of the subject. These earlier publications make it possible to limit the present section to a brief review of the evidence.

Structure and development.— In the first place the axial gradients, particularly the apico-basal or antero-posterior gradient, are often visible in the protoplasmic structure, density, vacuolation, or accumulation of yolk. Such structural gradations are very characteristic of eggs and early embryos, but in axiate plants they occur in relation to the growing tips of both stem and root at all stages of growth.[1]

A gradation in rate of cell division, growth, morphogenesis and differentiation is also a characteristic feature of physiological axes in both animals and plants. In axiate animals the rate of these processes is primarily highest at the apical or anterior end and decreases basipetally or in the posterior direction. In bilateral invertebrates it also decreases from the median ventral region laterally and dorsally, in bilateral vertebrates from the median dorsal region laterally and ventrally.[2] In axiate plants the growing tip continues its growth and division as long as it remains active as a growing tip. In relation to the growing tips of plant axes, gradations in cell size, rate of cell division, rate of growth of single cells and differentiation appear.[3]

Differences in rate of reconstitution at different levels of an axis are also of very general occurrence, the rate of reconstitution of apical or anterior parts decreasing basipetally or posteriorly. In pieces of *Tubularia* stem, for example, the time from section to emergence of the new hydranth at the distal cut end of the piece increases basipetally (Driesch, '99; Morgan, '01 b, '05, '06, '08; Child, '07 c; Hyman, '20 b). At the proximal end of the piece, however, conditions are different because the proximal end is subordinate to the distal end if not too far distant from it and the development of the proximal hydranth may be delayed or inhibited in short pieces, while in long pieces it may occur much more rapidly. Lund ('23) [4]

[1] For figures of structural gradients in plants see Child,'15 c, Figs. 18, 19, 21, 22, 38, 39.

[2] For figures of developmental gradients in animals see Child, '15 c, Figs. 10–17.

[3] For figures of developmental gradients in plants see Child, '15 c, Figs. 18–22, 35–41.

[4] In this paper Lund maintains that in *Obelia* there is no difference in rate of regeneration at different levels of the stem, but rather a difference in length of time between section and the initiation of regeneration. He regards regeneration as beginning only when the visible development of the hydranth begins and takes no account of the extensive cell activity which has long been known to begin soon after section in most cases. Earlier authors have preferred to regard this activity as part of the regenerative process since it is a normal and constant feature of formation of a new hydranth from a piece of stem. But whether we accept Lund's definition of regeneration or that of other authors, the data which

has found an axial difference in reconstitution period in *Obelia* similar to that in *Tubularia*. In my experiments on *Planaria dorotocephala* I have found similar, though slight differences in rate of development of the head at different levels, and Sivickis ('23, p. 145) has noted a similar difference in *P. lata*. The relation between the character of reconstitution and body level has been extensively studied in *Planaria* and it is a well-established fact that the frequency of normal heads decreases from anterior levels posteriorly in each zooid (Behre, '18; Child, '11 a, b, '16 b, '20 a; Sivickis, '23).

Susceptibility. — Differences in susceptibility to a very large number of external agents, probably to such agents in general, are characteristic features of the different levels of the physiological gradients.[1] In general the physiological gradients have been demonstrated as susceptibility gradients in various ways and by many different agents, physical and chemical. The investigation of susceptibility in its relation to the physiological gradients has brought to light certain general relations between susceptibility and physiological condition, or more specifically between susceptibility and rate of fundamental metabolic reaction.[2] These relations are briefly as

he presents constitute very definite evidence for the existence of a physiological gradient in the stem of *Obelia*. It is to be expected that the more active cells of more apical stem levels will make the physiological changes (dedifferentiation, activation, or whatever we may call them) which precede the development of the hydranth more rapidly than the less active cells of lower levels. After they have attained the condition in which, hydranth development becomes possible, they are probably much alike and morphogenesis may go on at the same rate at all levels, though Lund's curves indicate a difference in rate.

[1] Papers concerned with the demonstration of the susceptibility gradients as gradients in survival time under the action of various agents are as follows: Child, '13 b, '14 a, b, '15 a, '16 a, b, c, '19 b, e, '23 a, '23 d; Child and Hyman '19; Galigher, '21; Hyman, '16, '17, '20 b, '21; Hyman and Galigher, '21; MacArthur, '21. Further data on various plants, protozoa, ctenophores, hydrozoa, flatworms, echinoderms, annelids, fishes and amphibia, and the chick embryo are not yet published. In the other literature of the action of external agents on protoplasm numerous data indicating differential susceptibility along physiological axes appear, and it is of interest to note that various authors have observed axial differences in susceptibility to X-rays and radium in various organisms, both plant and animal. Recently Dr. M. A. Hinrichs has demonstrated the physiological gradients in *Stentor*, *Hydra* and *Planaria* as gradients in susceptibility to ultraviolet radiation and to sunlight after photochemical sensitization by eosin (Hinrichs, '23 b) and I have obtained further data along the same line on various forms, both plant and animal (unpublished). In all forms thus far examined the results obtained by photolysis are similar to those obtained with other agents.

[2] Behre, '18; Child, '13 a, b, '14 c, '15 b, Chaps. III—VII, '19 a, c, d, '23 a; Galigher, '21; Hyman, '16 b, '19 a, b, c, d, e, '20 a, '20 c; Hyman and Galigher, '21; Sivickis, '23. Recent criticisms by Lund ('18 a, b, '21 a) and G. D. Allen ('19 a, b, '20), bearing chiefly on the relation between susceptibility and metabolism have

follows: To a certain range of concentrations or intensities of agents which are experimentally determined to be above the limit of tolerance of the organism concerned and therefore strongly toxic or lethal in their action the susceptibility varies directly with, though not necessarily proportionally to, the general protoplasmic activity or rate of metabolism. To a certain lower range of concentrations or intensities, also experimentally determined for each species, the rate and degree of acclimation or acquirement of tolerance varies directly with, though not necessarily proportionally to, the general protoplasmic activity and the rate and degree of recovery after temporary exposure to a certain range of concentration or intensity varies in the same way. General protoplasmic activity is a vague term, but is used in order to avoid the implication that any particular component factor in protoplasmic condition is necessarily regarded as primary. Protoplasm is a system in which the dynamic changes are so closely correlated and integrated that we cannot point to any one as primary, moreover, it is possible that the initiatory change in a complex physiological process such as excitation is not always necessarily the same.

The data on susceptibility constitute some of the strongest evidence for the existence of such integration in the protoplasmic system. In the simpler organisms and the earlier stages of development of higher forms the susceptibility relations are in general similar for a great number of agents of different chemical constitution, e. g., cyanides anesthetics, acids, alkalies, various neutral salts, vital dyes, etc., and for physical conditions such as extremes of temperature.[1] This cannot possibly mean that all these agents and conditions act on living protoplasm in the same way or alter primarily the same factor in the system. Certainly the effects of the different agents and conditions are exerted primarily or chiefly upon different factors of the protoplasmic system, and the results show clearly enough that when any essential factor is sufficiently altered, the system as a whole is altered. In the less highly specialized protoplasms, therefore, we find little or no indication of regional differences in susceptibility specific for

been in part disposed of by Hyman's later work and other data soon to be published will dispose of others. As is evident to those familiar with the gradient conception, these criticisms appear to be due largely to misapprehension and in a number of cases are directed against views quite different from those advanced by us; consequently they require no consideration here.

[1] Recent work, in large part not yet published, has added to this list as follows: formaldehyde, various alkaloids, lack of oxygen, ultraviolet radiation and sunlight after photochemical sensitization.

particular agents. Among the lower invertebrates the differences in susceptibility to acids and alkalies seem to be more nearly specific than any other differences yet discovered in these forms (Child, '20 c, p. 158, J. W. MacArthur, '20), but these differences appear during the course of development and are not present in the earlier stages. And in the higher animals, even the vertebrates, the apparently specific relations between particular tissues or organs and particular agents are largely or wholly absent in the early stages. In general, the susceptibility gradients of the simpler organisms and the earlier stages of development are non-specific in relation to particular agents and conditions. This being the case, we may expect to find a relation between susceptibility and rate rather than kind of dynamic change in protoplasm. The chemical reactions of metabolism are essential factors in the activities which we call life, and among these the oxidations are regarded as of fundamental importance. With certain qualifications and limitations it appears to be true that the rate of oxidation is in some degree a measure of the rate of living. It has also been shown that in the less highly specialized protoplasms susceptibility to certain ranges of concentration or intensity of external agents is an indicator of rate of oxidation and may be used as a rough comparative measure of differences in rate. There is therefore a real experimental basis for the statement, that susceptibility is in general a measure of rate of metabolism or more particularly oxidation. In highly specialized organs and tissues specific susceptibilities to particular agents may appear and these may in some cases be related to qualitative factors of constitution rather than to rate of oxidation. Nevertheless the fact remains that in the less highly specialized protoplasms susceptibility is, within certain limits of concentration or intensity of agent and with proper technical procedure, a rough measure of physiological condition and more particularly of rate of oxidation. The existence of this general non-specific relation between susceptibility to the action of external agents and metabolic condition in protoplasm seems to me to be merely a special case under general physico-chemical laws which may be stated in more general terms as follows: The greater the velocity of changes concerned in the maintenance of, or approach to, dynamic equilibrium in a system, the more rapid and extreme the effect of sufficiently powerful external agencies in altering or destroying that equilibrium, and the more rapid the equilibration to, or recovery from, slight or temporary disturbances. In other words, the more active the system, the more sensitive it is to gross disturbances and the more rapidly

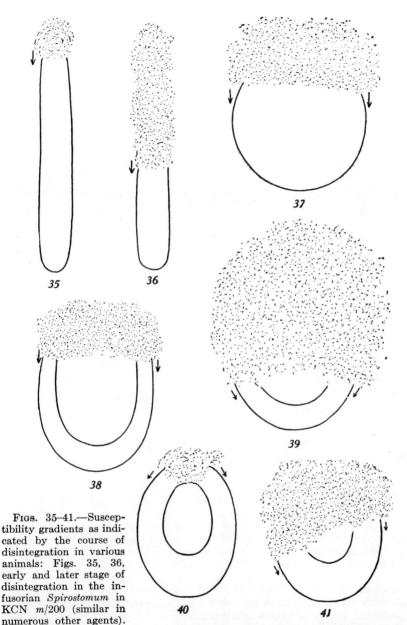

FIGS. 35–41.—Susceptibility gradients as indicated by the course of disintegration in various animals: Figs. 35, 36, early and later stage of disintegration in the infusorian *Spirostomum* in KCN *m*/200 (similar in numerous other agents). Apical end uppermost, body contracted; Fig. 37, disintegration of unfertilized egg of sea urchin, *Arbacia* in neutral red. Intact regions are stained deep red and decoloration accompanies disintegration; Figs. 38, 39, early and later stage of disintegration of blastula of medusa, *Phialidium* in KCN, *m*/100; Figs. 40, 41, early and later stage of disintegration of blastula of sea urchin, *Arbacia*, as observed in many different agents. The difference in rate of basipetal progress of disintegration in different meridians shown in Fig. 41, probably indicates an early stage of the differences between anterior and posterior in later larval stages. In each figure the arrows indicate the direction in which disintegration is progressing.

it equilibrates to slight disturbances. I believe the relation between susceptibility and metabolism in its simplest form is nothing more than this.[1]

Differences in susceptibility along an axis may be made evident in various ways. In highly toxic concentrations or intensities a definite gradient in the course of death and disintegration may appear and this may be preceded in motile forms by a gradient in loss of motility.

In Figs. 35–44 the course of death and disintegration along the chief axes of various organisms is indicated. In each case the same death and disintegration gradients have been observed with various agents. The portions figured as intact are still alive at the stages indicated: in ciliated forms, such as *Spirostomum* (Figs. 35, 36) and the hydroid and sea urchin blastulæ (Figs. 38–41) the cilia of the intact portions may continue movement until disintegration begins and in forms with muscular differentiation (Figs. 42–44) movement may occur almost up to the moment when disintegration begins. If the organisms are returned to the normal medium before the toxic action has proceeded too far, all, or nearly all of the intact portion of the body will recover. Numerous other figures of both plants and animals might be added.

When early developmental stages are exposed to toxic but non-lethal concentrations or intensities differential susceptibilities along an axis may appear in a differential modification of development. In inhibiting agents the most susceptible regions are most inhibited, but in a certain range of low concentrations or intensities they show the most rapid and most complete acclimation or development of

---

[1] Huxley ('22) has advanced the view that the susceptibility of cells may also vary with amount of surface exposed to the agent. This is undoubtedly true, but it may be noted that differences in exposure of cell surface in a particular body layer, or in the body surface, sufficient to affect susceptibility to any marked degree, usually arise secondarily in the course of differentiation. I have pointed out repeatedly that with the progress of differentiation various factors appear which alter the general relation between susceptibility and metabolic rate. Unquestionably difference in exposure of cell surface is one of these factors.

In Huxley's work the index of susceptibility appears to be change in behavior of the living cell as a whole, usually change in form. It cannot be assumed, however, without further evidence, that because a flattened cell shows marked change in form and a cuboidal or rounded cell little or none in a certain concentration of agent, the toxic action of the agent is greater upon the flattened cell. It is possible that change of form may occur in the flattened cell with very slight toxic action, while a greater degree of toxic action is necessary to produce visible change in the cuboidal or rounded cell. In other words, the change in form of the flattened cell does not necessarily mean a higher susceptibility in the sense in which I have used the word.

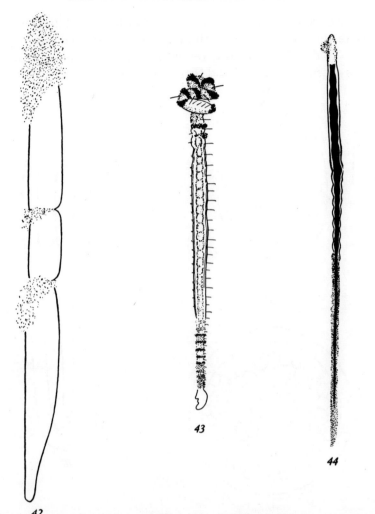

FIGS. 42–44.—Susceptibility gradients in flatworm and annelids: Fig. 42, a stage of disintegration of the rhabdocoel, *Stenostomum* in KCN, $m/1000$ (and many other agents). The figure represents a chain of zooids. The head of the anterior zooid, as most active region is most susceptible, that of latest formed, shortest zooid least susceptible. Ventral regions are more susceptible than dorsal; Fig. 43, a disintegration stage of obligochete, *Dero limosa*, showing primary antero-posterior, and secondary postero-anterior gradient, the latter resulting from development of new segments anterior to anal segment; Fig. 44, disintegration stage of *Limnodrilus claparedianus*, showing the double gradient (Figs. 43, 44 from Hyman, '16 a).

tolerance and after certain ranges of temporary exposure they recover most rapidly and most completely. In exciting or accelerating agents a differential acceleration of development may also occur at different levels of a gradient. All of these differentials appear as differential effects on rate of development, and in this way on size

and proportion of different parts. Four sorts of modification in two
opposite directions occur as the result of differential susceptibility
(Child, '16 d, '17 d). In differential inhibition the most susceptible
regions are most inhibited and therefore least developed. In differen-

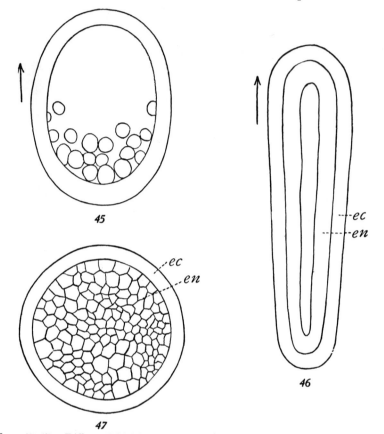

45

ec
en

ec
en

46

47

Figs. 45–47.—Differential inhibition in early development of hydrozoan, *Phialidium:*
Fig. 45, normal early stage of elongation of blastula and immigration of cells from basal
region to form entoderm; Fig. 46, normal elongated planula; Fig. 47, differential inhibition by KCN, acids, etc. Planula spherical without visible polarity. Excessive formation of entoderm has prevented development of enteric cavity. Arrows in Figs. 45 and
46 indicate direction of locomotion. The sperical planula of Fig. 47 is incapable of
definitely directed locomotion: (*ec*), ectoderm; (*en*), entoderm.

tial acclimation they are at first most inhibited, but later show more
acclimation and so are finally less inhibited than the less susceptible
regions. In differential recovery the modifications are essentially like
those of differential acclimation but they occur after return to the
normal medium. In differential acceleration the most susceptible regions are most accelerated and therefore relatively larger than normal.

Developmental modification through differential susceptibility is illustrated here by a few examples. Further data are presented in the following chapter in another connection. Cases of differential inhibition are shown in Figs. 45–52. In normal hydroid development immigration of cells to form entoderm (Fig. 45) and elongation of the blastula into the planula occurs (Fig. 46). In differential inhibition the original polarity may completely disappear, *i. e.*, the

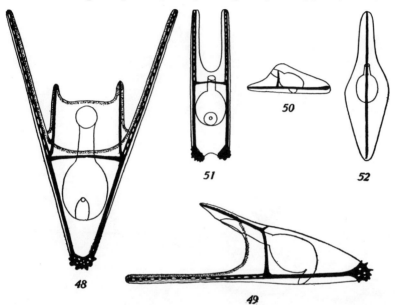

FIGS. 48–52.—Differential inhibition in larval development of sea urchin, *Arbacia:* Fig. 48, normal pluteus larva, basal view; Fig. 49, normal pluteus, side view; Fig. 50, differential inhibition by action of KCN throughout development, side view. Apical and anterior regions more inhibited than basal and posterior; Fig. 51, differential inhibition by temporary exposure to KCN, basal view. Anterior and median more inhibited than posterior and lateral; Fig. 52, greater degree of differential inhibition by temporary exposure to KCN, basal view. Median region so completely inhibited that a single median arm and skeletal rod develop instead of paired lateral structures.

apical region is most inhibited, the basal least and with a certain degree of inhibition the axial gradient is reduced to a level. In such cases the larva remains spherical, loses its definitely directed movement (Fig. 47) and does not develop further unless a new gradient arises in it (Chap. IX).

Figures 48–52 show differential inhibition in sea-urchin development. Figures 48 and 49 show normal pluteus larvæ in lateral and basal aspects. Figure 50 is a differentially inhibited larva in side view, and it is evident that the apical region, the oral lobe, is more inhibited than the basal region. Figure 51 is a basal view showing that anterior and median regions are more inhibited than posterior and lateral, and Fig. 52 is a more extreme inhibition in which the median region is completely inhibited so that the lateral arms arise as a single structure in the median line.

In differential acclimation, recovery and acceleration the modification of form is opposite in direction to that occurring in differential

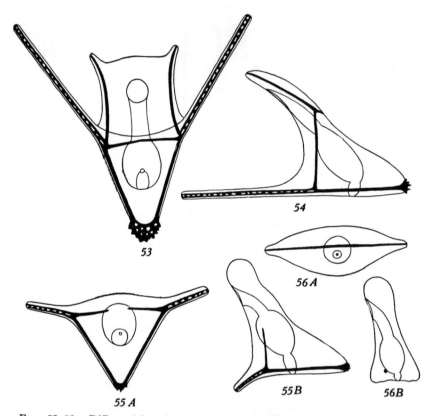

53

54

56 A

55 B

56B

55 A

Figs. 53–56.—Differential acclimation in *Arbacia:* Figs. 53, 54, basal and lateral views of a slight degree of differential acclimation; Fig. 55 (*A*), basal, (*B*), lateral view of more extreme degree of differential acclimation; Fig. 56 (*A*), basal, (*B*), lateral view of still more extreme modification. In all these cases apical, anterior and median regions are disproportionately large, as compared with basal, posterior and lateral.

inhibition. Figures 53–56 showing different degrees of differential acclimation in the sea urchin will serve as examples. Comparison of these figures with the figures of normal plutei (Figs. 48, 49) shows that in the stages figured of these differential acclimations basal regions are more inhibited than apical, lateral more than median, and posterior more than anterior. In the earlier stages of development the

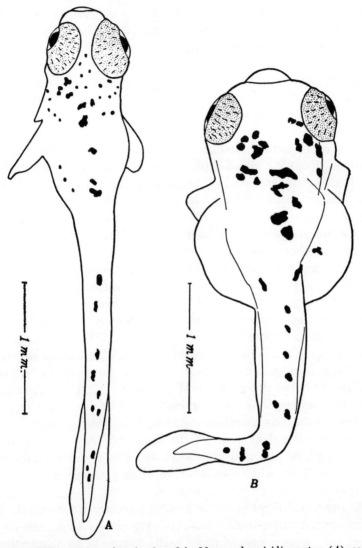

Fig. 57.—Differential acceleration in a fish, *Macropodus viridi-auratus:* (*A*), control developing under standard normal conditions; (*B*), exposed to atropin sulphate 1¾ hours during early cleavage. Rate of development and of heart beat more rapid than in control (by permission of J. N. Gowanloch from unpublished work).

reverse was the case, but apical, anterior and median regions have undergone acclimation more rapidly and to a greater degree than basal posterior and lateral regions, that is, differential acclimation is preceded by more or less differential inhibition. The changes in differential recovery and differential acceleration are similar in direction to these, and differential recovery, like differential acclimation, is preceded by differential inhibition. In differential accleration, however, there is no inhibition or retardation, but development is accelerated, from the beginning. Bellamy ('19) has been able to produce differential acceleration in amphibian development and Mr. J. N. Gowanloch has accomplished the same result with fishes. Figure 57 shows a case of differential acceleration (B) and normal control (A) obtained by Mr. Gowanloch with a low concentration of atropin.[1]

These experimental modifications of development through differential susceptibility afford a physiological basis for interpretation of a wide range of teratological forms in nature. In fact, differential susceptibility appears to be a fundamental teratogenic factor in all cases where the modification results from exposure of the embryo as a whole to the external condition concerned and not from direct mechanical or other injury to some part.

It is perfectly evident that the types of developmental modification are non-specific and essentially quantitative both in their relations to the axes and to the different protoplasms and external agents. Similar external agents and conditions produce the same sorts of modification in flatworms (Child, '16 b, '20 a, '21 c, Buchanan, '22), echinoderms (Child, '16 d), annelids (Child, '17 d), fishes (Stockard, '07, '21), and amphibia (Bellamy, '19, '22). Similarly in teratological forms of fishes produced by Werber ('16, '17) the indications of differential susceptibility are evident. And finally Newman ('17 a, '18) has shown that monsters resulting from hybridization in fishes may be interpreted in terms of the same differential susceptibility, i. e., as might be expected from what we know of differential susceptibility elsewhere, a differential susceptibility of one protoplasm to the other or of each to the other exists.

The most important point for present purposes is that all the data on differential susceptibility indicate very clearly that each physiological axis or direction of order exists primarily as a quantitative gradient in physiological condition in which differences in rate of oxidation and associated differences in protoplasmic condition are fundamental factors. As will appear later, these differences in physiological condition along the axes are of fundamental importance for the behavior of the organism as a whole.

Penetration. — Axial gradients in "permeability" or rate of penetration of various substances have been demonstrated in many forms

[1] Mr. Gowanloch has very kindly permitted this use of figures and data from his unpublished work.

both animal and plant. The regions more susceptible to the higher concentrations of external agents show in general a higher rate of penetration of such agents as vital dyes than less susceptible regions. But many facts indicate that permeability of living cells is itself closely associated with physiological condition and with metabolism as a factor in such condition. It has been pointed out elsewhere (Child, '21 a, pp. 40–42) that the susceptibility gradients cannot be interpreted in terms of permeability of cell surfaces as a physical condition independent of metabolism. There is no reason to believe that the permeability of living cells is independent of metabolism, moreover, a certain parallelism exists between rate of penetration of various substances and rate of oxidation. And finally the results of differential acclimation are opposed to the differential permeability, *i. e.*, it is the regions of higher permeability which acclimate most rapidly and to the greatest degree.

Oxidation-reduction reactions. — Certain oxidation-reduction reactions render the physiological gradients directly visible as color gradients resulting from the deposition of the products of oxidation or reduction at different rates or in different amounts at different levels of a gradient. For example, the different levels of a physiological gradient reduce potassium permanganate at different rates and in different amounts and so become visible as gradients in depth of brown or blackish color due to deposition of MnO_2, or other oxides in the protoplasm (Figs. 58–60). This reaction has proved to be a very delicate method for demonstrating the physiological gradients in many cases.[1] The indo-phenol reaction, an oxidation, has also been used in certain cases, the physiological gradients appearing as gradients in depth of blue resulting from deposition of the blue indophenol in the protoplasm (Child, '15a). The gradients have also been demonstrated in various plant and animal forms after staining with methylene blue as gradients in rate of reduction of the dye in the protoplasm.

Electrical potential. — The physiological gradients are also characterized by differences in electric potential. Observations have been made on many different forms, both animals and plants.[2] In general, in animals the higher levels, *i. e.*, the levels of more intense activity, of higher rate of oxidation, are electro-negative, galvanometrically,

[1] Child, '19 a, e, '21 d, '23 a; Galigher, '21; Hyman, '20 b, '22.
[2] See Child, '21 d, p. 90; Mathews, '03; Morgan and Dimon, '04; Hyde, '04; Hyman, '20 b, '23 a; Hyman and Bellamy, '22; Lund, '22; and some data in the work of Waller, '97, '03.

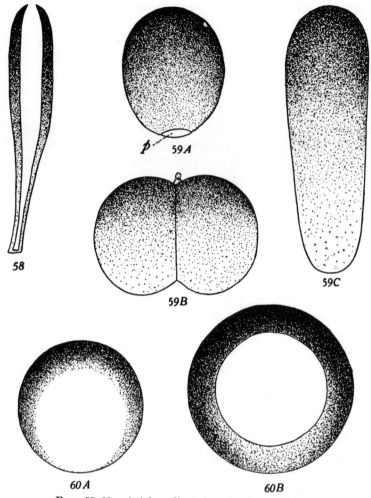

FIGS. 58–60.—Axial gradients in reduction of KMnO₄.

FIG. 58.—Reduction gradient in wall of sycon sponge split longitudinally.

FIG. 59A–C.—Reduction gradients in developmental stages of hydromedusæ: (A), in superficial cytoplasm of ovarian egg of medusa, *Stomotoca atra;* (p), area of attachment of egg in gonad; (B), in two cell stage of medusa, *Phialidium;* (C), a stage of reduction gradient in ectoderm of planula of *Phialidium.*

FIG. 60A–B.—Reduction gradients in sea urchin development: (A), in optical section of ovarian egg; (B), in optical section of early blastula.

to lower levels. In the algæ thus far examined the higher levels of a physiological gradient are usually electro-positive to lower levels. This difference of sign between animals and algæ may be connected with the fact that in the latter the reduction and syntheses connected with photosynthesis and its products overbalance the oxidations as factors in potential difference.   Further work is necessary, however, to determine whether this suggestion is correct.

The existence of characteristic differences of electric potential associated with the physiological gradients suggests the probability that the differences in rate of metabolism or oxidation along the gradient play an important part in determining these potential differences.   Moreover, the fact that the differences of sign at different levels are such as we should expect from the differences in metabolic rate known to exist increases this probability.   The evidence for this view is presented in the recent discussion of this question by Hyman and Bellamy ('22).   It should, however, be stated with some emphasis that this view by no means involves the assumption that differences in metabolic rate are the only source of potential differences in organisms.   Unquestionably there are many other sources of such difference, and other factors than metabolism may be concerned in the axial potential differences, but many lines of evidence indicate that the metabolic factor is of importance as a source of potential difference.

Galvanotaxis. — A relation of some sort between the galvanotactic reaction and the gradients exists, at least in many of the simpler animals, as Hyman and Bellamy ('22) have shown.   So far as observations go at present, forms with a simple polar gradient tend to orient themselves in the electric current so that the high end of the gradient is toward the negative pole.   The same reaction appears in various axiate organs such as cœlenterate tentacles.   In annelids with a second region of high metabolic rate at the posterior end, the two ends of the body are turned toward the negative pole so that the body takes U-shape.   In the arthropods and vertebrates the situation is commonly more complex, as might be expected in consequence of the high degree of modification of the primary gradients and the neuromuscular complexity.

At present any attempt at interpretation of this apparent relation between the gradients and the galvanotactic reaction can be little more than surmise.   Hyman and Bellamy suggest that the orientation is in some way connected with the fact that the region of highest metabolic rate is positively charged in relation to other parts, but they do not attempt to show how the positivity of this region determines orientation.   A. R. Moore ('23) has shown that in the earthworm a reaction very similar to, if not identical with, the galvanotactic reaction occurs when the current is passed transversely through a few body segments, as well as when the whole body is exposed to it, and that the nerve cord is necessary for conduction of the stimulus which brings about orientation of the parts not directly affected by the current. On the basis of these experiments he maintains that the galvanotactic reaction in the earthworm results from the action of the current on the nervous system. His experiments and interpretation do not, however, alter the fact that a relation of some sort exists between the polar gradient and the orientation, nor will it hold for some of the simpler organisms which have only a rudimentary nervous system or none. At present only the apparent fact of the relation between the gradient and the galvanotactic reaction need be noted: further work is necessary for any general interpretation of the mechanism of orientation.

Respiration. — And finally it has been possible in various cases to determine directly differences in rate of oxygen consumption and CO_2 production at different levels of physiological gradients.[1] This method of direct determination of respiratory exchange of different body levels meets with various difficulties, e. g., the effects of separating different body regions, the fact that it gives only total oxygen consumption or CO_2 production of all organs and does not afford any means of distinguishing between different organs or regions in which the gradients are not necessarily the same or in the same directions. For this reason the method has been used chiefly for simple organisms.

Organ gradients — The existence of a physiological gradient or gradients in various axiate organs of many organisms has been demonstrated by one method or another, or by several different methods. Such gradients have been observed in various specialized reproductive axes and in the "hairs" of algæ, in the larger flagellum of *Noctiluca*, in the tentacles of various cœlenterates, in the plate rows of ctenophores, the growing arms of echinoderm larvæ, the branchiæ and sensory tentacles of various annelids, the growing tail of ascidian and amphibian tadpoles. Dr. Hyman has found that the embryonic heart of fish and chick represents a physiological gradient with high region at the sinus end. Tashiro has found a gradient in CO_2 production in various nerves, and MacArthur and Jones a gradient in respiration rate in the nervous system as a whole. The most extensive work on the physiological gradient of any organ is that of Alvarez and his coworkers on the alimentary tract. They have found in the small intestine, for example, corresponding gradients in irritability, latent period, tone, rhythm, conduction, suscepti-

[1] Robbins and Child, '20; Hyman and Galigher, '21; Child, '23 a; Hyman, '23 a, b.

bility to various drugs, etc., and their work on stomach and colon shows the existence of similar gradients in those organs. Penfield has suggested the existence of such a gradient in the ureter.[1]

THE CONCLUSIONS FROM THE EVIDENCE

The different lines of evidence indicating or demonstrating the existence of physiological gradients are in remarkable agreement. They force us to the conclusion that physiological axes in the simplest terms thus far discovered, are gradients in physiological condition in the protoplasm, or some part of the protoplasm of a single cell or a cell mass, involving the fundamental metabolic reactions, as well as physical condition of the protoplasmic substratum. Moreover, the various methods indicate that the physiological differences at different levels of an axial gradient are primarily quantitative, rather than qualitative differences, *i. e.*, they are first of all differences in rate, amount, degree, rather than differences in kind, though qualitative differences may appear secondarily. Except as regards the apparently specific susceptibilities of certain tissues or organs to certain agents in the later developmental stages and mature forms, particularly of the higher animals, the different methods agree in their evidence concerning position, direction and course of the physiological gradients. That is to say, the differences in structure, rate of development, susceptibility, rate of penetration, rate and amount of reduction or of oxidation, electric potential, and, in cases where they have been determined, oxygen consumption and CO_2 production, all indicate the same regions of the organism as high and low ends respectively of a particular gradient and the regions between as intermediate in condition.

[1] Most of the published data on organ gradients may be found in the following references: on the hairs of algæ, Child, '17 a; cœlenterate tentacles, Child, '19 b, 21 d, Child and Hyman, '19, Hyman, '20 b; ctenophore plate row, Child, '17 c; arms of echinoderm larvæ, Child, '16 d, Galigher '21; nerve fibers, Tashiro, '14, '15 a, b, '17; nervous system, C. J. MacArthur and O. C. Jones, '17; alimentary tract, Alvarez, '14, '15 a, b, '16 a, b, '17 a, b, '18 a, b, c, '22; Alvarez and Mahony, '21, Alvarez and Starkweather, '18 a, b, c, '19, Alvarez and Taylor, '17 a, b, Taylor and Alvarez, '17; ureter, Penfield, '20 and references given. The physiological literature on the vertebrate heart indicates very clearly the existence of a gradient of some sort in this organ, with the sinus end as pacemaker. Hyman ('21) has demostrated a susceptibilty gradient in the embryonic fish heart and Mr. J. N. Gowanloch has been able to alter and obliterate the gradient experimentally through differential susceptibility and so to alter the course and direction of the beat (Gowanloch '23). Other data on branchiæ and sensory tentacles of polychetes, tails of ascidian and amphibian tadpoles and various other organs are still unpublished.

The relation of the gradients to the various organs and parts of the developing organism is also definite. The apical region or head arises from the high end of the major, or polar gradient, and the other organs at different levels of the gradient. In the axes of radiate parts the relation between gradient and localization is also definite and characteristic for the species. The tip of the cœlenterate tentacle, for example, represents the high end of the tentacle gradient. In most bilateral invertebrates, e. g., turbellaria, annelids, arthropods, the median ventral region, and in the vertebrates the median dorsal region arises from the high region of the bilateral gradients. In the various organs, appendages, etc., of bilateral forms, the symmetries or asymmetries are associated, at least during early development, with physiological gradients.

The evidence indicates further that the chief gradients appear primarily in the superficial regions of the cell or multicellular body. In many of the simpler organisms, e. g., many protozoa (Child, '14 b) and plant cells, they are present throughout life only in the ectoplasm or the superficial regions. On the other hand, in more highly specialized organisms with definitely localized, axiate internal organs, gradients are also present in these organs, so far as examined, though these gradients may differ in position and direction from those of superficial regions. As regards persistence or modification of gradients during the life history it has been found that the primary gradient or gradients may persist in many of the simpler organisms throughout life or even through various reproductive processes, but complications and modifications of various sorts may also occur (Child, '15 b, pp. 54, 60, '16, '17, '21 a, p. 26). The original polar gradient may be obliterated or reversed, as in the development of the hydroid from the planula (Figs. 22–24). In the process of budding in plants, hydroids and many other forms a new gradient appears in each new bud (Child, '19 b). In segmented animals, so far as examined, the lower end of the polar gradient becomes secondarily a region of high metabolic rate and from this new segments arise (Hyman, '16 a, '21, Hyman and Galigher, '21, Child, '17, Bellamy, '19). From the stage at which this posterior high region appears to the completion of segment development, or in some forms throughout life, the axis of the segmented animal represents a double gradient, both ends of the body being high ends with the low region at an intermediate level. The data obtained by Morgan and Dimon ('04) on electrical polarity in the earthworm show the double character of the axis, but their significance was not apparent when they were published. Again the origin of new radial axes about a circumference, such as the tentacles of a cœlenterate, the arms of a starfish, is associated with the origin of new gradients. Similarly the appendages of bilateral forms represent new gradients in more or less specialized tissues.

Except in organisms with indefinite or temporary axiation, such as *Amœba*, the changes in the gradients during development of the individual, whatever they may be, occur in an orderly and definite manner and sequence for each form. In many cases we are able to analyze to some extent the physiological conditions associated with the origin of new gradients and even to determine their origin experimentally, but in other cases we know as yet little or nothing of the conditions concerned.

The further investigation proceeds along these lines, the more certain it becomes that physiological axes in their simplest known terms represent quantitative gradations or differentials in physiological condition. This means merely that the simplest sort of physiological axis first becomes distinguishable as such a gradient. It does not necessarily mean that the axis always returns to its primary condition with each reproduction, nor does it mean that every individual axis is nothing more than such a gradient. It is possible that in some cases qualitative differences may exist along an axis from the beginning of that particular axis, but the facts indicate that the quantitative differences are the fundamental factors in axiate pattern.

SURFACE-INTERIOR PATTERN AND CELL PATTERN IN RELATION TO PHYSIOLOGICAL GRADIENTS

In pure surface-interior pattern the only differential is from the surface inward, all parts of the surface being alike (Chap. IV, p. 57, also Child, '21 a, pp. 23, 60–62). The cell itself is apparently a further development of such pattern, with nucleus and cytoplasm as the fundamental qualitative differentiations. Obviously interior rather than surface conditions are necessary for the formation of nuclear substance. There is no evidence to indicate that the cell is physiologically anything more than this, though those who regard polarity as a universal property of protoplasm must of course hold that all cells are fundamentally axiate.

Whether surface-interior pattern consists primarily in a quantitative physiological gradient like that of axiate pattern, but extending from all points of the surface inward, it is impossible to determine. External agents necessarily act from the surface inward, so that we cannot determine whether a susceptibility gradient exists. Direct investigation of the interior of such an organism is possible only by exposing it, *i. e.*, by making some part of it a surface. But the existence of physiological gradients of some sort from the surface inward in surface-interior pattern can scarcely be doubted. Excitation occurs primarily at the surface and if it is transmitted inward at all, is very probably transmitted with a steep decrement. Oxygen and nutritive substances enter through the surface and waste products must pass out through it, so the possibility of various concentration gradients between surface and interior exists. It seems probable that the surface-interior pattern is fundamentally like the axiate pattern in so far as it originates in quantitative differences in physiological condition, rather than in qualitative differences in constitution.

The presence of axiate pattern does not mean the disappearance or obliteration of surface-interior pattern. Surface-interior pattern appears in every organism, not only with relation to the external surfaces, but also to the internal surfaces. In fact, surface-interior pattern exists wherever living protoplasm is exposed to a non-protoplasmic environment, *i. e.*, wherever a surface occurs, and in many cases also in relation to two protoplasmic surfaces in contact, *e. g.*, two cells. In general, organisms represent patterns ranging from pure surface-interior patterns through various combinations of surface-interior, polar, radiate and bilateral patterns.

CHAPTER VIII

THE PHYSIOLOGICAL GRADIENTS IN RELATION TO LOCALIZATION AND DIFFERENTIATION

According to the Roux-Weismann theory of qualitative nuclear division, development is itself a distributing or sorting process in which the various determinants are assigned to their proper places. The localization of parts or characters results from this process and the differentiation of the cells is a matter of the determinants which they contain. As already noted in Chapter III, the data of observation and experiment have forced the abandonment of this theory, and it is now generally admitted that no such distributive process occurs in development. Morgan's assertion that each cell inherits the whole germ plasm expresses current views and indicates the change in our conceptions of heredity and development.

Experimental investigation has shown beyond question that physiological polarity and symmetry are factors in the localization of parts in individual development. If polarity and symmetry are primarily quantitative gradients in physiological condition, as maintained in the preceding chapter, it is necessary to show, first, that such gradients can serve as the basis for localization and differentiation of parts, and, second, that localization and differentiation can be experimentally controlled and altered by controlling or altering the gradients.

THE GRADIENTS AS A POSSIBLE BASIS OF LOCALIZATION AND DIFFERENTIATION

The general question how a quantitative physiological gradient can serve as the basis or starting point for the orderly and progressive complication and qualitative differentiation of parts which takes place in the development of the individual is of course important. The experimental data show conclusively that localization and differentiation do occur in relation to physiological gradients, but with our present fragmentary knowledge of protoplasm as a physico-chemical system we can do little more than point out probable or possible ways in which this may occur.

Localization in the physiological sense means the determination of the locus in protoplasm of some particular process, change or condition, commonly the specialization or differentiation of some organ or part. Differentiation, as the term is usually employed, is the appearance of directly perceptible, *i. e.*, morphological differences in structure and constitution in different parts or regions of an organism. In general differentiation may be described as the appearance in protoplasms of substances and structures of molar, *i. e.*, morphological magnitude, which were not originally present. Localization and physiological specialization of parts may occur without visible differentiation, *i. e.*, parts specialized in different directions are not necessarily different in gross morphological structure. Differentiation in the sense employed here is primarily a result or incident of certain degrees of specialization. It is not necessary to suppose that all specializations and differentiations involve qualitatively different chemical reactions or substances, but certainly many of them do and the essential question is how or whether such qualitative differences can arise in relation to the differences in condition at different levels of physiological gradient.

Differences in the velocity of a chemical reaction do not of themselves give rise to qualitatively different products, but in the protoplasmic system the different levels of a physiological gradient represent not merely differences in velocity of a single reaction, but differences in many factors, physical and chemical, *e. g.*, colloid dispersion, ionization, active mass of enzymes, concentration of various substances, probably water-content, and velocities of many different chemical reactions. These differences and probably others are all more or less closely interrelated and it is idle to speculate as to the primary factor: probably it is sometimes one, sometimes another, according to conditions. From what we know of non-protoplasmic physico-chemical systems it is evident that in so complex a system as protoplasm the possibilities of the origin of qualitative differences from differences originally quantitative are as numerous as could be desired (see Child, '21 a, pp. 90–97). Moreover, the fundamental chemical reactions in the protoplasmic system do not in general proceed to completion, or attain equilibrium, but in conquence of the entrance of nutritive substance and oxygen, the exit of CO_2 and other waste products, and the deposition of still others in inert form, they continue at a greater or less velocity throughout life. The relation between the rate of entrance of nutritive substance or of oxygen and the velocity of the oxidative reactions may be a factor in determining structural differentiation. If, for example, nutritive material enters a cell more rapidly than it is oxidized, it may accumulate as unoxidized or partially oxidized "reserves," *e. g.*, fat, or yolk in animal eggs, starch in plant cells, etc. The parts which become specialized and differentiated as regions or organs bearing reserves are in general regions of low oxidative metabolism. In the plant, for example, the reserves do not in general accumulate where they are formed, but in the regions of low respiratory activity. As Vöchting ('78, '84, '87, '00, etc.) and other botanists have shown, it is possible to determine the localization and differentiation of such reserve organs in regions of the plant where they never appear normally and to determine their dedifferentiation and redifferentiation into ordinary axes by changes

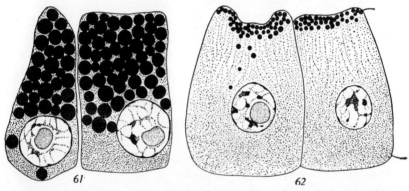

61   62

FIGS. 61, 62.—Pancreas cells of toad: Fig. 61, fully loaded and almost quiescent; Fig. 62, almost completely discharged after prolonged stimulation (from Child, '15 b, after preparations loaned by R. R. Bensley).

in conditions which are not specific but primarily quantitative. The plant responds to the quantitative change with qualitative effects.

Similarly in the animal body a decrease in rate of functional oxidative metabolism may result in the accumulation of fat in various cells and increase in metabolic rate in its disappearance. There is no indication that the changes in metabolism in such cases are anything more than quantitative, but the results are qualitative.

Again, the loading of the gland cell accompanied by very definite and conspicuous structural differentiation (Fig. 61) occurs in the presence of nutritive substance when the cell is unstimulated and the oxidation rate is low but when the cell is stimulated and the rate of oxidation increases "discharge" occurs and the differentiation of the loaded stage disappears (Fig. 62). Many differentiations are undoubtedly very similar in character to these, though often more stable and less readily reversible.

In many animal eggs yolk accumulates during the ovarian growth period and a gradient in rate and time of deposition or in amount of yolk is often visible. This gradient corresponds to the physiological gradient in the egg, the yolk being deposited earlier, more rapidly, or in larger amount at the lower levels of the gradient. In eggs in which nutrition enters chiefly or wholly at one point, this may be

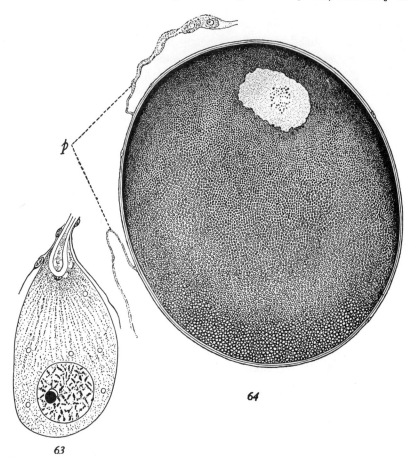

Fig. 63.—Half grown ovarian egg of *Sternaspis scutata*, showing the peduncle with vascular loop extending into cytoplasm of egg. The attached pole becomes basal, the free pole, apical (from Child, '15 b).

Fig. 64.—Section of ovarian egg of frog, showing yolk gradient; (*p*), pedicle by which egg is attached (from preparation loaned by A. W. Bellamy).

the chief factor in determining that region of the egg as the low end of the gradient. The ovarian egg of *Sternaspis*, for example, is attached by one pole, and a vascular loop enters the egg through the pedicle of attachment (Fig. 63). Apparently nutritive substance enters chiefly through this pole, which becomes the basal entodermal pole of the

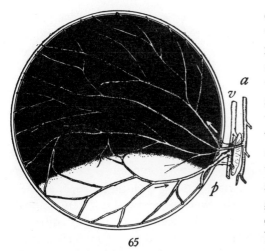

65

F‍IG. 65.—Semi-diagrammatic view of ovarian egg of frog, showing a characteristic arrangement of arteries and veins: (*a*), artery; (*v*), vein; (*p*), pedicle (from Bellamy, '19).

egg. On the other hand, the free end of the egg is more exposed to the fluid of the ovarian cavity and this exposure may conceivably be more effective than the vascular loop in providing for respiratory exchange and determining the pole of the egg as apical. But whether the gradient of the *Sternaspis* egg is determined chiefly by one or by both of these differentials, the primary difference is quantitative rather than specific. Nutritive substance undoubtedly reaches all parts and respiratory exchange undoubtedly occurs in all parts. In various other invertebrate eggs the relations between polarity and attachment are very similar to those in *Sternaspis*, the free pole becoming apical and the high end of the gradient, the attached pole basal and the low end.

In the frog's egg a yolk gradient also appears (Fig. 64) although the whole egg in later stages is inclosed in a capillary network (Fig. 65). The visible structure of the

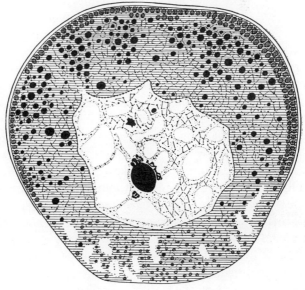

66

F‍IG. 66.—Axial section of full grown egg of *Chætopterus pergamentaceus* before maturation, indicating the structural differentiation of the cytoplasm in relation to the axis (from F. R. Lillie, '06).

unfertilized egg of the annelid *Chœtopterus* (Fig. 66) as described by F. R. Lillie ('06) suggests that here more or less morphological differentiation has occurred in relation to the physiological gradient which is present in this egg (Child, '17). But Lillie ('08) has shown that this visible differentiation is not the fundamental factor in the polarity of the egg, since by means of centrifugal force the various spherules can be carried into different regions of the egg without altering essentially the course of development.

The point which I wish to emphasize in this connection is that an apico-basal physiological gradient is present in all animal eggs examined, including various cœlenterates, echinoderms, annelids, mollusks, amphibia — whether distinct visible axial differentiation is present or not. Apparently different eggs develop very different degrees of specialization in relation to the gradient before fertilization. It is sufficiently evident, however, that the gradient may serve as the basis or starting point of differentiation. If the gradient is present before yolk formation begins, yolk may accumulate more rapidly or in greater amount at the lower levels. On the other hand, the accumulation of yolk about the region of entrance of nutrition may perhaps itself originate a gradient. The differences determined by such a gradient may lead not only to qualitative differences in reaction at different levels, but they may determine differences in rate of cell division, turgor, viscosity, etc., which become factors in determining further relations of the parts concerned. There is every reason to believe that gastrulation with all its consequences results from differences originally quantitative, rather than qualitative.

In fact, localization and differentiation during embryonic development apparently consist in large measure of the origin of specific qualitative from non-specific quantitative differences, although it is often a matter of viewpoint where we shall draw the line between these two categories. The data of developmental physiology and differentiation considered without theoretical preconception afford the strongest support to this conclusion, and there seems to be no other which will account for all the facts in physico-chemical terms.

Both synthesis and breakdown of various substances are going on in protoplasm. If for any reason the rate of synthesis of certain molecules exceeds the rate of decomposition, or if the molecules once formed are relatively stable under the conditions in the cell, an accumulation of these molecules will occur in the cell and it will become qualitatively, and if the process goes far enough, morphologically different from other cells in which decomposition keeps pace with synthesis.

Apparently just such differences as these occur at different levels of a physiological gradient. The different regions of a cell or the different cells along a gradient become qualitatively different by the appearance in their cytoplasm of different substances. It seems to be true, moreover, that cells which represent lower levels of a gradient tend in general to accumulate non-protoplasmic substances to a larger extent than those of higher levels. This is certainly true in the plant, in which cells of the growing tip and higher levels consist wholly or largely of granular "embryonic" protoplasm, while at lower levels fluid vacuoles and other inclosures appear in increasing volume. In animals also differences of this sort appear to some extent. The nerve cells, for example, which represent the high ends of the chief axial gradients, seem to retain a "protoplasmic" structure to a higher degree than many other cells of lower levels in the gradients: in these latter we find various sorts of inclosures and non-protoplasmic structures and in some the original protoplasmic structure has largely disappeared. Skeletal and supporting tissues generally develop from cells representing relatively low levels of a gradient.

As I have pointed out repeatedly, this conception of the significance of the gradient in localization and differentiation is not necessarily in conflict with current views, concerning the importance of chemical or transportative correlation, hormones, etc., but may merely supplement them. It is evident that as soon as qualitative regional differences do arise, or probably when the quantitative differences become sufficiently great, the basis for transportative or chemical correlation is established. In the case of the polar differentiation of the animal egg, for example, the yolk of the one hemisphere is largely used as nutrition in the growth of the other, i. e., the polar differentiation becomes the basis of a transportative correlation between the two hemispheres of the embryo. This is a factor in determining further differences and so on until the final relations of ectoderm, mesoderm and entoderm and their products are established.

DATA OF OBSERVATION AND EXPERIMENT

Since the physiological gradients are characteristic of physiological polarity and symmetry, at least in the earlier developmental stages and since localization and differentiation of parts occur along these gradients, a certain relation, real or apparent, must exist between the gradients and the developmental processes. As a matter

of fact, we find the apical region or the head of the organism arising
from the high end of the gradient and the other organs characteristic of each species arise in order at various levels of the gradient.
These facts, however, are merely suggestive, not demonstrative.
From them alone we might as readily conclude that the physiological gradients and the developmental phenomena are both determined by some more fundamental factor, as that localization and
differentation are deter-
mined by and result from
the gradients.

The experimental modi-
fication and obliteration of
gradients, and the deter-
mination of new gradients
afford m o r e conclusive,
though strictly speaking

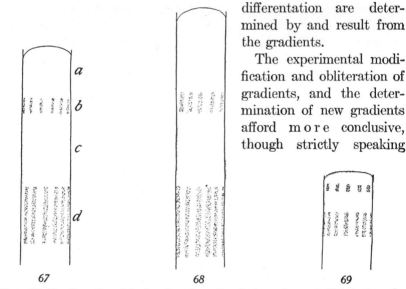

67   68   69

Figs. 67–69.—Lengths of hydranth primordia of stem pieces of *Tubularia* under
various conditions: Fig. 67, under standard normal conditions; Fig. 68, under conditions which accelerate metabolic, *e. g.*, high temperature, slight dilution of sea water
rate; Fig. 69, under conditions which decrease metabolic rate, *e. g.*, low temperature,
inhibiting chemical agents. The primordia show four regions: (*a*), pretentacular or
oral; (*b*), distal tentacular; (*c*), intertentacular; (*d*), proximal tentacular (from Child,
'15 c).

not absolutely demonstrative evidence. As I have pointed out elsewhere (Child, '15 b, pp. 128–142), altering the physiological condition either in the direction of depression or of excitation alters
the length of the gradient. If the gradient is a factor in the
localization of organs we may expect to alter their relative lengths
or distances apart as we alter experimentally the length of the gradient, and this proves to be the case. In the regulatory development
of the hydranth of *Tubularia* from pieces of stem the hydranth primordium is formed inside the perisarc, the two sets of tentacles being
represented by longitudinal ridges, as indicated in Figures 67–69. In
pieces of like physiological condition, from a given level of the stem,
and kept under the same environment the length of the primordium

and of the four regions composing it is fairly constant (Fig. 67).   Under conditions accelerating metabolism it is longer (Fig. 68) and under depressing conditions it is shorter (Fig. 69).

In the reconstitution of pieces of *Planaria dorotocephala* into new individuals localization of parts can be similarly controlled.   At a

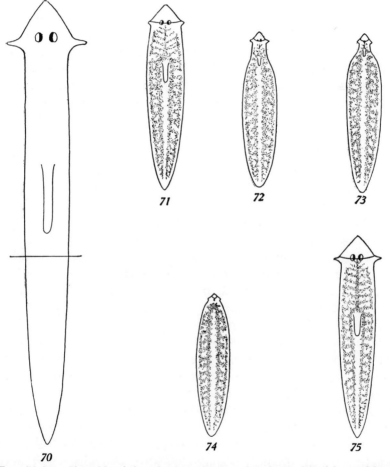

FIGS. 70–75.—Size of head, length of prepharyngeal region and position and length of pharynx in reconstitution of *Planaria dorotocephala* under different conditions: Fig. 70, outline indicating level of section; Fig. 71, reconstitution under standard laboratory conditions; Figs. 72–74, different positions and lengths of regions and organs with different degrees of inhibition; Fig. 75, reconstitution with high metabolic rate at high temperature (from Child, '15 c).

temperature of 20° in well-aërated water the isolated postpharyngeal region of Planaria — the portion posterior to the transverse line in Figure 70 — gives rise to a new animal like Figure 71, the pharynx being somewhat anterior to the middle, the region anterior to it differentiating as a prepharyngeal region and that posterior remaining practically unchanged. Under depressing conditions the head is smaller, the new prepharyngeal region shorter and the pharynx arises nearer the head, the difference from normal increasing with the degree of depression (Figs. 72, 73). Under a sufficient degree of depression reconstitution is practically limited to development of a minute head, almost no traces of reorganization of the anterior region of the piece into a prepharyngeal region occurring and the pharynx being entirely absent (Fig. 74). Changes in physiological condition in the opposite direction determine a longer prepharyngeal region and localization of the pharynx at a more posterior level (Fig. 75). Similar alterations in localization of the pharynx have been observed in a polyclad according as the cephalic ganglia are present or absent. Among the polyclads pieces do not give rise to new heads except when some portion of the cephalic ganglia, or in some cases, of parts of the nerve cords near them are present. When the pieces remain headless the new pharynx arises nearer the anterior end than when a head is present or develops (Child, '05).

Another line of evidence appears in the modification of development by means of differential susceptibility. Attention was briefly called to such modifications in connection with the discussion of susceptibility in the preceding chapter, but it is necessary to consider these modifications somewhat more at length at this point in their relation to localization and differentiation of parts.

Taking up first the question of obliteration of gradients or axes, it is evident that if the gradient represents the axis, obliteration of the gradient ought to result in obliteration of axial localization and differentiation. The obliteration of a gradient through differential susceptibility results from the fact that the levels of higher metabolic rate in a gradient are more susceptible and are therefore more depressed by inhibiting agents than the levels of lower rate. Consequently the gradient becomes less steep and with a certain degree of differential inhibition its steepness may attain zero, i. e., it may be obliterated. When a gradient is obliterated in this way in early stages of development, we find that further development shows no indication of the order corresponding to that particular gradient.

The obliteration of the apico-basal gradient in the hydroid larva was mentioned in the preceding chapter (pp. 82, 83, Figs. 45–47). After obliteration the larvæ are apolar so far as can be determined, both as regards the existence of physiological gradients and the capacity for axiate development and axiate motor behavior. They remain spherical indefinitely, even when returned to water, unless they are sub-

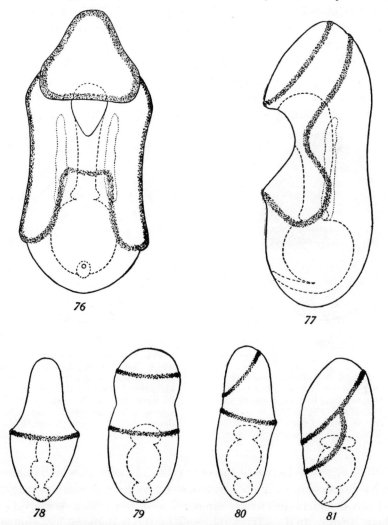

Figs. 76–81.—Obliteration of bilaterality in larval development of starfish, *Asterias forbesii:* Fig. 76, normal larva, oral view; Fig. 77, normal larva, side view; Figs. 78, 79, radially symmetrical, Figs. 80, 81, slightly bilateral modifications of development in KCN, $m/200000$. The ciliated bands are indicated by shading, the entoderm is drawn in broken lines, the cœlom sacs, if separated from entoderm, in dotted lines.

jected to a new differential in environmental conditions sufficient to determine a new gradient, or gradients. When this occurs, axiate development proceeds again, but the new axis or axes may arise in any direction with respect to the original (see pp. 123–125).

Obliteration of bilaterality in the starfish larva is readily brought about by the same methods. The normal larva of *Asterias* is distinctly bilaterally symmetrical in form (Figs. 76, 77), but when development from the eight, or the sixteen cell stage on takes place in KCN, m/200,000 at temperatures ranging from 20° to 24° the larvæ show various degrees of modification resulting from differential inhibition. A large percentage of these larvæ are either completely radially symmetrical in structure (Figs. 78, 79) or show some slight indications of bilaterality in the position of the ciliated bands (Figs. 80, 81)

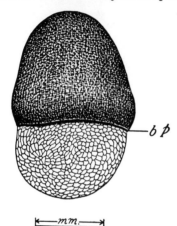

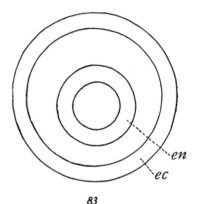

82

FIG. 82.—Radially symmetrical frog embryo: a differential inhibition resulting from exposure of unsegmented egg to LiCl *m*/10.62 for 76 hours; then 20 hours in water; (*bp*), blastopore lip (from Bellamy, '19).

83

FIG. 83.—Sea urchin larva from which all visible indications of polarity and symmetry have been obliterated through differential inhibition by KCN (many other agents give same result): (*ec*), ectoderm; (*en*), entoderm; mesenchyme cells scattered between ectoderm and entoderm, not shown.

or other organs. Larvæ of the sea urchin, *Arbacia*, in which bilaterality has been completely obliterated, so far as distinguishable structural and physiological differences are concerned, have been described elsewhere (Child, '16 d). With the same methods Bellamy has almost or completely obliterated bilaterality in amphibian embryos (Fig. 82).

By means of somewhat more extreme inhibiting conditions it is possible to obliterate completely, not only the bilaterality, but the polarity of echinoderm embryos. In the case of the sea urchin such forms lose their definitely directed movement and remain spherical in form indefinitely. Structurally they consist of a spherical ectodermal vesicle containing a spherical entodermal vesicle, and in the cavity between these a few mesenchyme cells (Fig. 83). Even when they are returned to water, such larvæ may live for weeks without further development. Moreover, susceptibility tests show that the polar susceptibility gradient characteristic of normal larvæ is completely absent. In these cases, then, all the gradients have been obliterated and with their disappearance, the capacity for axiate development and differentiation has also disappeared, and the animal no longer

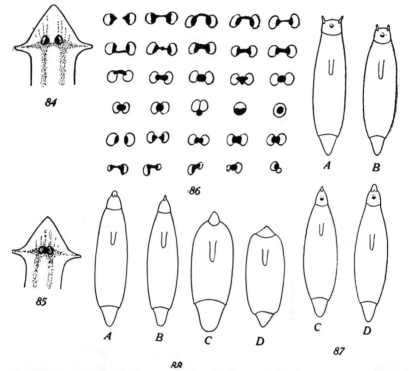

Figs. 84–88.—The head forms appearing in the reconstitution of pieces of *Planaria dorotocephala:* Fig. 84, normal head; Fig. 85, teratophthalmic head, development of median region inhibited; Fig. 86, various degrees of teratophthalmia; Fig. 87 *A–D,* teratomorphic heads, showing the range of forms. The degree of medio-lateral, differential inhibition is always greater than in teratophthalmia; Fig. 88 *A–D,* anophthalmic heads representing a still greater degree of medio-lateral differential inhibition.

shows even axiate motor behavior, but merely rolls about in one direction or another indefinitely. Dr. J. W. MacArthur permits me to state that he has produced by the same methods apolar starfish larvæ similar to those of the sea urchin (Fig. 83).

With less extreme degrees of differential inhibition acting at early stages of development, it is possible to inhibit more or less completely the development of higher levels of a gradient, while less susceptible levels proceed more or less rapidly. In this way proportions may be altered in such manner that the parts representing the higher levels of a gradient are reduced relatively to those representing the lower levels, or even completely inhibited in development. Differential inhibitions of this sort in the sea urchin larva were briefly described and figured in the preceding chapter as examples of differential susceptibility (pp. 83–94, Figs. 48–52). With the same methods and a wide range of agents, Dr. MacArthur has obtained similar modifications in the starfish and various other echinoderms, and Bellamy ('19, '22) has described numerous cases in the frog which illustrate the same principle.

Some of the most interesting modifications resulting from differential inhibition concern bilateral organs. In most if not all bilateral animals metabolic rate and susceptibility decrease primarily from the median ventral, or the median dorsal, region laterally (see pp. 81, 92).

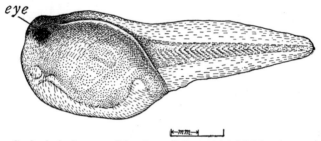

Fig. 89.—Cyclopia in frog, resulting from differential inhibition by treatment with LiCl, $m/7$ for three hours in early gastrula stage. The single eye is in the median plane beneath the surface and is seen through the body wall (from Bellamy, '19).

Consequently an inhibiting agent inhibits the median region more than the lateral, and bilateral organs may be approximated to the median line. The different forms of head in the regulatory development of *Planaria dorotocephala* (Figs. 84–88) can all be experimentally determined in this way and represent different degrees of differential inhibition in the medio-lateral axis (Child, '16 b, '20 a, '21 c; Buchanan, '22; Sivickis, '23). Under proper conditions forms representing differential acclimation and differential recovery can also be obtained (Child, '21c). Similar medio-lateral differential modifications in the larval development of the sea urchin have already been noted (Chap. VII, Figs. 51, 52). Cyclopia in fishes (Stockard, '07, '09, '10, '11, '21) and forms intermediate between this condition and normal are likewise different degrees of differential inhibition in the medio-lateral gradient. Bellamy has produced similar medio-lateral differential inhibitions in Amphibia (Fig. 89).[1]

[1] See also Bellamy, '19, pp. 344–46, Figs. 23, 24; '22.

The changes in localization and differentiation in differential acclimation and recovery and in differential acceleration are, as already noted, in the opposite direction from those characteristic of differential inhibition. Differential acclimation in the sea urchin was shown in Figures 53–56 with Figures 48, 49 representing normal larvæ for comparison. Bellamy's work on the amphibia, unpublished work by MacArthur on several species of echinoderms and my data on the sea urchin and *Planaria* (Child, '16 d, '21 c) show that differential acclimation and recovery determine changes in localization and differentiation in the same direction as regards any particular axis in all these forms and without specific relation to any particular agent.

The fact may be emphasized in passing that in these experiments, as elsewhere, polarity and symmetry appear as non-specific or quantitative regional differentials in a specific protoplasm. The production of anaxiate or modified forms does not require any particular agent or action, but polarity and symmetry can both be obliterated or modified by a large number of widely different agents and conditions. The obliteration or modification of the axes depends simply upon the differential susceptibility of different levels of the gradient which constitutes physiologically the axis.[1]

The data on modification of development through differential susceptibility leave no room for doubt that differentiation is very closely associated with, and dependent upon, the physiological gradients. When the gradients are altered, localization and differentiation are altered, and when a gradient is obliterated, differentiation does not occur in that particular axis. Moreover, these changes are determined by changes which are primarily non-specific or quantitative. We do not have to use particular agents to obliterate specific primordia, but by obliterating the gradient at a sufficiently early stage, we can prevent a primordium from developing and attaining a stage of specific differentiation. Similarly, by altering length and slope of the gradients we can alter localization of organs along the axes represented by the gradients. And finally, we shall

[1] Recently Dr. M. A. Hinrichs ('23 a) and I have observed independently that the same developmental modifications, resulting from differential susceptibility at different levels of the gradients, can be obtained in the sea urchin with ultraviolet radiation and with sunlight after photochemical sensitization as with other agents. With proper procedure either differential inhibitions like Figures 50–52 or differential recoveries like Figures 53–56 can be obtained. No attempt has been made thus far to obtain differential acclimation with continuous exposure, but there is little doubt that with a certain range of intensity it will occur.

see in the following chapter that the appearance and establishment of new gradients determines axial differentiation in new directions.

The data on developmental modification through differential susceptibility not only do not require the postulation of symmetrical or asymmetrical molecules (Harrison, '21) or a space lattice (Przibram, '21), but they are difficult to interpret in such terms, for it is highly improbable that agents of widely dissimilar constitution acting upon protoplasm in widely different ways, can all produce the same stereochemical changes, nevertheless, with proper concentration, period of exposure, etc., they do produce similar developmental modifications, not only in a single species, but in widely different species.

LOCALIZATION AND DIFFERENTIATION OF THE NERVOUS SYSTEM IN RELATION TO THE PHYSIOLOGICAL GRADIENTS

The problem of the origin and development of the nervous system as it appears in the light of our present knowledge concerning the physiological gradients has been considered at length elsewhere (Child, '21 a). Here it is possible only to refer briefly to a few points concerning localization and differentiation. In axiate animals the chief aggregation of nervous tissue is localized in the apical region or head, the region which primarily possesses a higher metabolic rate than any other part. Similarly the postcephalic portions of the central nervous system arise from the regions of highest rate in the symmetry gradients (see Child, '21 a, Chap. VI) and the progress of nervous differentiation in the posterior direction is an expression of the antero-posterior gradient.

As might be expected from its position in the gradients, the nervous system becomes morphologically distinguishable earlier than other definitive organs. Evidently then, its development, at least in its earlier stages, is independent of other organs which arise later. In short, the central nervous system arises from the dominant regions of the chief axial gradients and becomes, with its receptors, the organ *par excellence* of functional dominance or control in the behavior of the individual organism. As I have tried to make clear, the facts seem to me to indicate that the nervous system represents the morphological and physiological development and complication of the excitation-transmission relation which in its simplest form originates from the non-specific differences in physiological condition at different levels of a physiological gradient. If this is true, it follows, since the physiological gradient originates as a protoplasmic reaction to local or differential action of an external factor, that, physiologically speaking, the nervous system itself originates in protoplasmic behavior.

The nervous system shows relations not only to the axiate, but to the surface-interior pattern.   Sensory cells very generally are definitely arranged with reference to a surface.   The epithelio-muscle cell of hydra (Fig. 90) probably represents a simple excito-motor apparatus originating in relation to surface-interior pattern (Child, '21 a, Chap. XIII), the receptor or sensory end being at the surface, the effector or motor portion in the elongated contractile base, and the conductor between the two.

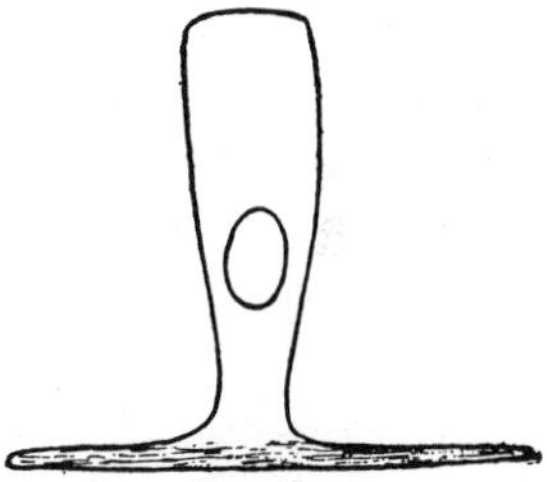

If this conception of the rôle of the physiological gradients in localization and differentiation of the nervous system is

Fig. 90.—Epithelio-muscle cell of hydra.

correct, they must play a part not merely in determining the general region from which nervous structure develops, but also in determining the polarity of individual neuroblasts, the localization and direction of outgrowth of axons, etc.   In Chapters X and XI of "The Origin and Development of the Nervous System" this question was discussed and a modified form of Kappers' ('17 and references there given) hypothesis of determination of neuroblast polarity and outgrowth by bioelectric currents was advanced.   According to this hypothesis the electric currents are primarily associated with the general axial gradients and so determine neuron polarity in relation to these gradients.

The suggestion advanced as to the manner in which the physiological polarity of the neuroblast is electrically determined is, briefly stated, that the neuroblasts are electrically polarized by the bioelectric currents to which they are exposed and that such polarization determines physiological polarity.   The higher levels of a physiological gradient are electro-negative galvanometrically to lower levels.   According to current conceptions the higher levels must therefore be internally electro-positive to lower levels.   Consequently when a cell becomes polarized by exposure to an electric current the region or pole which becomes internally electro-positive to other parts will become the high end of a physiological gradient, a region of outgrowth and of dominance.

In the discussion of this hypothesis, it was assumed that the membranes of the neuroblasts are impermeable at least to positive ions to such an extent that these ions accumulate within the cell on the side toward the bioelectric cathode and that this polarization determines the polarity of the neuron. This suggestion was advanced because it seemed to fit the facts in the case better than any other. It may, however, be pointed out that it represents only one of two possibilities of electrolytic determination of physiological polarity. If the cell membranes are highly permeable to both positive and negative ions, the positive ions will leave the cell on the cathodic and enter on the anodic side, while the negative ions will pass out on the anodic and enter on the cathodic side. Under such conditions the polarization of the cell will be opposite to that which occurs in cells with relatively impermeable membranes and the internally positive region of the cell will be determined on the side toward the anode.

According to this conception physiological polarity may be determined by an electric current in two opposite ways, depending upon conditions of permeability to positive and negative ions.

As already pointed out, this hypothesis of electric determination of physiological and particularly of neuron polarity is nothing more than an attempt to call attention to possibilities along this line.[1] The general physiological gradients are present in axiate animals and the evidence indicates that bioelectric currents are characteristic features of them, but extensive experimental investigation is necessary in order to determine whether these currents affect the neuroblasts in the manner suggested or in some other way, or whether they affect them at all. As a beginning along this line it may be noted that Ingvar ('20) has recorded the determination of direction of outgrowth of cells in tissue cultures, and Lund ('21 a) has determined polarity in pieces of hydroid stems by electric current, the apical ends being determined on the side toward the anode.

We are accustomed to say that the reflex arc represents the functional unit in the nervous system. The conception of origin of the nervous system under consideration here amounts essentially to saying that the physiological gradient is the simplest, the most generalized, and the primary reflex arc in the individual and so constitutes the physiological basis for the structural and functional development of all other arcs.

It is perhaps necessary to point out that this conception of ner-

[1] Recently Kappers ('22) has criticized my hypothesis at length, but since it was intended as nothing more than a suggestion and since experimental data on which to base definite conclusions are lacking, discussion of these criticisms can be little more than an academic exercise and is quite unnecessary here.

vous origins does not in any way conflict with data or theories of heredity. Heredity is concerned with potentialities of development and differentiation, but here we are concerned with the realization of hereditary potentialities in the individual. Hereditary potentialities of nervous development and differentiation exist in most animal protoplasms, but for the development of an individual nervous system certain physiological conditions are necessary, and I have endeavored to show that those conditions arise primarily in certain non-specific relations between a living protoplasm and environmental factors. When we say that the physiological gradient is the basis of the reflex arc we do not in any sense deny that each particular kind of protoplasm possesses hereditary potentialities which determine the characteristics that distinguish structurally and functionally the reflex arcs and the nervous systems of one species from that of another. We mean merely that for the realization in an individual of these hereditary potentialities of a specific protoplasm a physiological gradient is a primary and necessary factor.

CONCLUSION

There can be no doubt that a quantitative physiological gradient provides various possibilities for localization and differentiation and the experimental evidence indicates that changes in the gradient determine changes in localization and differentiation and that obliteration of the gradient obliterates, so far as can be determined, the axis which the gradient represents. If the physiological gradients were products or results of some underlying molecular or other structural polarity or symmetry we should not expect to find that obliteration of a gradient through differential susceptibility would obliterate the axis which it represents. As a matter of fact, however, we find that when a gradient is obliterated in early developmental stages localization and differentiation along that axis cease and we are not able to show that the axis is still present. These experimental data obtained with widely different animals are highly significant as indicating that the gradient is itself the physiological basis of the axis, rather than a consequence or incident of some sort of molecular or other protoplasmic structure.

CHAPTER IX

THE ORIGIN OF THE PHYSIOLOGICAL GRADIENTS

It was shown in the preceding chapter that the gradients and axes can be obliterated in organisms through the differential susceptibility of different levels. The question of their origin now arises. If polarity and symmetry are inherent in the molecular structure of protoplasm, as many zoölogists still maintain, changes can be brought about only by the modification of that structure and we have to assume that the conditions which brought about the change have done it by altering molecular structure. Leaving out of account the fact that if polarity and symmetry in general are matters of molecular structure, we ought to find some indication of optical axes in protoplasm, this hypothesis involves us in other difficulties, some of which are pointed out below.

If, however, the physiological gradient itself is the basis of polarity and symmetry all the assumptions of molecular structure and change, in favor of which there is no actual evidence, become entirely unnecessary. From this viewpoint polarity and symmetry are primarily dynamic in character, and molar or regional, rather than molecular in magnitude. Admitting this, it evidently ought to be possible not only to obliterate old polarities and symmetries, but to determine new axes experimentally, by exposing the protoplasm to a differential in action of some external factor which will determine in one way or another a physiological differential, *i. e.*, a physiological gradient. Moreover, since the physiological gradients are apparently primarily quantitative we do not need to employ specific factors to determine them. Any factor that will determine a more or less persistent quantitative differential in the protoplasm ought to be adequate.

As a matter of fact we can determine physiological gradients and axes experimentally by differential exposure in many animal and plant protoplasms and in many other cases the data of observation indicate that in nature physiological axes very often arise in the same way, though it is evident that in some cases they persist from earlier individual or cell generations.[1]

[1] For earlier discussions of this question see Child, '21 a, Chap. III, also '15 c, pp. 96–101, 132–4, 142–9.

DETERMINATION OF PHYSIOLOGICAL GRADIENTS BY LIGHT

Light has long been recognized by the botanists as a factor of great importance in determining both polarity and symmetry in plants through its differential action on different parts or regions. The determination of polarity in the egg of *Fucus* through the action of light has already been noted (pp. 58–61, Figs. 16–18). The action of light in determining polarity is much the same in the spore of *Equisetum* (Stahl, 1883). Polarity may also be determined by light in the alga, *Bryopsis* (Winkler, 1900 a). In certain liverworts light determines dorsoventrality and in various algæ the thallus is radially symmetrical when illumination is equal on all sides and bilateral when it is unequal or unilateral. According to Jenkinson ('09) light may play some part in determining bilaterality in the frog's egg.

It is important to note that in all these cases the molar regional differential in light action appears to be the important factor rather than any stereochemical or other orienting action upon the proto-plasmic molecules. Exact knowledge concerning the nature of light action is, however, lacking. The fact that a certain range of wave length toward the blue-violet end of the spectrum is significant in determination of polarity in *Fucus* (Hurd, '19, '20) suggests a chemical effect.

DETERMINATION OF GRADIENTS BY ELECTRICITY

Little is known as yet concerning electricity as a factor in determining axiation in animals. As already noted, Ingvar ('20) has observed the determination of apparent polarity in tissue culture by the electric current and Lund ('21 a, c) has reported determination of polarity in pieces of hydroid stem by the same means. The suggestions advanced in the preceding chapter and elsewhere (Child, '21 a, Chap. XI) concerning the rôle of bioelectric currents in determining neuron polarity are as yet without experimental basis, though it seems difficult or impossible to account for the facts in any other way than through some sort of differential action of the bioelectric currents on the cells. I am inclined to believe that future investigation will show that electric factors in the proper intensity and relation are highly effective in determining physiological gradients and so axiation. As regards the manner in which the electric current acts nothing definite is known, but, as suggested above (pp. 111–112), it seems to be possible to account for the facts by changes in electrical polarization of cells or cell masses and the effect of such change upon metabolic rate and physiological condition in general.

DETERMINATION OF GRADIENTS BY GRAVITY

Gravity as a possible factor in determining specific localization and differentiation has been considered in an earlier chapter (pp. 54–55). Here we are concerned with its possible action in originating and establishing physiological gradients. In various plants radial and bilateral symmetry show essentially the same relation to gravity as in other cases to light. Such plants or parts are radially symmetrical when their longitudinal axes coincide with the direction of gravity and dorsoventral when in other positions. It has been known, for example, that in pieces of stems of various plants in horizontal position, roots tend to appear on the lower and shoots on the upper side, and it has been experimentally demonstrated that the essential factor in such cases is gravity. Within recent years Loeb ('17 a, b, '19, '20 and other papers) has repeated many of the older experiments and added some further data, besides attempting an interpretation of the action of gravity in terms of transport of chemical substances, hormones, or formative substances. In these cases the action of gravity does not obliterate the preëxisting polarity but merely modifies it to some extent. Thus far no case is known in which gravity determines polarity in the egg, the spore or the growing tip of the plant as light does in various cases. In general, gravity is far less important than light in determining axial relations and forms in plants. Loeb ('92) has described the determination of polarity by gravity in an animal, the hydroid *Antennularia*. Up to the present this case remains unique. Morgan ('01 a) and Stevens ('02, '10) have shown that gravity is certainly not essential in this case, since polarity may be determined by other factors.

As regards the way in which gravity produces its effects we are even more in the dark than as regards the action of light and electricity. Transport of specific substances has often been postulated since Sachs, and Loeb in his recent papers ('17 a, b, '19, '20) attempted to interpret the facts in essentially these terms. This transportative conception fails, however, to account satisfactorily for many facts and interpretation must apparently be sought along other lines. It is perhaps permissible to call attention to a suggestion recently cited by Harvey ('20, p. 367) from a personal communication of R. S. Lillie. This suggestion is essentially that the distribution of sap by gravity may determine differences in electrical conductivity, and so differences in bioelectric currents in different regions. It seems probable at any rate that the action of gravity will prove to be primarily quantitative rather than specific as regards different regions of the plants. As regards polarity its action is not fundamentally different from that of light, which is apparently primarily quantitative. In other words, the action of gravity in determining polarity or symmetry, so far as such action occurs, is probably essentially like that of other external factors, a determination in some way of a quantitative gradient in physiological condition.

NEW GRADIENTS IN REGULATORY DEVELOPMENT AND AGAMIC REPRODUCTION

The appearance of new axes in many cases of regulatory development is very evidently associated with differential action of an external factor, even though the factor of the environmental complex which is chiefly or primarily concerned has not been determined.

New gradients determined by differential exposure. — Pieces 10 mm. or more in length from the stem of the hydroid *Tubularia* (Fig. 91) usually develop a hydranth first at the apical, and slightly later at the basal end (Fig. 92) when both ends are equally exposed. That the new polarity at the basal end is determined by the action of some external factor is clearly shown by two facts: first, it was not originally present, and second, if the basal end is closed by wax, paraffin, etc., or even buried in the sand, the new polarity fails to develop. In general, the shorter the piece of stem isolated the less clearly does the original polarity appear and the more rapidly do new polarities arise in response to external differentials. As I have pointed out elswhere (Child, '15 c, pp. 96–102) this general disappearance of the original polarity with decrease in length of the piece is to be expected if polarity is a physiological gradient, because the shorter the piece the more nearly are its two ends physiologically alike. But if polarity is a molecular phenomenon it is difficult to account for its disappearance with decreasing length of piece. Such short pieces of the stems of *Tubularia*, *Corymorpha*, and various other hydroids may give rise to single (Figs. 93, 94) or to biaxial forms (Figs. 95–98), according as a single or a double gradient is determined. In the biaxial forms one of the axes is obviously new and determined in relation to the cut surface at that end. In general, the shorter the piece the more frequent biaxiality, and this fact shows very clearly that as the length of piece decreases the external factor becomes more effective than the original polarity.

Similar biaxial forms appear in short pieces of planarians (Figs.

99–101) and it is possible to increase their frequency experimentally by partially obliterating the original gradient by means of anesthetics or other inhibiting agents at the time of, and for a certain period after section (Child, '15 c, p. 149).   In all these and in many other cases

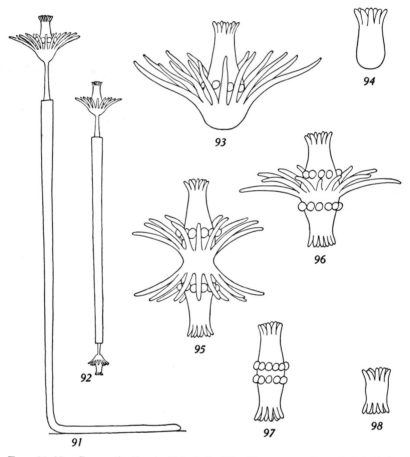

Figs. 91–98.—Reconstitution in *Tubularia:* Fig. 91, young, unbranched individual; Fig. 92, usual result of reconstitution in a long piece of stem with origin of a new gradient at aboral (lower) end; Figs. 93, 94, single apical structures from short pieces; Figs. 95–98, biaxial apical structures from short pieces (from Child, '15 c).

the direct exposure to the medium of the cells at the cut ends, permitting a more rapid respiratory exchange than in other regions where the body wall is intact, and the growth and cell division following the wound are undoubtedly factors in establishing the new axes. These new axes are in all cases represented by physiological gradients and these gradients apparently result simply from the gradation

in exposure and its effects from the cut surface inward. Hypotheses
of reversal in orientation of cells or molecules are quite superfluous,
and there is no reason to believe that exposure at a cut surface can
bring about such changes.

**Differential exposure after experimental obliteration of original
gradients.** — In *Corymorpha*, a hydroid much like *Tubularia*, except
that most of the stem is naked, the original polarity of stem pieces
(Figs. 102–105) or even single or double hydranths (Figs. 106–109)
can be obliterated through differential inhibition with various agents
and then on removal of the inhibiting agent a new polarity arises,
determined by the differential between the free surface and that in
contact (Figs. 104, 105, 108, 109). Since the new polarity is indicated

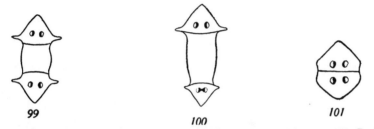

Figs. 99–101.—Biaxial heads from short pieces of *Planaria*: Figs. 99, 100, *P. dorotocephala*, Fig. 101, *P. simplicissima* (from Child, '21 a).

by a gradient involving differences in rate of respiration, the rate
being highest on the free surface, it seems probable that the gradient
is not some peculiar reaction to contact and its absence, but rather
a matter of the difference in oxygen supply and perhaps in rate of
CO_2 removal between free and attached surfaces. Similarly in the
development of sponges from dissociated cells (H. V. Wilson, '07,
'11 a) the polarity of the new individual is evidently determined by
the differential between the free surface and the surface in contact
with the substratum.

Determination of new gradients by localization of growth. —
The case of the sea-anemone *Harenactis*, in which it is possible to lo-
calize new axes by means of injury and the resulting growth (Child,
'09, '10 b, '15 c, pp. 146–9), requires mention here. When short cy-
lindrical pieces are cut from the body of this animal as indicated in
Fig. 110, *a*, *b*) and most of the mesenteries removed from inside them,
they close, as indicated in Figure 111, so that apical and basal cut surfaces of the body wall unite about the whole circumference and more
or less new tissue arises along the line of union. This method of closure
gives rise to " rings " or doughnut-shaped forms and the line of union

usually comes to lie somewhere on the outer surface in consequence of a peculiar revolution of the ring upon itself, like the movement in a vortex ring, presumably an attempt at orientation.   From both sides of the line of union tentacles and tentacle-groups arise, some bilateral, others radial and still others asymmetric (Figs. 112, 113).   The tentacle-groups tend to appear in regions where the two cut surfaces did not fit closely together and where consequently considerable growth

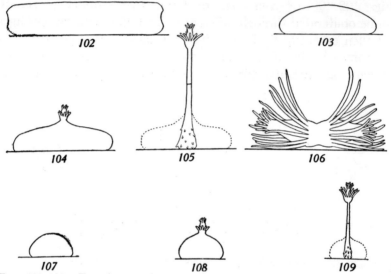

Figs. 102–109.—Experimental determination of new polarity in pieces of stem of *Corymorpha:* Fig. 102, a piece of stem after isolation; Fig. 103, reduction and "melting down" in dilute alcohol; Fig. 104, appearance of new hydranth on upper side of mass after return to sea water.   This polarity is at right angles to original axis; Fig. 105, later stage of new individual, with dotted lines indicating earlier outline of piece as preserved by thin perisarcal secretion; Fig. 106, a short piece which has developed biaxial hydranths and is therefore bipolar; Fig. 107, reduction of biaxial piece in dilute alcohol involving disintegration of tentacles and dedifferentiation of hydranth bodies; Fig. 108, appearance of new hydranth on upper surface of piece after return to water, the new polarity being at right angles to the former bipolar axes; Fig. 109, later stage of new individual, with dotted lines indicating earlier outline of piece as preserved by perisarcal secretion (from Child, '15 c).

of new tissue occurs, giving rise both to body wall and mesenteries. Where the cut edges were closely apposed and little new growth has occurred, few or no tentacles arise.   These facts led to the experiment of injuring locally a portion of the cut body wall by repeated snipping and complete removal of mesenteries.   Such regions were found to give rise to larger and more nearly normal groups of tentacles than regions where less growth occurred.   Figure 114 shows a case in which a normal axis arose from such an injured region.   In this case the new axial gradient originates in the gradation in rate of metabolism, growth, etc., which has its high region in the area of injury and greatest development of new tissue. That the kind of symmetry which arises may differ widely in different cases according to the shape and extent of the regions of more active growth is indicated by the

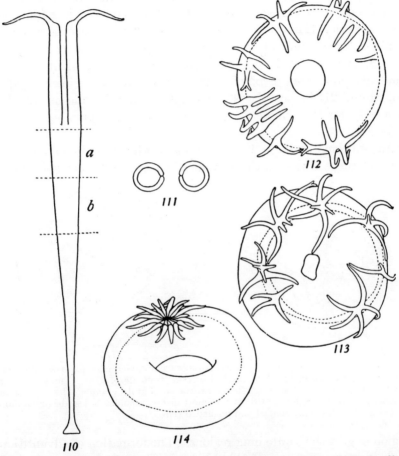

Figs. 110–114.—Localization of new axis in sea anemone, *Harenactis*, by localized injury and growth: Fig. 110, outline of animal indicating pieces, *a*, *b*, used; Fig. 111, closure of pieces, oral end uniting with aboral end about whole circumference to form a "ring"; Figs. 112, 113, Tentacle groups developing along the line of union of oral and aboral cut ends in such rings; Fig. 114, a new normal axis localized by localized injury with resulting growth in a certain region of circumference.

various symmetries of the tentacle-groups in Figures 112 and 113. In connection with this case of the localization of a new axis by determination of more rapid growth through local injury, a statement of Harrison's concerning the amphibian leg primordium is of interest. He says: "The limb rudiment may be thus regarded, not as a definite circumscribed area like a stone in a mosaic, but as a center of differentiation in which the intensity of the process diminishes as the distance from the center increases, until it passes away into an indifferent region. Many other systems, such as the nose, ear, hypophysis, gills, seem to have the same indefinite boundaries, which may even overlap each other" (Harrison, '18, p. 456). It is perfectly clear from this statement that Harrison regards the primordia of these various organs as physiological gradients in a more or less specialized cellular region of the embryo, though he does not believe that such gradients are the fundamental factors of physiological axes. In a more recent paper (Harrison, '21) he postulates a molecular symmetry and asymmetry as a basis for the symmetry relations in the amphibian leg (see pp. 126–128).

Adventitious buds. — There are many other cases in which a new axial gradient arises as the physiological gradient from a localized

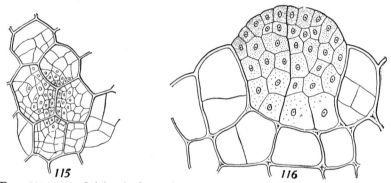

FIGS. 115, 116.—Origin of adventitious buds from epidermal cells of *Begonia* leaf: Fig. 115, surface view; Fig. 116, vertical section (from Regel, '76). The shading indicates gradient in protoplasmic structure from uniformly granular, deeply staining cytoplasm in more deeply shaded cells, to more or less vacuolated, less deeply staining cytoplasm in less deeply shaded and unshaded cells.

region of growth to adjoining regions. The formation of adventitious buds in plants is a case of this kind. In *Begonia*, for example, buds arise from the specialized epidermal cells of the isolated leaf, or in some cases without isolation (Regel, '76). In these buds the new gradient is directly visible as a gradient in cell size and rate of division and protoplasmic content (Figs. 115, 116). New axes appear in the same way in many other plants. While certain regions of the leaf or other parts usually show more or less predisposition to adventitious bud-formation as compared with others, the localization of each individual bud in a particular epidermal cell or cell group must be due to a slight fortuitous difference between this cell or cell group and others about it. Such difference determines that this cell or group shall react more quickly than those about it to the altered conditions and this reaction originates the new gradient and the new plant axis. When we say that the difference is fortuitous, we mean merely that we do not know the particular factors concerned in determining it. Some definite factor or group of factors is of course concerned in each case. Moreover, whenever a gradient originates in response to such action, the specific constitution of the protoplasm at once becomes a factor in determining its further development.

Similar processes of "adventitious" budding are of frequent occurrence in animals, particularly in regulatory development. In short pieces of the naked stem of the hydroid, *Corymorpha*, the cut ends close rapidly and since there is no perisarc there is no such differential exposure as in pieces of *Tubularia*, but all parts of the surface are exposed alike, unless in contact with the substratum. Such pieces may give rise to single or to biaxial forms like those of *Tubularia* (See Figs. 93–98) but they often give rise to three or even more axes or partial axes (Figs. 117–121). In such cases, at least one or more of the axes must be adventitious in origin. The buds in these cases represent only the apical regions of individuals but they are of course none the less new axes and must be localized by slight regional differences in cells or cell groups.

Cases like Figures 119–121 show remarkable combinations of extreme apical and extreme basal structures without any intermediate stem region. The basal structure usually appears on that side of the piece in contact with the bottom of the dish, the apical structures at the two cut ends, or if the piece rests on one cut end, this end develops basal structures and the other apical structures. In very short pieces this determination of polarity in relation to the substratum and the differential exposure of the pieces may be quite independent of the original polarity (Child, '23 c).

Adventitious gradients in embryonic development.—In the embryonic development of the hydrozoa the development of new adventitious axes is readily induced. The normal course of development has already been briefly described (p. 63). When early development occurs under a certain range of inhibiting conditions, *e. g.*, low concentrations of KCN, HCl, or even CO_2, the blastulæ remain spherical, are apparently apolar (p. 82), and in the higher non-lethal concentrations may fail to develop further, even though they remain alive for weeks. With a less extreme degree of inhibition, or if they acclimate to a sufficient degree, they may give rise to new axes, but under

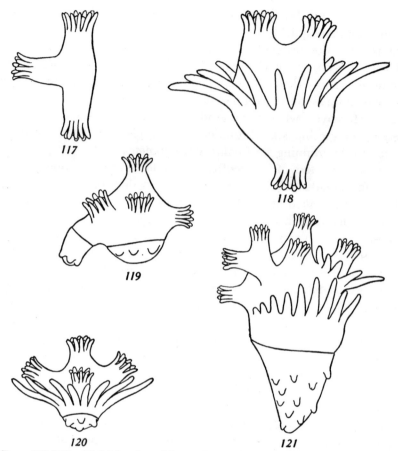

FIGS. 117–121.—Multiple adventitious polarities in reconstitution of short pieces of *Corymorpha* stem: Fig. 117, 1/16 piece from 125 mm. stem, three manubria with distal tentacles, no stem; Fig. 118, 1/16 piece from 125 mm. stem, biaxial, one axis with two manubria and one set proximal tentacles, other axis with one manubrium; Fig. 119, 1/8 piece from 80 mm. stem, four manubria with distal tentacles and two basal ends; Fig. 120, 1/33 piece from 100 mm. stem, four manubria with distal tentacles, one set of proximal tentacles and one basal end; Fig. 121, 1/23 piece from 120 mm. stem, six manubria with distal tentacles, only one with both distal and proximal tentacles, a second incomplete set of proximal tentacles below the manubrial complex, one basal region.

such conditions the axes are stolons not stems,[1] and very commonly not merely one but two or more appear, and in all possible relations to each other (Figs. 122–126). Here again, with the partial or com-

---

[1] The less specialized hydroid stolon characteristic of this and various other species is a slightly inhibited gradient. Stems can be transformed into stolons by a certain degree of inhibition or depression and transformed back again by removing the inhibiting factor and the embryonic development of stems or stolons can be experimentally controlled in the same way (Child, '23 b).

plete obliteration of the original axis new adventitious axes appear. Under good environmental conditions, *i. e.*, after removal of the inhibiting agent, all of these new axes may transform into hydranth-bearing stems.

Partial or even complete adventitious reduplication of axes is not infrequent in embryonic development, and differences, obviously

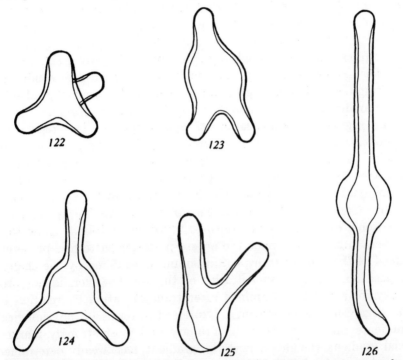

Figs. 122–126.—Multiple adventitious polarities in inhibited embryonic development of hydrozoan, *Phialidium:* Figs. 122, 123, development in HCl, $m/5000$, in the one case four, in the other three stolon axes; Figs. 124–126, development under conditions of crowding and excess of CO_2, the first with three, the second and third with two stolon axes. In all figures the outer heavier outline indicates perisarc, the inner lighter line, surface of cœnosarc.

fortuitous, and differing in different embryos, may be concerned in localizing the new axes. Many other cases of partial or complete embryonic reduplication may be called adventitious, which means only that the conditions determining the new gradients and axes are not uniform and constant in all cases, but differ without definite order in different cases, *i. e.*, are fortuitous.

In all cases these adventitious axes are represented by physiological gradients and it is evident that the gradients are not predetermined but are reactions to local conditions. These duplications, particularly the partial duplications and partial multiplications such as seen in *Corymorpha* (Figs. 117–121) are not readily accounted for in terms of inherent molecular or other structural polarity, but they present no difficulties to the conception of polarity as fundamentally a dynamic gradient of organismic magnitude.

Dichotomy, twinning and related processes.— Discussion of this group of phenomena is postponed to the following chapter and it need only be noted here that dichotomy and twinning from a single egg consist fundamentally of equal division of a dominant region, or of the replacement of a single dominant region by two of equal rank. The localization of the new axis may be determined by conditions resulting from differential growth in relation to the original gradients, or by conditions in the environment of the dominant region.

The regulatory reduplication of appendages. — The regulatory reduplications of appendages particularly in arthropods and amphibia [1] afford interesting examples, both of the appearance of new axes — in this case appendage axes or partial axes — and of peculiar axial relations of the reduplicated parts with respect to each other. Considering briefly the case of the amphibian appendages, Harrison's experiments on transplantation of limb-buds show that in these transplanted buds the antero-posterior pattern is predetermined at the time of transplantation and not altered by the change in position. The dorsoventrality of the leg, however, is not predetermined, but is determined after transplantation by relation to the organismic environment. Expressed in terms of physiological gradients this means that the primary and most strongly marked axial gradient, the antero-posterior gradient, has already determined a persistent physiological differential in the limb-bud, while the less strongly marked dorsoventral gradient has not yet determined a persistent differential. Further experiment may show the possibility of influencing through position on the body both dorsoventral and antero-posterior relations in the limb-bud (see Wilhelmi, '22).

The most interesting features of these transplanted limb-buds are the development of supernumerary limbs by the origin of new limb axes through division or budding of the original axes and the asymmetry relations of the limbs thus formed. One or two supernumerary limbs may arise so that the limb-complex may consist of two or three limbs. Harrison's statement of the axial relations of such appendages to each other is as follows: (1) The long axes of duplex

---

[1] See Bateson, '94, Harrison, '21, Przibram, '21, and references given by these authors.

or multiplex appendages lie in one plane. (2)   Two adjacent members form in structure and position the image of each other, as reflected from a plane mirror bisecting the angle between the respective axes and perpendicular to the common plane of the two axes (Figs. 127, 128).   Since the supernumerary limbs are usually of later origin than the original bud it is evident that their asymmetry is determined in some way in relation to that of the original bud.   The asymmetry of the amphibian leg expresses itself in regional differences in rate of metabolism and growth and the axial form of the leg is the result of such differences.   On the basis of Harrison's stereochemical hypothesis of symmetry and asymmetry the origin of these regional differences remains obscure; as yet we know nothing of the physiology of this particular process of reduplication except that it is associated in some way with the disturbances brought about by the experiment.   Undoubtedly the limb-bud is more or less inhibited for the time being, particularly when grafted into a bodily environment differing from the normal.   Under these conditions it must be less effective than the bud *in situ* in dominating the surrounding region, and physiological isolation with the appearance of new buds may occur, as is probably the case in various other processes of reduplication.

The asymmetry of the supernumerary limb or limbs is obviously determined in some way in relation to that of the primary limb, but until we have more complete knowledge of the processes of reduplication only suggestion is possible.   There can be no doubt that differences in electric potential are associated with the regional differences in cellular activity, rate of growth, etc., which constitute the more obvious indications of the asymmetry of the limb.   If bioelectric currents of any appreciable strength result from these differences, such currents may be important or even fundamental factors in determining the relations of the limbs to each other.   And in the same way the bioelectric factors associated with the axes of the body on which the limb-bud is grafted may influence its axial relations, at least as regards dorsoventrality.

Recently Przibram ('21) has considered at length a great variety of reduplications of parts in animals and has attempted to interpret their axial relations in terms of a hypothetical space lattice.   Such interpretation is purely speculative, absolutely no evidence being presented for the existence of such a space lattice in any case.   It seems probable that future experimental investigation will provide a basis for a much simpler physiological interpre-

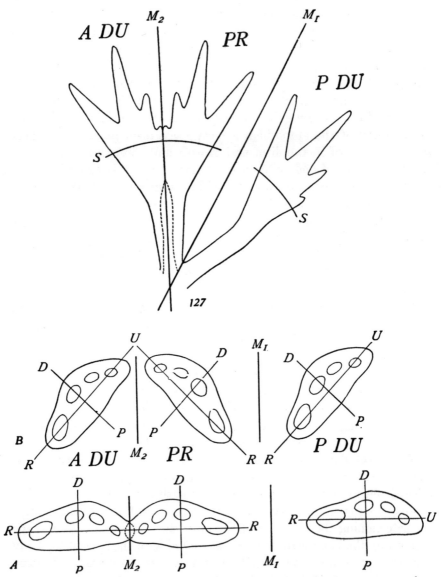

Figs. 127, 128.—Diagrams of reduplicated amphibian legs, showing symmetry rela-tions: (PR), primary leg; (P DU), posterior reduplication; (A DU), anterior reduplica-tion; (M_1 M_2), planes of symmetry, "mirror planes," between the two reduplications and the primary leg; (M_1) is radial (R) since the radial borders of the two legs, (PR) and (P DU), which are symmetrical with respect to it face each other; (M_2) is ulnar (U) since the ulnar borders of the two legs, (PR) and (A DU), face each other; (D), dorsal surface; (P), palmar surface. In the sectional diagram, Fig. 128A the mirror planes are radial (M_1) and ulnar (M_2). In Fig. 128B the mirror planes are radiodor-sal (M_1) and ulno-palmar (M_2). (From Harrison, '21.)

tation of the various phenomena of regulatory reduplication than the speculations concerning a space lattice offered by Przibram. Even if the space lattice is present it is by no means clear how it can determine physiological polarity and symmetry and their modifications as we find them.

THE ORIGIN OF THE GRADIENTS IN EGGS

The determination of polarity by light in the eggs of certain algæ has already been mentioned (pp. 58–61). In most other plants the polarity of the egg and embryo shows in general a very definite relation to its organismic environment, though practically nothing is known concerning the determining factors in particular cases.

In many animals a relation exists between the polarity of the egg and its ovarian environment in the gonad. For example in *Chœtopterus* (F. R. Lillie, '06), *Sternaspis* (Figs. 63, 66, pp. 98–9) and various other invertebrates in which the growing ovarian egg is attached to the parent body by one portion of its periphery, the apical pole arises on the exposed free surface, the basal pole at or near the region of attachment and the physiological gradient corresponding to this polarity appears. It seems reasonable to believe that the polarity of such eggs is determined by the differential in the ovarian environment. The nutritive substances which give rise to yolk probably, in some cases certainly (Fig. 63), enter the egg chiefly at the attached pole, while respiratory exchange must occur most readily through the free surface or some part of it. In the hydromedusa *Phialidium* the egg axis is apparently determined by a similar differential, the egg region most exposed to the sea water becoming apical, the opposite end basal (Child, '21 a, p. 54, Fig. 1). Such differentials provide conditions for the origin of an axial gradient as a physiological reaction of the egg cell to its environment.

According to Boveri ('01 a, b) the attached pole of the sea urchin egg cell becomes apical, the free pole basal, but Jenkinson ('11) maintains that, the attached pole becomes basal, the free pole apical. In the absence of definite knowledge any discussion of possible factors is useless. In some of the higher animals, also, the attached pole of the egg apparently becomes the apical pole, perhaps because in these forms the presence of a circulatory system or of impermeable egg membranes determines a more rapid respiratory exchange through the attached region than elsewhere. And finally, it is possible that in some eggs the gradient persists from earlier cell generations and so is inherited, as in many cases of fission. Such inheritance is, of course, not Lamarckian but represents merely the persistence through cell division of a regional cytoplasmic differential.

Concerning the origin of symmetry in eggs and embryos, we know even less than concerning the origin of polarity. In the frog the point of entrance or direction of movement of the spermatozoön is commonly believed to be a factor in determining bilaterality (Roux, '85. '87, '95, Bd. II), but Jenkinson ('07, '09) maintains that various other factors may also be concerned. Brachet ('11) finds, however, that in eggs induced to develop parthenogenetically by puncture there is no relation between bilaterality and the meridian of puncture, and concludes from this fact that the egg possesses a primary bilateral symmetry which is labile and subject to alteration by entrance of the spermatozoön. Whatever its origin may be, the regional symmetry differential is physiologically distinguishable in a quantitative way in early developmental stages (Bellamy, '19). In the echinoderms there is no definite evidence of bilaterality until after development has begun, but it is distinguishable physiologically as a gradation before it is distinguishable structurally (Child, '16 a, Jenkinson, '11). In the annelids and mollusks bilaterality is both morphologically and physiologically distinguishable in the first cleavage and in many insects it is indicated even before fertilization by the shape of the egg.

As regards the origin of bilateral symmetry in eggs and embryos various possibilities exist. It may in some cases be determined by ovarian conditions, in others by conditions connected with maturation or fertilization, in still others by conditions arising later in development. It is also possible that in some cases bilaterality, like polarity, may persist from earlier cell generations and so be inherited by the individual, but this again is not Lamarckian inheritance. According to Bartelmez ('12), for example, bilaterality is distinguishable in very early ovarian stages of the pigeon's egg and is presumably hereditary.

It is probable that the theories of polarity and symmetry most widely current are responsible in part for the state of our knowledge concerning the origin of polarity and symmetry in embryonic development. As long as these characteristics of organisms are regarded as matters of molecular structure and orientation, the problem of their origin is in the same category as other problems of molecular structure and orientation. Experimental possibilities are limited to the modification of polarity and symmetry by modification of molecular structure and orientation, and since we are far from any definite knowledge of the molecular structure concerned or of its changes, the whole matter has only a speculative interest. Actually, however, there is no real evidence in support of these theories of polarity and symmetry and a good deal against them. They are essentially speculative hypotheses which have been advanced, chiefly by morphologists, in the absence of experimental physiological data. When we take the facts as they stand, viz., that polarity and symmetry appear primarily as non-specific molar or regional physiological differences which can be determined, altered or obliterated by non-specific environmental action, and that we cannot find, by the methods of optics or otherwise, any positive indication of a molecular or static polarity or symmetry in protoplasm, it is evident at least that such hypotheses have no adequate basis at present. As a matter of fact, the conception of the physiological gradient as the primary factor in polarity and symmetry is the only theory which is based on actual evidence from experiment.

THE ORIGIN OF SURFACE-INTERIOR PATTERN

In an earlier chapter (pp. 57–61) it was noted that surface-interior pattern represents a more generalized relation to environment than axiate pattern. In this pattern the only fixed differential is between surface and interior, consequently the relation to environment and the behavior of surface-interior organisms are less specialized than in axiate organisms. So far as different regions of the surface are concerned, the surface-interior organism possesses the highest degree of versatility, i. e., any reaction may be performed by any region, the environmental factors determining which region shall react in a particular case.

While it is probable that some cells and perhaps many microörganisms possess only surface-interior pattern, at least during some stages of their life history, we find surface-interior, together with axiate pattern in most forms. Surface-interior pattern does not disappear when axiate pattern arises, but exists in all organisms. Every exposed surface, every epithelium, every cell, whether in contact with inorganic environment or with other cells, possesses a surface-interior pattern. In epithelial cells this pattern usually appears as an axis in relation to the surface-interior differential (see Figs. 61, 62), i. e., the pattern is axiate as regards the cell, but surface-interior as regards the epithelium as a whole.

That this kind of pattern is directly related in some way to a differential of some sort between surface and interior or between a more exterior and a more interior region, cannot be doubted. We often see the pattern in its simpler forms appear as the direct consequence of exposure of protoplasm. Except in the more highly specialized protozoa in which the ectoplasm has attained a more or less definite morphological form, isolated pieces of cells usually become more or less spherical in form and if they contain nuclei, behave in all respects like whole cells. It is a familiar fact that the differences between ectoplasm and entoplasm in *Amœba* are determined by difference of exposure. Regions exposed to the external environment acquire the structure and behavior of ectoplasm and ectoplasm carried to the interior acquires the structure and behavior of entoplasm. Plasmolyzed or otherwise isolated portions of plant cells containing nuclei secrete cellulose over the exposed surface. In some forms of cell division morphological cell membranes or boundaries, "cell-plates," appear in the cytoplasm without any relation to exposure to non-protoplasmic environment. Such cases do not conflict in any way with the views advanced here. No one doubts that the localization and development of the cell plate or membrane is determined by certain physico-chemical factors associated with nuclei or cytoplasmic regions or both. In short the environment in such cases is intra-protoplasmic or intercellular.

Multicellular masses develop, at least superficially, some degree of epithelial pattern and arrangement, when brought into a definite differential to environment, whether intra- or extra-organismic. Early developmental stages of animals usually show this epithelial pattern in some form (Fig. 45) and in later stages it appears on both external and internal surfaces (Fig. 46). In plants also cell layers differentially exposed show a surface-interior pattern related to the differential exposure.

Most of us do not hesitate to conclude that in each individual case of surface-interior pattern the differential exposure is a factor directly concerned. The particular kind of surface-interior pattern which develops in any given case is of course determined first of all by the hereditary constitution of the protoplasm, but differential exposure is necessary in each case for the appearance or realization of the pattern. The rôle which we assign to the environmental factor in these cases differs of course according to our conception of organismic pattern, but it seems evident that surface-interior pattern does not arise *de novo*, independently of environmental factors.

The question whether the cell originated as a surface-interior pattern has been touched upon elsewhere (Child, ' 21 a, pp. 23, 60–62).

According to this conception, the localization and differentiation of the nucleus as a definite organ has been determined by conditions characteristic of the interior of a mass of protoplasm. Such a conception of nuclear origin does not conflict in any way with the rôle assigned to the nucleus in inheritance. The persistence of the nucleus from one cell generation to another merely means that the pattern which has been established is persistent or hereditary. Nevertheless, the growth of nuclear substance, even now is apparently possible only in the interior of a mass of protoplasm. In the case of the spermatozoön for example, life is narrowly limited (Cohn, '18) and the intake of nutrition and synthesis of new nuclear substance apparently does not occur unless the sperm head reaches the interior of a mass of protoplasm. The change in form of the sperm head induced by Loeb and Bancroft ('12) outside the egg cytoplasm seems to be largely or wholly a matter of imbibition and swelling and there is no evidence that any synthesis of new protoplasm occurs. These and various other facts indicate very clearly that in the persistence and growth of nuclear substance in cells environmental factors, i. e., "interior" conditions, as well as hereditary constitution, are concerned.

THE ORIGIN OF NEW GRADIENTS IN RELATION TO HEREDITY

Taking the data of experiment and observation as they stand, polarity and symmetry appear primarily as physiological gradients. When the gradients are obliterated, polarity and symmetry disappear and when new gradients are determined by the differential action of environmental factors, new polarities or symmetries, or both, appear. In many cases gradients once established persist through agamic reproduction and perhaps also through gametic reproduction and so are inherited by the new individuals, but the only logical conclusion in the light of all the facts seems to be that even in such cases the gradients in the first instance must arise through differential action of external factors. And finally, if we accept the conclusions of the geneticists and cytologists, the mechanism of heredity does not afford any basis for such regional molar differences as the physiological gradients. To refer again to Morgan's statement: "Each cell inherits the whole germ plasm" (Morgan, '19, p. 241): granting that this statement is correct, it is evident that the factors which determine that different cells behave differently in development cannot be sought in the germ plasm alone, but must consist in some external differential which brings about the realization of certain of the hereditary potentialities in one cell or cell group and others in other cells or groups. In his earlier statement Morgan suggests the existence of regional cytoplasmic differences, but makes no attempt to account for the origin of such differences (see pp. 22–23). The physiological gradients, originating in external differentials provide an adequate physiological basis for such differences, and if we accept Morgan's statements, the differences must arise in the final analysis in relation to environmental factors. The hereditary constitution of each protoplasm reacting to the external differential gives first the physiological gradient and then, on the basis of this, development and differentiation.

In fact not only the data of experiment and observation in the field of developmental physiology, but current theories of heredity force us to the same conclusion, viz., that environmental factors are concerned in determining the order and the "wholeness" which constitute the individual. The hereditary potentialities may be in large measure or in many cases wholly independent of each other, as the particulate theory of heredity maintains, but the individual, in each cell of which only certain of the potentialities inherent in it are realized in development, is none the less physiologically a whole. There is in fact no conflict between the particulate conception of heredity and the conception of the organism as a whole, unless we attempt to derive the wholeness from the particulate character of the hereditary potentialities. Such an attempt can lead only to the dilemma in which Morgan apparently finds himself (Morgan, '19, pp. 241–246). In the light of present biological knowledge the only possible conclusion seems to be that the individual organism represents in each case the behavior of the hereditary potentialities of the "germ plasm" in relation to certain environmental factors.

Even this conception, however, does not involve the conclusion that heredity has nothing to do with the origin and development of new gradients. In the first place, the hereditary potentialities of excitation and reaction must be present, and since particular protoplasms are so constituted that they are more sensitive to certain environmental factors than to others, the gradients of polarity and symmetry may be determined by different factors in different protoplasms.

Again, the hereditary mechanisms may play a part in determining the particular factors to which the reproductive element is exposed. Admitting for the sake of argument that the differential exposure of ovarian eggs of various species determines their polarity (see pp. 98–100), it is evident that the complex of metabolic, morphological and physiological conditions which lead up to and determine the differential exposure and the factors to which the egg is exposed,

8

7

depend primarily upon the hereditary potentialities of the protoplasm from which the parent body, including the ovary, develops.

In still another way heredity is unquestionably concerned in the origin of new gradients in protoplasms. The differential action of the external factor merely initiates the physiological gradient. The final results depend upon the hereditary constitution. Some protoplasms, e. g., Amœba, are incapable of maintaining for any great length of time the differential externally determined. In many other protoplasms, when once established it persists throughout life or even through reproduction. Moreover, the development of the gradient beyond a certain stage is undoubtedly rather a matter of protoplasmic constitution than of the external factor. When the action of the external factor has once determined a certain degree of metabolic and structural differential, we see that in most protoplasms the gradient may persist and determine a definite course of development and differentiation quite independently of further differential action of the external factor. In the alga Fucus, as we have seen, only a few hours' exposure to light of a certain intensity is necessary to determine a gradient which becomes the axis of the plant and plays a large part in determining its form and the relations of its parts. In short, heredity is a factor in determining the special characteristics of each physiological gradient in each particular species, such, for example, as its length at each stage of development, its slope or steepness, i. e., the curve of each of its component factors, oxidation, colloid dispersion, water-content, etc. It follows, of course, that heredity is concerned in processes of budding, fission, etc., although the gradient is the physiological factor directly concerned in determining the localization of the bud and the time of its appearance, and even though each new bud develops a new polarity, as in axiate plants, hydroids, etc.

This relation between heredity and the physiological gradients has always been regarded as a fundamental, though self-evident aspect of the gradient conception and it has been something of a surprise to find critics of the conception apparently believing that it was an attempt to interpret, not only individual development, but the differences between different species in terms of differences in metabolic rate.

The only question which remains for consideration in this connection is whether protoplasm can autonomously give rise to a gradient and so autonomously determine its own polarity or symmetry or both. Is an autonomous molar or regional segregation or stratification of substances possible in such a way as to give rise to the graded quantitative differences characteristic of physiological axes? In various publications Morgan has postulated a stratification of materials as a feature of polarity (*e. g.*, Morgan, '07, Chap. XVII), but though he has suggested that such stratification results in some way from tension, it is not entirely clear whether he regards polarity as primarily autonomous or as originating under the influence of external factors. Loeb ('16 b) seems at times to regard a regional segregation of materials as occurring autonomously, though he also conceives it as occurring under the influence of external factors such as gravity.

It has been stated by various authors that the visible structure of animal eggs altered by centrifuging shows more or less tendency to return to normal (*e. g.*, Gurwitsch, '05, Conklin, '10). This might perhaps be regarded as indicating a capacity for autonomous stratification or arrangement, but the fact that centrifuging does not alter the polarity of the egg (Lillie, '08, Conklin, '10) indicates that a differential of some sort still exists in the original axis, and this differential, whether it be represented by an elastic structure as Conklin has suggested, or by a physiological gradient, is undoubtedly the factor which determines the restoration of the normal visible structure. In any case the granules which are displaced by centrifuging are not essential factors in polarity, for that may persist unchanged, whatever their location. It may be said that at present there is no evidence to indicate that a regional stratification of materials, a physiological gradient or any sort of physiological polarity or symmetry of organismic magnitude can originate autonomously in protoplasm. The protoplasm of an axiate organism, such as the hydroid, from which polarity and symmetry have been experimentally obliterated, may remain alive for a long time without showing any indication of a reappearance of polarity or symmetry (pp. 83, 123). In such cases the hereditary potentiality of axiate organization is still present, for if we expose the apolar mass to a new external differential, a new polarity, a new physiological gradient, arises and development once more goes on.

In every such case, and, I believe, in all cases, the external differential determines that an actual physiological gradient shall arise, but the specific constitution of the protoplasm, in other words, heredity, is always a factor in determining the particular characteristics of the gradient in that protoplasm. If we admit that polarity and symmetry are fundamentally such physiological gradients, this distinction between the realizing factor and the hereditary factor is inevitable and the necessity for it self-evident. Nevertheless, certain critics of the gradient conception have maintained that features so definite and constant as polarity and symmetry in organisms could not be of external origin. Such a position results simply from misapprehension. Even though a gradient may originate in a differential excitation, the constitution of the protoplasm in which it arises makes it as definite and constant a thing as that constitution itself. That is to say, given certain environmental conditions, a physiological gradient in a particular protoplasm will possess certain definite and constant characteristics.

CHAPTER X

PHYSIOLOGICAL DOMINANCE AND PHYSIOLOGICAL ISOLATION

The existence of a relation of dominance and subordination between parts in plants has long been recognized by botanists, though the physiological basis of this relation has been obscure. While under ordinary conditions the dominance of the growing tip over other regions and parts of the axis is the most conspicuous and characteristic relation of this sort in axiate plants, the growing tip is not the only region which dominates or controls other parts. Apparently any region of sufficiently rapid respiratory exchange may dominate a less active region. This relation of dominance and subordination and the physiological isolation of parts from the influence of the dominant region (see pp. 62, 157) are the primary factors in determining the order and arrangement of branches and other parts in axiate plants.

Attention has been called elsewhere (Child, '15 b, Chaps. IX, X, '15 c, Chaps. IV, V, '21 a, Chap. V) to the fact that this relation of dominance and subordination is characteristic not only of axiate plants, but also of axiate animals, and not only in development but in the special functional relations resulting from development. I have endeavored to show further (Child, '21 a) that this relation of dominance and subordination is primarily a dynamic feature of the physiological gradient and so of the physiological axis, that it is fundamentally excitatory and transmissive in character, and that it represents the physiological basis of the relation of dominance and subordination which we find in the reflex arc as the physiological unit of the nervous system (see Herrick, '24, Chaps. XVII, XVIII).

It was pointed out in the earlier discussions of the subject that the high end of a physiological gradient differs from other levels as a region of excitation differs from an unexcited or a less excited region and the control or dominance of the high end over other levels depends primarily upon this fact. From this viewpoint there is physiological continuity between the simple physiological gradient and the reflex arc. It was mentioned in Chapter IV above that the relation of dominance and subordination is a general characteristic of organ-

138

ismic pattern and we have now to consider the actual working of the relation in nature and experiment.

It has also been pointed out (Child, '15 c, Chaps. IV, V) that physiological isolation of parts may occur, *i. e.*, a part may be isolated from the controlling or determining action of a dominant region, while still in physical continuity with that region. Some data have been presented to show that physiological isolation can be experimentally controlled and modified, that it plays a fundamental rôle in regressive development and physiological rejuvenescence of parts and in fission, budding and many other reproductive processes. These earlier considerations make it possible to review the chief facts and conclusions rather briefly in the present chapter, but some space is devoted to discussion of certain aspects of the subject not previously considered.

PHYSIOLOGICAL DOMINANCE AND SUBORDINATION IN PLANTS

The existence of this relation of dominance and subordination in axiate plants and its significance for the development of buds and branches and so for the form of the plant as a whole, has long been familiar to botanists. In general, the apical or chief vegetative tip of an axis dominates the axis and inhibits, retards or determines the course of development of other buds or growing tips along the axis. In the absence of the chief vegetative tip the tip of the most nearly apical bud or buds dominates all lower levels, in the absence of this the next lower bud, and so on toward the basal end of the axis.

This relation exists not only for the main stem, but also to a greater or less degree within each subordinate axis, *e. g.*, a lateral branch. In like manner the root tip dominates levels below it within a certain range and lateral root tips dominate their own axes to some degree. This relation of dominance and subordination also appears more or less clearly in various other plant organs or organ complexes.

Certain characteristics of this relation in plants are of particular interest here. In the first place the relation is not simply an apparent or formal relation resulting from stereochemical or other structural features of the plant protoplasms, but it is a real physiological control involving energy changes. The experimental evidence indicates that dominance is associated in some way with the liberation of energy in living protoplasm and it appears at present to be true that the region or part in which intensity or rate of energy-liberation is highest dominates other regions of lower intensity or rate. In fact the relation of dominance and subordination in the plant is fundamentally associated with, and determined by the physiological gradients. The high end of the gradient dominates other levels and in partial gradients, *i. e.*, isolated pieces, the highest level present dominates lower levels.

The experimental demonstration of dominance in plants is most readily accomplished through physiological isolation, *i. e.*, through the removal of subordinate parts from the influence of a dominant part and observation of their behavior following such removal. The various methods and the results of physiological isolation are considered below (pp. 151–160), but it may be pointed out here that the effects of the trimming and pruning of plants are dependent primarily upon this relation of dominance and subordination in the plant axes.

PHYSIOLOGICAL DOMINANCE AND SUBORDINATION IN ANIMALS

The existence in postembryonic stages of most axiate animals of a functional relation of dominance and subordination of nervous or transmissive character is a familiar fact. In general, the apical region or head, or more specifically the central nervous system and the sense organs of the apical region or head, dominate other levels to a greater or less degree by means of nerve impulses, and we can also distinguish the relation of dominance and subordination at the various postcephalic levels of the central nervous system. In similar manner the central nervous organs of a particular level of the longitudinal axis constitute to some degree functionally dominant regions of the minor body-axes. In annelids and arthropods, for example, the segmental ganglia, situated in the median ventral region exercise a functional nervous dominance over lateral and dorsal regions of the segment. In vertebrates the median dorsal spinal cord similarly dominates lateral and ventral regions. So far as our knowledge goes, such dominance and subordination are always definitely related to the chief physiological gradients of earlier developmental stages, the high end of a gradient becoming the dominant region of that particular gradient.[1]

[1] But in the brains of the higher vertebrates there appears to be considerable modification of the primary axial gradients resulting from the development of numerous "centers" or regions of secondary dominance, the correlation centers. The progressive elaboration of these centers has been reviewed by Herrick ('24, Chaps. XVII–XIX) who expresses the opinion that in their more highly developed forms, and notably in the cerebral cortex, these correlation centers become the regions of highest dominance of the body. Herrick's account includes a discussion — largely theoretical — of the probable physiological factors involved in the transfer of the region of highest dominance from the periphery in primitive reflex arcs to the deep-seated cerebral cortex of higher mammals.

Functional dominance and subordination also appear in many axiate organs and organ complexes and here, as in the more general relations, the high end of a physiological gradient becomes the dominant region. The ctenophore plate row has been discussed in earlier publications (Child, '17 c, '21 a, pp. 212–220) and I have called attention to the fact that the relations of the plates in the row constitute an almost diagrammatic example of dominance and subordination in relation to a physiological gradient. Alvarez and his co-workers [1] have demonstrated the existence of the physiological gradient and of a functional relation of dominance and subordination in stomach, small intestine and colon. Hyman ('21) has found that the embryonic vertebrate heart is a physiological gradient and that the sinus region which later becomes the pacemaker represents the high end of this gradient. Gowanloch ('23) has been able to modify the development and even to reverse the direction of beat of the heart in fishes by means of differential susceptibility.

Undoubtedly in other axiate organs, such as the ureter (Satani, '19, Penfield, '20), the fallopian tubes, the contractile blood vessels of various animals, etc., functional dominance and subordination are similarly related to physiological gradients.

In "The Origin and Development of the Nervous System," Chap. XIII, it was pointed out that the reflex arc itself is fundamentally a relation of dominance and subordination, that the development of the reflex arcs in the individual is evidently related in a definite way to the physiological gradients and their developmental modifications, and finally that the gradients as excitation-transmission gradients constitute the general physiological basis out of which the reflex arc arises, through functional specialization and morphological differentiation.

Dominance and subordination, however, appear in animals, not only in the special functional relations of postembryonic stages, but also as factors in growth and differentiation of parts, agamic reproduction in nature and the regulatory reconstitution of new individuals from isolated pieces. Some fourteen years ago attention was called to the existence of a relation of dominance and subordination in the hydroid *Tubularia* (Child, '07 a, c, '12 b) and Rand's work on hydra (Rand, '11, '12) led him quite independently to recognize the dominance in organization and development of the apical body-region in that form.

[1] Alvarez, '14 a, '15 a, b, '16 a, b, '17 a, b, '18 a, b, c, '22; Alvarez and Mahony, '21; Alvarez and Starkweather, '18 a, b, c, d, e, '19; Alvarez and Taylor, '17 a, b.

In the reconstitution of isolated pieces of *Planaria* it has been found that a piece from any level of the body is capable of determining the development of all parts posterior to its own level, even though it remains completely headless. On the other hand, if it remains headless, such a piece never develops any trace of parts anterior to its own level in the body, but if even a rudimentary head develops, then all parts normally characteristic of the regions intermediate between the head and the level from which the part was taken develop.[1] In fact the study of *Planaria* has demonstrated beyond question, first, that the head region, or more properly speaking, the high end of the major physiological gradient in the body of *Planaria* determines the organization and development of the parts and organs of levels posterior to it, so far as these are not already present, and second, that the development of a new head on an isolated piece is not, physiologically speaking, a replacement of missing parts by the piece, but actually occurs in spite of the piece. That is to say, in order that a new head shall develop on a piece, the cells at the anterior cut surface, which give rise to the head must be active enough as compared with the rest of the piece to be physiologically independent of it. If these cells are dominated by other parts of the piece, no head develops. Consequently, as repeated experiment with various agents has shown, the head-frequency (*i. e.*, the frequency of head development in pieces of like size from animals of like size taken from a standardized stock), may be increased by conditions which inhibit the metabolism of other parts of the piece. Similarly head-frequency is decreased when the rate of metabolism of other parts of the piece is increased in relation to that of the head-forming cells.

These experiments have led to the conclusion that the reconstitutional development of such pieces is essentially similar to embryonic development, in that determination and control in the organization of the new individual proceeds from the anterior end posteriorly. The formation of the new head on an isolated piece is not determined by the piece but is a "self-differentiation." The only effect other parts of the piece can have on head-formation is a negative, inhibitory effect. The head, once established as a region of high metabolic rate, determines the organization and differentiation of levels posterior to it, so far as these are not already present.

---

[1] For these data and various others bearing upon the question of dominance and subordination in *Planaria* see Buchanan, '22, Child, '10 a, '11 b, c, '12 a, '14 d, e, '16 b, '21 a pp. 100–102, Figs. 8–12.

It has long been known to students of regulatory development in the lower animals that in isolated pieces of *Planaria* the missing parts anterior to the level of the piece do not develop in order proceeding anteriorly, with the head appearing last. The fact is that, no matter what the level from which the piece is taken, the new head begins to develop first at the anterior cut surface of the piece and other parts arise either by redifferentiation of the old parts posterior to the cut surface or by later growth of new tissue posterior to the new head (Figs. 129–131). This is true not only for *Planaria* but for many if not for all forms in which the regulatory development of new apical regions or heads occurs on isolated pieces. For example, in the hydroid *Tubularia*, whatever the level at which the stem is cut, the new hydranth arises at the apical end of the piece (see Figs. 67–69, 91–98). In the case of the earthworm Morgan ('97, '02) observed that when more than five segments were removed from the anterior end only five segments regenerated. Similarly, in various limicolous oligochetes only a certain number of segments characteristic for each species develops anew at the anterior ends of species when more than that number of segments are removed (Hyman, '16 a). In the species studied by Hyman the intermediate regions are formed by later redifferentiation of some of the old segments. In pieces from the more posterior levels of the body then the new head is "out of place" since the parts which normally lie between it and the level of the piece on which it develops are not present. If we regard the development of the new head as determined by the piece these facts remain inexplicable, but as soon as we recognize that the new head is, so far as the rest of the piece is concerned, a self-differentiation and that the region from which it arises dominates levels posterior to it because it represents the region of highest metabolic rate in the piece the difficulty disappears. In regulatory, as in embryonic development, the so-called law of antero-posterior development holds, and the apical end or head constitutes the first step in the formation of a new individual. The chief physiological difference between the reconstitution of a piece and embryonic development is that in the former case the development of a new posterior end is determined by the regions already present in the piece even in the absence of a head, while in embryonic development the whole individual is determined from the apical or anterior end posteriorly.

That the apical or cephalic portions of the central nervous system develop independently of other parts is indicated by various facts. In the case of *Planaria*, Flexner ('98) and Keiller ('10) showed that the

ganglia of the new head may develop quite apart from and independently of the cut ends of the nerve cords in the piece, the connections
being established later by outgrowth from the new ganglia. The fact
determined by Goldfarb, ('09), that in the earthworm a new head and
new ganglia will develop at the anterior cut surface even after the
ventral cord is removed from several segments posterior to the end,
also indicates the independence of the cephalic ganglia. The experiments of Fischel ('10, '14) and Waelsch ('14) indicate that in amphibia
and birds the earlier embryonic stages of the central nervous system
arise independently of other parts. Moreover, Spemann ('18, '21)
and Mangold ('20) have shown that the region anterior to the dorsal
lip of the blastopore in the amphibian embryo, i. e., the region which
plays a large part in the formation of the cephalic nervous system, not
only develops independently of other parts after a certain stage, but
dominates or determines their development. Spemann, in fact, has
called this region the "organizer."

Peripheral parts may influence the development of the central nervous system in later stages, at least in the higher animals as Shorey
('09) has shown, and the incomplete or retarded differentiation or
small size of certain nervous regions or centers in the absence, incomplete development, or lack of functional connection of peripheral
parts normally associated with them is a general rule in the higher
animals. Levi has found a correlation between the size of nerve cells
and the size of the animal, i. e., supposedly the size of the area inner-
vated by each cell, and Terni has demonstrated this correlation experimentally.[1] Nevertheless, all the evidence at hand indicates that in
the lower animals and in the earlier stages of the higher animals the
central nervous system develops independently, or almost independently of other parts, and the apical or cephalic portion of it independently of other levels of the nervous system itself (see, also, Child, '21 a,
pp. 125–128).

It was noted above (pp. 101–110) that the localization of organs
along an axis may be experimentally altered by altering the length or
steepness of the gradient. At present it seems possible to interpret
these facts only in terms of dominance and subordination in relation
to a physiological gradient.

The facts, considered from the physiological viewpoint, permit little
doubt concerning the significance of dominance and subordination
in both embryonic and regulatory development and in both animals
and plants. There is, in fact, good ground for believing that the re-

[1] Levi, '97, '06, '08, '16, '19; Terni, '14, '19.

lation of dominance and subordination is a necessary expression and consequence of the existence of a physiological gradient. Moreover, a physiological continuity apparently exists between the relation of dominance and subordination in development and that which appears in later stages as a characteristic feature of nervous function. Thus we reach once more the conclusion that between the simple physiological gradient, the localization and differentiation of organs and the complexities of nervous control a physiological continuity exists.

PHYSIOLOGICAL INDEPENDENCE OF PARTS AND ORGANS IN RELATION TO DOMINANCE

We must of course expect to find that dominance and independence go hand in hand, *i. e.*, that so far as one region or level of a gradient or physiological axis dominates another, it is independent of that other. This fact is strikingly illustrated by normal embryonic development, in many agamic reproductive processes and in the regulatory development of isolated pieces. In embryonic development, for example, the organs representing the high ends of the axial gradients develop before other parts (Child, '15 c, pp. 67–72). In processes of budding in plants, the apical end, the growing tip of each particular axis, is the first part of that axis to be established (Child, '15c, pp. 83–87), and in budding and fission in animals, as in embryonic development, the region representing the high end of a particular axis or gradient develops first. Again in the regulatory development of short isolated pieces of the lower animals such as hydroids, flatworms, etc., only the parts representing the apical or anterior end of the body may appear (Figs. 93–101, also Child, '15 c, pp. 96–101). In other words, a short piece isolated from any level of the body may transform completely into an apical structure or head, other parts being completely absent. No other region or level of the body has ever been seen to originate in this way in regulatory development, *i. e.*, in complete independence of other parts. The development of organs representing lower levels of a gradient is always determined by the presence of higher levels. Relative independence of course exists in the gradients of minor axes. The development of the median ventral trunk region in most, if not all, bilateral vertebrates and of the median dorsal region in vertebrates, is relatively independent of the development of lateral and dorsal, and lateral and ventral regions respectively. In axiate organs as well we find a similar independence in development of the regions representing the high ends of the gradients.

Functionally also a given level of a gradient is relatively independent of lower levels, and the apical or anterior end is therefore the most independent region of all. In the simpler animals this functional independence in relation to the gradient appears most clearly. It has been observed in many invertebrates that regions of the body apical or anterior to a region of excitation are but little affected by it, while regions basal or posterior to it are much affected. If an annelid or a turbellarian be cut in two, the piece anterior to the cut is but little affected and soon recovers its normal behavior, while the levels posterior to the cut are much affected (Norman, '00). In the higher animals and even in man the functional independence of higher levels still persists to some extent, but the autocratic or oligarchic pattern of relations of the simpler animal and plant axes has undergone modification in the direction of democracy and representative government in the course of evolution (Child, '21 c, pp. 248–267).

MOSAIC DEVELOPMENT

Both the Roux-Weismann theory of qualitative nuclear division and the theory of the segregation of formative substances in the cytoplasm of the egg involve the assumption that different cells or cell groups of the embryo go through the developmental processes independently of each other. According to these conceptions, the developing organism is a mosaic of these independent parts, which enter into relation with each other only in later stages.

Omitting discussion of the theories, the experimental data show that in some animals development even from the beginning, actually appears to be of this character. In such cases we find that, at least within certain limits, parts of the egg, isolated cells or cell groups of early stages, or organ primordia continue their development with little or no change, i. e., as if the other parts were present.[1] In some forms this apparent independence of parts already exists to a greater or less extent in the egg at the beginning of development, while in others cells or parts isolated in early stages react to the altered conditions by change in the course of development, but in later stages such reaction becomes more and more narrowly limited. Evidently then development of apparently mosaic character appears to very different degrees and in different stages in different forms. At the

[1] Without attempting a complete or extensive bibliography, the following papers are cited: Conklin, '97, '02; Driesch and Morgan, '95; Fischel, '97, '98; Roux, '95, Bd. II; E. B. Wilson, '92, '93, '94, '96, '03, '04; Ziegler, '98, Child, '00. Further references will be found in these papers.

one extreme are forms such as the annelids, mollusks and ctenophores, in which at least certain regions are so fixedly predetermined at the beginning of cleavage that isolation from other parts does not alter their behavior to any marked degree. At the other extreme are eggs like those of the sea urchin, the medusa, etc., in which isolation of parts is followed by extensive regulatory change. In such forms whole embryos may develop from single isolated blastomeres or other parts of embryos, but with certain limitations as regards size of pieces, regions of embryo represented and stage of development, which differ in different species. Even in such cases a gradual determination or fixation of differences in different regions or cells occurs in the course of development, so that in general as development progresses the regulatory plasticity of earlier stages disappears or becomes more and more limited. In some forms, however, in which metamorphosis involves extensive development of new parts, the larval stages preceding metamorphosis may show a high degree of mosaic behavior, while later stages have a high regulatory capacity. Such relations appear in the polychete annelids, the mosaic character of early development having to do with larval organs.

How are we to account for these differences? In the more extreme mosaic type of development the parts appear to develop, or, more strictly speaking, are able to develop up to a certain point independently of each other and in the regulatory types, physiological correlation between the parts appears to be an essential factor, since the course of development is altered by isolation. A very simple interpretation of this series of facts is possible in terms of physiological gradients. In the more extreme mosaic types of development, e. g., annelids and mollusks, specialization or differentiation at different levels of the gradient has occurred to such an extent that isolation at a certain stage does not alter the course of events during a certain period of development following that stage. It is of interest to note further that in the annelid and mollusk this specialization is apparently established first in the upper levels of the primary gradient, i. e., the regions which give rise to the anterior regions of the larval body, and particularly the ectodermal regions. In fact, the lower levels of the gradient, which give rise to the ectoderm, mesoderm and entoderm of the postcephalic regions are not so highly specialized. In the annelid these regions remain capable of growth and formation of new segments up to late developmental stages, or throughout life, and even in the adult isolated pieces of postcephalic regions are capable of more or less extensive regulatory development, often of development of complete new individuals. If specialization and differentiation have any relation to the physiological gradients, we should expect them to appear first or to be more stable at the higher than at the lower levels of a gradient because of the differences in metabolic rate at the different levels.

Whenever a sufficient degree of such specialization exists, development will appear to a greater or less extent as a mosaic of independent processes in different cells or regions, *i. e.*, the regulatory capacity of isolated parts will be more or less limited. In annelid and mollusk eggs and in some other forms, in which the upper levels of the polar gradient have already attained such specialization at the beginning of cleavage, early development appears to be largely a mosaic of independent processes. In the egg of the jellyfish, on the other hand, none of the levels of the polar gradient has become fixedly specialized at the beginning of development, consequently in this form early development appears as a correlative process, *i. e.*, extensive regulation follows isolation of parts. In fact it is only in advanced stages of development of the hydroid that any marked degree of fixity of differentiation takes place and then it is limited to the extreme apical end of the gradient, *i. e.*, to the hydranth, and even this is capable of a considerable degree of regulation in many hydroid species.

If what has been said in preceding sections concerning the dominance and independence of the high end of the polar gradient and of the apical end or head developing from it is correct, it is evident that the early development of this region must always be of the mosaic type, so far as its relations to other parts are concerned. That is to say, its specialization is independent of that of lower levels of the gradient. According to this view this is the only primary or fundamental mosaic feature of development. Apparent independence of other parts does not mean primary or even actual independence, but merely a certain degree of specialization or differentiation resulting from physiological correlation in earlier stages. Such specialization may limit the regulatory capacity of the parts and make it possible for them to continue their development with little or no change for a time after isolation.

Even in the case of the apical end or head, its independence of other parts does not result from inherent qualities of its cells but merely from the fact that it represents the high end of a gradient. When the gradient is obliterated, it fails to develop (pp. 104–107) and when new gradients are experimentally localized new apical ends or heads appear. We must conclude then that so far as any determination of the apical end or head by other parts is concerned, development is always a mosaic, at least in its earliest stages, but that the apparent independence of other parts is always secondary and the consequence of their specialization or differentiation as particular levels of a gradient. The fact that some subordinate parts are able to continue their development with little change for a time after isolation does not necessarily mean that they were actually independent of other parts before isolation. It means rather that their ability to react to the altered conditions by alteration in the course of development is more or less limited in range, or that reaction occurs slowly.

THE DOMINANT REGION AS A PACEMAKER

The idea of a functional pacemaker, that is a region or part determining or controlling the rate of certain activities in other parts, has long been familiar to physiologists. Physiological investigation of the vertebrate heart and its rhythmic activities has demonstrated beyond a question that a certain region at or near the sinus end of the heart normally controls the rate of beat. If this region is inhibited in its activity, e. g., by cold, or is removed, the function of pacemaker may be taken up by the region adjoining, and by inhibition of this region the function of pacemaker may again be transferred to the adjoining intact region and so on. Similar functional pacemakers exist at the upper end of the stomach, the small intestine and the colon and at the upper end of the ureter, and, as in the heart, the function of pacemaker may be transferred successively to lower levels by inhibition or removal of the normal pacemaker.[1] In the case of the heart, the alimentary tract and the ureter, regions or levels normally subordinate may also become pacemakers for a part or even for the whole organ if sufficiently excited, even though the normal pacemaker be still present and functioning.

In the plate row of the ctenophore the apical region is normally the pacemaker (Child, '17c, '21a, pp. 212-220), but when the apical region is inhibited or more basal levels are physically isolated from it, the most apical level present or intact becomes the pacemaker and any level of the plate row may be made a pacemaker by sufficient stimulation. Undoubtedly a functional pacemaker exists in many

[1] For the heart see Eyster and Meek, '21, also Gowanloch, '23; for the alimentary tract see papers by Alvarez and co-authors in bibliography and for ureter, Penfield, '20.

other organs, *e. g.*, the elongated tubular hearts and contractile blood vessels of various invertebrates, the Fallopian tubes, the vas deferens.

In the case of the heart, the alimentary tract, and the ctenophore plate row it has been shown experimentally that the pacemaker represents the high end of a physiological or metabolic gradient characteristic of the organ concerned. When we turn to the development of axiate organisms, we find that the axes are represented primarily by physiological gradients similar, so far as we can determine, to those characteristic of the heart, the alimentary tract and the ctenophore plate row. Moreover, we find that in such a gradient the high end is dominant and controls or determines conditions at lower levels within a certain range of distance. In fact, the high end of such a gradient is essentially a development pacemaker. To take the case of the plant, for example, the growing tip which is the high end of the chief axial gradient controls the development of buds and branches at lower levels. If this tip is removed or inhibited the growing tip of the next lower bud or branch takes up the function of pacemaker, etc. Except that in the heart, alimentary tract and ctenophore plate row a rhythmic excitation is the conspicuous feature, the relations in these gradients of specialized organs and in the axial gradients of axiate plants and animals are very similar. Moreover, the facts indicate that dominance and subordination in development, as well as in the rhythm of heart beat and peristalsis, is fundamentally a relation based on excitation and transmission. The high end of an axial gradient dominates lower levels, because it differs from them as a more strongly excited region differs from one less strongly excited.

Taking the facts as they stand, they point very definitely to two conclusions. First a pacemaker, whether functional or developmental, represents primarily the high end of a physiological gradient, or a region so strongly excited as to alter a preëxisting gradient or determine a new one. Second, wherever a physiological gradient is established a relation of dominance and subordination, of pacemaker and follower, must exist to some degree and within a certain range. And not only do the facts point us to these conclusions, but current theories of heredity make it necessary to discover or postulate some sort of controlling and ordering factor to account for the orderly, definite and correlated character of individual development. If every cell inherits the whole germ plasm, as Morgan maintains, there are only two ways of accounting for the orderly, definite and relatively constant course and character of specialization and differentiation of cells and cell groups in development. Either it must depend upon a relation of physiological dominance and subordination, of pacemaker and follower, which is determined in the final analysis by differences in behavior or reaction of different cells or regions to a differential in environment, or else it is the expression of the control and ordering of physico-chemical factors by a metaphysical factor, which we may call entelechy or something else, as we choose. There is, I believe, no escape from this alternative. The phenomena of individual development are inconceivable without a controlling and ordering factor, a pacemaker of some sort, either physiological or metaphysical, and the evidence points very clearly to the existence of a physiological pacemaker in the high end of the physiological gradient.

PHYSIOLOGICAL ISOLATION

It is a familiar fact that the physical isolation of parts of the body of organisms is in general followed by changes in their behavior. In the higher animals the specialization of structure and function is so great that such physically isolated parts soon die, though under properly controlled conditions, e. g., in tissue culture media, even small groups of cells may be kept alive for long periods and may grow and divide. In the simpler animals such physical isolation of parts, if not carried too far, is followed by dedifferentiation of some or all of the cells of the isolated piece and this in turn is followed by a new developmental process which gives rise either to a complete new individual (Figs. 129–131) or to the more apical or anterior portions of such an individual (Figs. 95–98). Such a process is known as regeneration, form regulation, restitution, reconstitution. It involves a change in behavior and structure from that of a part toward that of a whole organism.

Among the lower plants every cell of the body may be capable, when physically isolated, of transforming into a new growing tip and so into a new individual, but in the multiaxiate higher plants physical isolation of pieces containing buds, merely determines the outgrowth of some of the buds. In such cases there is simply the substitution of one axis for another, rather than the development of new axes.

It appears to be true then that a physiologically isolated part of an organism tends in general to lose its characteristics as a part and to become or approach the conditions of a new whole individual. The capacity for such reconstitution is greatest in the simpler organ-

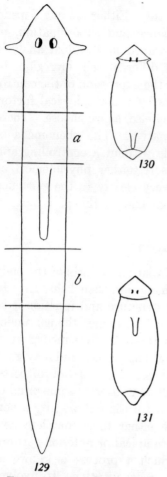

129

FIGS. 129–131.—Reconstitution of pieces of *Planaria dorotocephala* from different levels: Fig. 129, outline of body indicating levels, (*a*) and (*b*), from which pieces are taken; Fig. 130, reconstitution of (*a*); Fig. 131, reconstitution of (*b*). In Fig. 130 only the head, in Fig. 131, the head with a short region of the body behind it, develops from the new tissue at the cut surface: in Fig. 131 almost the whole prepharyngeal, and the pharyngeal regions are formed by reorganization of the regions posterior to the cut surface (from Child, 21 a).

isms, because the greater degree and fixity of specialization in the higher forms, particularly the higher animals, limits their potentialities of change in behavior.

It is very generally admitted that the changes which occur in physically isolated pieces of organisms are in some way the results of their isolation. That is to say, their original development as parts of the individual was determined by their physiological relations with other parts and primarily, as I have tried to show, by their position in a physiological gradient or gradients. When we isolate such a part physically, *e. g.*, by section, we of course isolate it from the action of the physiological factors which have made it the particular part it is. If its specialization as such a part is not fixed, it does not persist in the absence of physiological factors which determined it and dedifferentiation occurs. The course and character of the reconstitutional process in a particular case depends on the axial relations. In some isolated pieces the old gradients persist (Figs. 124–126), in others new gradients arise (Figs. 102–109).

Various reasons have been given repeatedly for believing that the physiological relations in a gradient must be primarily excitatory-transmissive in character, *i. e.*, that the high end of the gradient differs from other levels as a region of excitation differs from an unexcited or less excited region (Child, '15 c, '21a; see also Chaps. XI and XII below). Transmission of excitation with a decrement unquestionably plays an important part in the origin and establishment of the gradients.   According to this conception physiological dominance is fundamentally an excitatory and transmissive relation.   In the absence of specialized structural paths and in at least some nerves, the excitatory change usually undergoes a decrement in physiological effectiveness and finally a point is reached beyond which it is ineffective.

Under such conditions the range of dominance must be limited by the decrement in transmission.   In other words, at a certain distance from the dominant region its control becomes ineffective.   The range of dominance may differ widely with different conditions: for it may be very short in early embryonic stages in which the conductivity of protoplasm for excitation is rather low, and it may increase during development until in the nerves of vertebrates it is certainly very great and is regarded by many as unlimited (Child, '21 a, pp. 223 –228).   Again, experiment has shown that the range of dominance varies with rate of metabolism in the dominant region.   Decrease in rate determines decrease in range of dominance and vice versa.

Since the range of dominance is limited, particularly in the earlier developmental stages and in simpler organisms throughout life, the possibility exists that under certain conditions some portion or portions of the body may come to lie beyond the range of dominance, even though they are still in protoplasmic or cellular continuity with it. For isolation brought about in this way the term "'physiological isolation" has been used (Child, '11 e.)   In the simpler organisms, in which the isolated part is capable of reacting to the altered conditions, the result of physiological isolation is essentially the same as that of physical isolation.   The physiologically isolated part or region tends to lose its characteristics as a part and to develop into a new individual.

In many processes of budding, fission, etc., in both plants and animals the occurrence of physiological isolation can be demonstrated in various ways, or very clearly indicated.   Such isolation is probably concerned in some way and to some extent in all processes of agamic reproduction.   For example, one indication of physiological isolation of a part is the partial or complete inability of the animal to control it.   Such a condition is very clearly shown in *Planaria dorotocephala*. After the animal attains a certain length the posterior region of the body is no longer under complete control of the anterior region under ordinary conditions, though when the animal is strongly excited this region is often brought under control.   Sooner or later this posterior region reacts independently of the anterior region by attaching itself to the substratum in reaction to some slight stimulus, while the anterior region continues to creep forward. When such reaction occurs the body in front of the attached region may become greatly

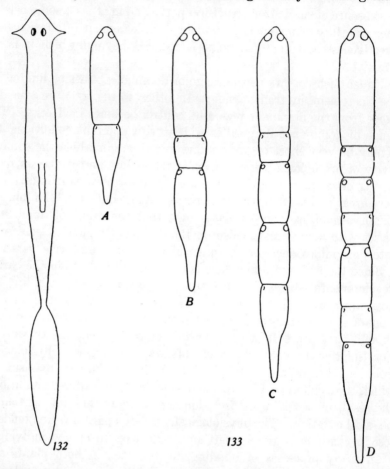

Fig. 132.—The act of fission in *P. dorotocephala:* through an independent motor reaction the posterior zooid attaches itself to the substratum while the anterior zooid continues to advance until rupture occurs.

Fig. 133.—*Stenostomum*, showing various stages in the formation of chains of zooids: (*A*), first fission; (*B*), second fission of anterior zooid; (*C*), second fission of posterior zooid and third fission of anterior zooid; (*D*), third fission in anterior, second and third zooids. Comparison of figures shows that distance from head of zooid to fission plane next posterior differs according to degree of development of head, being least in zooids with least developed heads and greatest in those with most developed heads.

stretched (Fig. 132) and if the animal has sufficient strength, or if the degree of excitation of the anterior region does not become so great that the posterior region is brought under control, fission results.

In many other animals physiological isolation results in actual development of the new individual before separation occurs. The flatworm *Stenostomum* serves as an example (Fig. 133). Here the range of dominance and therefore the distance of the fission plane from the head in each new fission differs according to the development of the head and nervous system, *i. e.*, with the range of dominance in that zooid. The zooid in which

nervous system is most est length before a new fis- earlier the stage of de- nervous s y s t e m, the when fission begins. Even changes or changes in be- rence of physiological iso- onstrated by the presence dients, as indicated by KMnO₄, electric potential (See Chap. VII). In va- has been shown that there which physiological isola- strictly speaking, four cerned in physiological possible to determine and through all four of these

Increase in size.— may result from increase organism, this increase bringing certain parts be- yond the range of domi- nance in that individual. Budding and fission re- sulting from increase in length of an axis are cases in point. In *Planaria* (Fig. 132) and *Stenosto-*

development of head and advanced attains the great- sion plane appears and the velopment of the head and shorter the zooid at the time where no morphological havior appear, the occur- lation may often be dem- of new physiological gra- susceptibility, reduction of or respiratory exchange rious earlier publications it are four possible ways in tion may occur, or, more factors which may be con- isolation, and it has been c o n t r o l its occurrence factors.

Physiological isolation in length or size of the

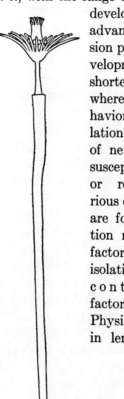

Fig. 134.—*Tubularia*, showing physiological isola- tion of tip of stolon with consequent development of a new hydranth.

mum (Fig. 133) fission commonly results from increase in length of the polar axis and consequent physiological isolation of the posterior end. In the hydroid, *Tubularia*, the basal end of the stem forms a holdfast and gradually grows along the substratum as a stolon (Fig. 91, p. 118), but when the length of the stem plus stolon, *i. e.*, the dis- tance of the stolon tip from the dominant hydranth region, becomes sufficiently great, the tip of the stolon transforms into a new hydranth (Fig. 134). In various other species of hydroids the formation of a new hydranth bud is possible only at a certain distance on the stem from an active hydranth and this distance varies with the activity of the hydranth. Numerous other cases of physiological isolation and fission, budding or some other form of agamic reproduction might be mentioned.

Decrease in dominance. — A decrease in activity, or removal of the dominant region may bring about physiological isolation. Such isolation and the following reproduction may occur without any increase in size of the organism concerned. That physiological isolation and outgrowth of buds in plants can be experimentally induced by removal of the growing tip or by retarding its metabolism has long been known to botanists. In animals similar results can be obtained. In *Planaria*, for example, removal of the head favors development of the posterior zooid and fission (Child, '10 a, '11 d). In *Tubularia* removal of the apical hydranth or inhibition of the development of a hydranth at the apical end of a stem or stem piece is a factor in bringing about physiological isolation at the basal end and so favors or determines development of a hydranth there (See Fig. 92, also Child, '07 a, d). As noted in Chapter VI, Wood-Jones has described relations of dominance and subordination in the staghorn corals which are almost identical with those in multiaxial plants. In these corals, removal of the apical dominant zooid of the branch results in physiological isolation of parts below and some of the lateral zooids undergo transformation into apical zooids of new branches.

Both botanists and zoölogists have repeatedly called attention to the occurrence of various processes of agamic reproduction under "unfavorable conditions" and such reproduction has often been regarded as an adaptation directed toward preserving the life of the species under the unfavorable conditions. Doubtless it serves this purpose in many cases, but physiologically it results from decrease or obliteration of dominance because of the fact that the dominant region is more susceptible than other parts to the injurious conditions. The individual disintegrates physiologically into two or more smaller individuals. The "unfavorable" conditions under which such reproduction occurs are in general conditions which decrease metabolism and so shorten or more or less completely obliterate the gradient because of the differential susceptibility of different levels (see pp. 80–84).

Block. — Physiological isolation of subordinate parts may also be brought about by physiological block, *i. e.*, by blocking or obstructing through physiological change the passage of the correlative factor at some point in its course from the dominant to the subordinate region. McCallum ('05) brought about some degree of physiological isolation in the bean seedling by subjecting a short zone of the stem to vapor of an anesthetic. More recently Bellamy and I have found a zone

135   136

FIGS. 135, 136.—Physiological isolation by low temperature block in scarlet-runner bean: Fig. 135, physiological isolation and growth of buds in axils of cotyledons by zone of low temperature on internode next above them (petiole of leaf was broken after outgrowth of buds); Fig. 136, physiological isolation and growth of buds in axils of first foliage leaves by zone of low temperature on internode next above them.

of low temperature a very effective means of blocking the correlative factor in various plants (Child and Bellamy, '19; Child, '20 b, '21 b.) The result of such an experiment on the scarlet-runner bean is shown in Figures 135, 136. In the normal bean plant the buds in the axils of the cotyledons and of the first foliage leaves do not grow out because they are inhibited by the chief growing tip, or in its absence by other growing tips apical to them which reacts to isolation more rapidly than they do. The cooling to 3°–5° C. of a zone of the stem twenty mm. or more in length blocks the dominance of the growing tip or other buds and the buds of the axil next below the cooled zone grow, as Figures 135, 136 show. Such cooling produces no perceptible physical injury and after removal of the low temperature the inhibiting action of the growing tip is again effective below the cooled zone, unless the isolated buds have become so active during the period of isolation that the chief growing tip is no longer able to inhibit them.

In the course of these experiments it has been found that within a certain range of temperature the effectiveness of the block varies with the length of the cooled zone. For example, at a temperature of 4°–5° a cooled zone 25–30 mm. in length may be ineffective as a block, but with the same temperature a cooled zone 80–100 mm. is effective. With sufficiently low temperature, e. g., 2°, a cooled zone 25–30 mm. long is effective as a block at any level of the stem, but with higher temperatures, e. g., 4–5', the farther away the cooled zone from the buds to be isolated, the less effective it is as a block. These facts suggest that with the higher temperature the inhibiting factor is not completely blocked and that in the normal parts of the stem below the cooled zone it gradually recovers its normal intensity or effectiveness. When the cooled zone is near the buds to be isolated the length of normal stem below the zone is not sufficient for such recovery, but when the zone is far away it is sufficient. Another possibility is that the correlative factor itself is weaker at the lower level and therefore more completely blocked by a given length of zone at a given temperature than at the higher level.

And finally, it is important to note that the blocking by low temperature of the inhibiting action of the growing tip on buds below does not block the passage of water and salts in the opposite direction. Plants with a cooled zone of stem do not wilt and the stem continues to grow above the cooled zone. To determine whether the cooled zone blocks the downward transport of substances is not so easy, but by using different plants and different parts it has been possible to make it highly probable that the blocking of such transport is not the essential factor in the physiological isolation (Child, '21 b.)

In the course of his experiments on *Bryophyllum* Loeb[1] has advanced various hypotheses in the attempt to interpret the relation of dominance and subordination in plants. These hypotheses are in terms of transportative correlation, an attempt to account for the facts by assumptions concerning the flow or distribution or flow of sap or of certain nutritive substances in it or by the assumption of the production by the dominant growing tip of inhibiting substances. As I have pointed out elsewhere, the results of the low temperature experiments indicate, if they do not demonstrate, that the re-

[1] Loeb, '15 a, b, '16 a, '17 a, b, c, d, e, '18 a, b, c, '19, '20 a, '23.

lation of dominance and subordination in plants is primarily rather a matter of transmission of excitation, than, as Loeb maintains, of transportation of substance.   On the basis of other experiments Harvey ('20) has recently reached essentially the same conclusion.

It has long been known that nerve impulses in animals may be blocked by cooling, compressing or partially anesthetizing a zone of the nerve, but the blocking of the correlative factor concerned in the general relation of dominance and subordination in the physiological gradients of animals has not yet been attempted.   There is, however, every reason to believe that with the proper technique such blocking can be accomplished in the same way as in the plant.

Local action on the subordinate parts. — Finally, physiological isolation may occur in still a fourth way, viz., by direct excitation of, or other local action on, a subordinate part of such a degree that it is no longer sensitive to the control of the dominant region.   Physiological isolation occurs in such cases because the subordinate part after excitation itself becomes the high end of a new gradient, and the excitation-transmission changes from the originally dominant region are obliterated in passing up this gradient (pp. 195, 200), or, if they do reach the part in question are no longer effective in controlling it because of its increased activity.

This sort of physiological isolation sometimes occurs in the buds of plants through the action of external factors favorable to growth. In the case of *Bryophyllum*, for example, the buds in the notches of leaves are ordinarily inhibited by the chief growing tip, even in moist air, but when a leaf is immersed in water while still attached to the parent plant some of the buds will often develop new plants even though the chief growing tip of the parent plant is growing actively and inhibiting all other buds.   Similarly, the direct action of external factors on the growing tips of runners may induce their transformation into new plants before the length of the runner has become sufficient to bring about physiological isolation of the tip in the ordinary way.

The development of biaxial forms from pieces in various hydroids and in *Planaria* (Figs. 92-101) and in other forms are cases in which this factor of physiological isolation plays a part.   The development of a new hydranth or a new head at the basal or posterior end of the piece occurs because the external differential determines a new gradient from the cut surface inward, *i. e.*, in the opposite direction to the original gradient, and in spite of its presence.   The new gradient determines first the new apical end and then so much of the body as the length of the piece and the lengths of new and old gradients permit. In these cases the new polarity arises more readily because the removal of the original hydranth or head and the isolation of the short piece have weakened dominance in the original direction.

Physiological isolation in development of repetitive series.—Physiological isolation is also unquestionably a factor in the development of repetitive series of parts, e. g., segments, series of tentacles, the mesenteries of sea anemones and corals, the "gills" of mushrooms, the order of leaves, branches, and other parts in plants. Each region of growth dominates a certain area and a new region of growth can arise only outside this area. In this way physiological isolation of neighboring cells from the dominance of a growing part such as a tentacle, usually in consequence of growth of the organism, may determine the localization and development of another tentacle at a certain distance from the first in the region which reacts most rapidly to the isolation. In short, the principle of physiological isolation applies to the process of repetition of parts as well as to the repetition of whole individuals.

Combinations of the different factors. — It may be noted, in conclusion that a particular case of physiological isolation is not necessarily determined by the action of a single one of the four factors, but two or more of them may be concerned. For example, growth may partially isolate a region and a temporary or permanent decrease in dominance or a direct stimulation of the region, or both may complete the process. Again, conditions bringing about decrease in dominance may also partially block the passage of the correlative factors, and so on. In all probability many cases of physiological isolation in nature represent such combined action of more than one of the four factors. But, however it is brought about in any particular case, the occurrence of physiological isolation shows, not only that dominance is a real physiological factor in development, but also that in the less highly specialized protoplasms it is limited in range and that this range can be controlled and altered in various ways.

DICHOTOMY, TWINNING AND AXIAL REDUPLICATION IN RELATION TO PHYSIOLOGICAL ISOLATION

In the preceding section it has been shown that physiological isolation plays a fundamental part in the reproduction of new individuals and the reduplication of parts from regions which are originally subordinate parts of an individual. There are, however, certain reproductive processes which involve the dominant region more or less directly, rather than the more distant subordinate parts. In many plants the growing tip divides at certain stages, or periodically, into two, or sometimes more than two growing tips of equal physiological rank which give rise to two or more similar and equivalent axes. Such division of an axis into two is commonly called dichotomy and in various algæ, liverworts and other forms it is a normal form of branching (Fig. 137). In various animals also such equal division of a dominant region occurs, either in normal development or under pathological or experimental conditions. It may

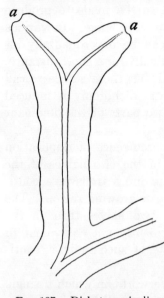

FIG. 137.—Dichotomy in liverwort, *Metzgeria:* the growing tip divides periodically into two growing tips, (a, a,) of equal physiological rank and each of these gives rise to a new axis.

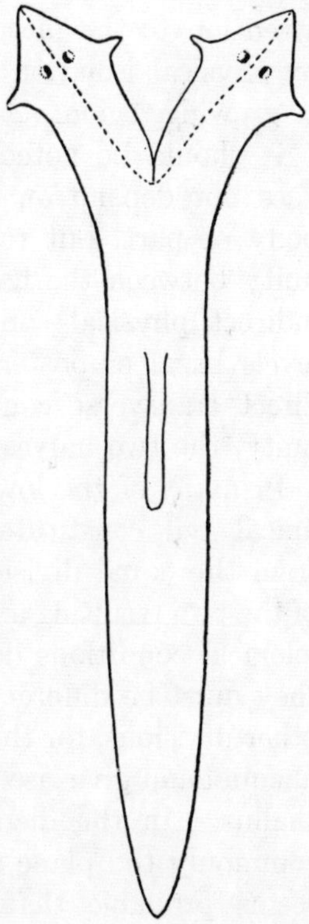

give rise in some cases to complete and separate individuals, in others to partially double or multiple individuals, e. g., double-headed forms, or to double or multiple parts, such as the reduplicated legs of amphibia (Figs. 127, 128, pp. 126–129), crustacea and various other forms. It is a familiar fact that dichotomous duplication of an axis can be experimentally produced in many cases by partial or complete physical isolation of the halves of the dominant region. If a planarian is split longitudinally into two halves, each half reorganizes into a whole animal, or, if we split only the anterior end and prevent the cut surfaces from uniting, each half of the head, or of the separated portion, becomes a whole and a form with two anterior ends results (Fig. 138). Dichotomous division of the posterior end may be accomplished in the same way.

FIG. 138.—A two-headed *Planaria* produced by partial longitudinal splitting. Dotted line indicates approximate boundary between old and regenerated tissue.

In the sea anemones and various other cœlenterates forms with double apical ends can also be produced by such physical isolation of the halves of the apical region. The amphibian limb-bud which would normally give rise to a single leg can be made to produce two legs by splitting it longitudinally at an early stage. In various plants dichotomous division of the axis can be experimentally induced by splitting the growing tip longitudinally for a short distance. Numerous other cases might be mentioned, but these suffice to call attention to the fact that such experimental dichotomy is induced by physical isolation from each other of two parts of the dominant or growing region.

It should be noted, however, that the occurrence of duplication does not depend on complete separation of the two halves of the body or part, but rather upon the loss of direct transverse continuity between the halves of the dominant or growing region. The indirect physical continuity between the two halves through the levels basal or posterior to the split is evidently not equivalent to direct transverse continuity, since, in spite of such indirect continuity, the two halves become wholes.

In many of the lower plants, such as liverworts, in which a single apical cell constitutes the growing tip proper, dichotomy results from the equal division of this cell in a plane vertical to the plane of the two resulting axes. We know nothing of the intracellular physiological conditions determining such division, but it is evident that they must be different in some way from those which determine the other divisions, for these latter take place in other planes, are usually unequal and give rise, not to growing tips but to the other cells of the thallus. In the dichotomous divisions the plane of dichotomy is commonly the plane of the flattened thallus (Fig. 137), therefore it seems probable that differential physiological conditions of some sort in definite relation to this plane determine both occurrence and plane of dichotomy.

In plants with multicellular growing tip dichotomy involves the division of the tip into two multicellular tips, but cell division is not necessarily directly concerned. In animals also a dichotomy of the apical or anterior dominant region obviously involves a division of a dominant region or growing tip into two. Except in certain colonial, normally branching forms such dichotomous division of the chief body axes in animals occurs under either pathological or experimental conditions and gives rise to so-called double monsters, partial, or sometimes complete twins, in short to all degrees of duplication.

The case of the armadillo. — In the nine-banded armadillo investigated by Patterson and Newman and discussed at length with references to the original papers by Newman ('17 b, Chaps. II, III; '23,
Chap. VIII), the single embryonic vesicle gives rise normally to four
complete embryos. In certain other species of armadillo larger num-
bers of embryos are produced normally from the single ovum. Since
this embryonic division in the armadillo is a normal phenomenon and
has become well known through the work of Patterson and Newman
and since Newman has advanced a physiological interpretation of it,
it serves well as a starting point for interpretation. According to
Newman the division is the consequence of a quiescent period in early
development. During this period in which development is retarded
or inhibited for some unknown reason, the original dominant region
loses its dominance because of decreased activity and parts of the embryonic vesicle previously subordinate, or perhaps parts of the dominant region itself, become physiologically isolated. In consequence
of such isolation four new radially situated dominant regions arise
and develop into four embryos.

In Newman's earlier account he conceives this process of reduplication as the simultaneous formation of a number of equivalent radially arranged apical regions in the ectodermic vesicle. Two of these
favored by position with respect to the bilaterality of the uterus, become the "primary" embryos, two others the "secondary" embryos,
but all four are equivalent as regards origin (Newman, '17 b, pp. 50,
51). According to his later views, however, the process is apparently
conceived as consisting of two successive fissions of the vesicle, the direction of the first determined by a differential of some sort associated
with the bilaterality of the uterus, that of the second by undeter-
mined conditions (Newman, '23, Chap. VIII). Patterson ('13) regarded the process of reduplication as a double budding and Stockard ('21) has accepted his view. Newman's contention that the process is rather a double fission than budding is based on the supposed
dichotomous character of the divisions without persistence of the
original dominant region. As regards the first duplication this contention seems well founded for, as far as the evidence goes at present,
this duplication appears to be a true dichotomy. As regards the second duplication, however, the evidence is somewhat less conclusive,
though it seems to suggest dichotomy, rather than lateral budding
with persistence of the dominant region of the primary embryo.

Newman's assumption of obliteration of an original single dominant
region may be correct, but it is not the only way of accounting for

the facts. If there is a differential in the uterine environment of the embryonic vesicle such that two lateral regions of it are more favorably situated, for example, as regards respiratory exchange, or other physiological conditions, these two regions may be directly determined as dominant apical regions in spite of the presence of the original dominant region. Such a process of duplication is essentially a process of physiological isolation by "excitation of subordinate parts" (p. 159), except that the parts accelerated in this case may be parts of the original dominant region. If the first duplication in the armadillo occurs in this way, the original dominance is obliterated, not by the quiescent period, but directly by the bilateral differential in the uterus. Very probably both factors are concerned. The chief purpose of this discussion is to call attention to the fact that the data of observation, even in a case so extensively investigated as this of the armadillo, do not yet permit us to reach definite conclusions concerning the physiological factors involved, but merely serve as a basis for pointing out the possibilities. It appears that we do not certainly know whether this case of double twinning represents two successive dichotomies or a simultaneous tetratomy or a polytomy with persistence of four members. Nor is it certain whether one, or both of the duplications, if there are two, results from a loss of dominance and physiological isolation during a quiescent period, or whether the two primary, or all four polarities are directly determined by local differentials in spite of a preëxisting original polarity.

As the facts stand, they suggest that the axes of the two primary embryos are directly determined by the bilateral environmental differential in the uterus, but whether after obliteration of an original dominance by a quiescent period, or in spite of it, I do not think we can as yet determine. In any case, however, this interesting embryonic reduplication, in spite of its uniformity and constancy, cannot be accounted for in terms of heredity alone. It represents the behavior under certain physiological conditions of a specific protoplasm with certain hereditary potentialities.

Other processes of dichotomy and twinning. — Turning to other cases of dichotomous duplication, twinning, etc., in multicellular forms, it is evident that we know no more concerning the physiology of the process than in the case of the armadillo. Whenever a growing tip or an axis divides dichotomously, the position of the two new tips or axes with reference to each other must be determined either by a differential of some sort, such as a double symmetry gradient already present in the region concerned, or by some differential in environmental conditions within the organism or external to it, which localizes two active regions instead of one.

The physiological processes concerned in dichotomy may differ in different cases. In dichotomy in the lower plants there is usually no evidence that any inhibition, quiescent period, or loss of dominance is necessary. The apical cell divides equally, the division plane coinciding with the median plane of the thallus, and each half remains an apical cell. The plane of division is usually definitely related to the bilaterality of the thallus, which in turn may be determined originally by light or by some other environmental factor. In plants with multicellular growing tip and in multicellular animals dichotomy is not primarily a matter of cell division, but involves changes in rate of activity in cell masses, and essentially the same questions arise as in the case of the armadillo.

It appears to be true that flattened growing tips and blastoderms present conditions relatively favorable for the occurrence of di-

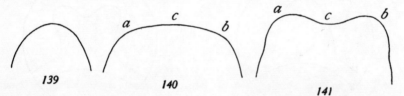

FIGS. 139–141.—Diagrams illustrating dichotomy of a growing region in consequence of growth and flattening in a plane at right angles to the main axis. Further explanation in text.

chotomy in the plane of the flattening. A brief consideration will serve to indicate the conditions which may be concerned in such a case. A growing region of this sort may be at first radially symmetrical (Fig. 139), but differential growth, determined either by its relations to other parts of the organism, or directly by some external differential, brings about a flattening at right angles to the polar axis (Fig. 140). Such flattening may itself determine a differential in the growing region between the middle portion, c, and the two lateral regions, a and b (Fig. 140). The regions a and b are more favorably situated than c as regards nutrition, since they are nearer the less active cells of lower levels from which they can obtain food, while c is surrounded on all sides by cells with a high rate of metabolism and growth. As regards respiratory exchange also the conditions are more favorable at a and b than at c, particularly if the surface of these regions is curved as indicated in the diagram. If such a differential becomes sufficient, the activity of c may in time be somewhat inhibited, while a and b retain or increase their activity and so become distinct growing and dominant regions (Fig. 141, a, b), separated by a less active region, c. In this way a true dichotomy may result from differential growth of a dominant region determined by conditions acting at right angles to the polar axis. It seems probable that many of the dichotomies which occur normally or occasionally in nature are of this sort, the differential transverse growth of the dominant region being determined by different factors in different cases. In certain plants, for example, dichotomy occurs at right angles to the direction of incident light, while in animals other conditions, probably in many cases conditions connected with respiratory exchange, are concerned.

Moreover, if a flattened dominant region is inhibited by an external chemical or physical agent and then undergoes acclimation or

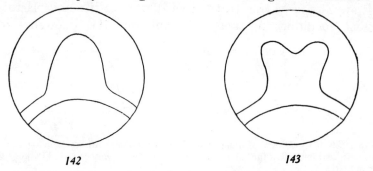

142   143

Figs. 142, 143.—Diagrams of early developmental stages of fish to illustrate dichotomy of anterior end of embryonic area: Fig. 142, normal; Fig. 143, dichotomy.

recovery, it is evident that conditions are more favorable for such acclimation or recovery at a and b than at c (Fig. 140). Consequently dichotomy of an axis may sometimes be brought about experimentally by the action of inhibiting factors.

The occurrence of different degrees of dichotomy and twinning as a teratological phenomenon in the embryonic development of fishes has been noted by various investigators. Such dichotomy gives rise to all degrees of twinning, from double-headed monsters to complete normal twins. Recently Stockard ('21) has described such dichotomies experimentally determined by inhibiting conditions and has interpreted them in terms of loss of dominance and physiological isolation of a subordinate region with budding. Even though some cases of unequal twins may be accounted for in this way, the frequent cases of equal twins present difficulties to this interpretation. It seems much more probable that these are true dichotomies and that they arise in some one of the ways described above. The fish embryo presents exceedingly favorable conditions for the occurrence of such dichotomy. The dominant region of the embryo develops as a broad flattened area upon the yolk (Fig. 142), *i. e.*, it is normally flattened transversely and is therefore a favorable substratum for the appearance of dichotomy in the manner indicated in Figures 140 and 141. Stockard has produced such dichotomous fish embryos by low temperature and by insufficient oxygen. It is evident at once that in the flattened embryonic area the differential exposure of lateral borders and median portion of the dominant region may determine physiological differentials like those indicated in Figure 141 above. Something of this sort apparently happens in many cases. The originally single dominant region becomes two, not simply because of loss of dominance of one region over another, but because the shape of the dominant region favors the appearance of a differential between lateral and median portions and this differential determines two dominant regions (Fig. 143) and consequently a greater or less degree of twinning, according to conditions.

It seems to be true that those forms in which the dominant region in early stages is a flattened area spread out over yolk give rise more frequently to such dichotomies than other forms. In the chick, for example, such dichotomous twinning is not infrequent. There may be other conditions not yet recognized which also favor dichotomy, but, taking the facts as they stand, the shape of the dominant region appears to be a factor of considerable importance in the occurrence of dichotomy in both plants and animals, consequently the conditions determining the shape must be regarded as conditions predisposing to dichotomy.

In many cases of complete twinning from a single ovum the embryos may be more or less widely separated from each other. The possibility may be pointed out that in some such cases duplication may have been brought about in some way at a stage before a single embryonic area was established, rather than by fission of such an area. What conditions have been concerned in such cases and whether such twins represent physiological isolation in consequence of inhibition of a single dominant region in the early blastoderm or earlier, or direct determination of axes by environmental differentials in spite of an original dominance, we do not know.

Situs inversus viscerum and mirror imaging in twinning. — In partial duplications in vertebrates it is often found that the usual visceral asymmetry is reversed in one of the components. Mirror imaging in the reduplication of amphibian limbs has been discussed in the preceding chapter. In his recent book Newman ('23, Chaps. XII–XIV) has described and figured numerous cases of these symmetry relations, consequently detailed description is unnecessary here. We have as yet no experimental evidence for analysis of these relations and little more than surmise is possible as regards the conditions concerned (see p. 127). I wish, however, to point out that both situs inversus and mirror imaging indicate that the components concerned affect each other or are affected by a common factor. In short, the symmetry relations, whether determined by bioelectric, or by other conditions associated with the physiological gradients, represent in each case a reaction of the specific protoplasm to environmental conditions.

The problem of polytomy. — It is a question of some interest whether a number of new axes, either of individuals or of organs, with a definite localization and arrangement, can arise simultaneously through polytomy of a single dominant region or of a general substratum. Many apparent cases of such polytomy occur. In many plants, for example, branches, the parts of flowers, etc., appear in whorls and among animals the tentacles of cœlenterates and the rays of the starfish apparently represent equivalent parts which, so far as appearances are concerned, must have originated simultaneously. A priori, the simultaneous orderly origin and localization of such parts in a definite and constant pattern appears physiologically impossible without preëxisting differentials of some sort determining the radius in which each part shall arise. But when we examine the origin of such parts more closely we find that, at least in many cases, they do not arise simultaneously. Among plants many whorls and multiple radial parts are known to originate as compressed axes, the radial arrangement and equivalence being secondary. That is to say, the parts arise successively in a regular order and sequence in relation to an extremely short axis. There is considerable evidence of similar conditions in animals. In the development of certain sea anemones the tentacles do not appear simultaneously, but in a definite order and position with respect to each other. In the buds of hydra also and in pieces undergoing reconstitution it can often be seen that the tentacles do not appear simultaneously, but in order, and small isolated pieces often give rise to one tentacle only. In many other cases among the cœlenterates there is at present no indication of such a definite order in appearance of tentacles and the process of their localization appears to be a true polytomy. In the reconstitution of a piece of *Tubularia* stem, for example, the tentacle ridges seem to appear simultaneously about the whole circumference (Figs. 67–69) and in the development and reconstitution of hydranths in various other hydroids the tentacle buds seem to arise simultaneously about the whole circumference (Figs. 91–98, 117–121). If these processes are true polytomies, as they appear to be, and not successive buddings, we have as yet no basis for physiological interpretation of them. As regards the echinoderms, the earlier development shows clearly enough that the more or less equiradiate form of later stages is secondary and not the result of a true polytomy.

Polytomy in anaxiate forms is of frequent occurrence, *e. g.*, the multiple cell divisions in protozoan and other cysts, but in such cases we merely have the localization of cell boundaries with relation to the positions of nuclei rather than the origin of new axes. It is perhaps still a pertinent question whether true polytomy, *i. e.*, simultaneous multiple division of an axis, does occur in any case of orderly and definite axial multiplication, and if it does occur, we have then to inquire how the particular axes are localized and how the arrangement of the whole series of axes, *e. g.*, a ring of tentacles, is determined.

THE LIMIT OF INDIVIDUAL SIZE

If the conception of dominance and physiological isolation discussed in this chapter is correct, it follows that unless other factors are concerned, the length of any individual axis must be determined by the range of dominance. If the length of the axis increases beyond the range of dominance, or if the range of dominance decreases below the length of the axis, or if dominance is otherwise interfered with, physiological isolation occurs and a new individual may arise. In the plants and the simpler animals these are apparently the chief factors in determining the size of the individual and, as might be expected, individual size shows very wide variation according to conditions.

Another factor or group of factors is concerned in determining size, particularly in the more highly specialized organs and organisms. This is the decrease and cessation of growth with the progress of differentiation. Even in the plants such organs as leaves and parts of flowers usually lose the ability to grow during the course of development, though in some cases it reappears after processes of dedifferentiation, as in adventitious buds from epidermal cells of leaves. In animals which do not reproduce asexually the rate of growth decreases during later development and increase in size finally ceases or becomes very slow.

There is no doubt that in animals with well-developed nervous system the range of dominance increases greatly in the course of development and sooner or later exceeds by far the actual size of even the largest individual. The nerves of the higher, if not of all vertebrates, are capable of conducting impulses to very great, perhaps to indefinite distances (see Chap. XI), but the size of the vertebrate body is very definitely limited. The limiting factors in these cases are the factors which limit growth, not those which limit dominance.

Even in the higher animals, however, the range of dominance may be very low in early developmental stages and particularly during the development of the nervous system the increase in range must be very great. If this is true, physiological isolation may occur in early stages, even though the individual is of very small size, and may be impossible later, although the size is much larger. For example, segmentation, which is probably a limited reproductive process in which a certain degree of physiological isolation is concerned, may occur, even in the higher vertebrates in early developmental stages, but not in advanced life.

Nevertheless certain cases of apparent physiological isolation do occur in mature life and particularly in old age, viz., the neoplasms, especially the malignant forms. In these the isolating factor seems usually, if not always to be an irritation of the cells concerned, i. e., it is isolation by local action on the subordinate part (see p. 159), though perhaps some decrease in the effectiveness of dominance with advancing age may also play a part. In some cases the cells of neoplasms show more or less differentiation, but in the extreme malignant type they grow and divide indefinitely and this indefinite growth constitutes their malignancy. Whether such growth is the result of continued action of the factor which initiated the growth, or whether the cells have lost their ability to differentiate, is not certain. The point of chief importance for present purposes is that physiological isolation is apparently concerned in the initiation of many, if not all sorts of neoplasms, as well as in normal reproductive processes.

THE FORMATION AND ISOLATION OF SEX CELLS

The evidence along both morphological and physiological lines indicates that the sex cells are as much a part of the body as other cells, that the genesis of the egg and spermatozoön from the primitive germ cell is a process of differentiation and of senescence comparable to that occurring in other body cells, and finally, that the fully developed gamete, whether male or female, is a physiologically old cell, approaching death, and that the initiation of development leads to regressive development and rejuvenescence (Child, '15 b, Chaps. XIII, XIV).

The sex cell may retain physical continuity with the protoplasm of other body cells up to a late stage, or it may lose this connection early and undergo its later development in the fluid of the gonad, or, as in many annelids, in the body cavity. Its loss of continuity with other cells seems at first glance to be a process quite different from physiological isolation. Certainly neither growth beyond the range of dominance nor decrease in dominance are involved and it seems highly improbable that dominance is blocked from the sex organ. If physiological isolation is concerned apparently it must occur through local action on the subordinate part, i. e., the sex cell. It seems to be true that the loss of direct continuity with other cells follows the loss of physiological significance of such continuity for the growing egg or sperm. In many annelids, for example, connection of the egg with other cells has no appreciable nutritive or respiratory function and is lost very early, the fluid of the body cavity serving as nutritive and respiratory medium. In many other forms eggs receive their nutrition through the region of attachment, and continuity persists through the whole growth period, as in the case of *Sternaspis* (Fig. 63), the sea urchin and starfish, most cœlenterates and many other forms. In the case of the male cell the nutritive requirements are usually much less than for the egg and the fluids of the gonad adequate as nutritive and respiratory medium, consequently continuity with other cells may be lost very early. According to this view the isolation of the sex cells within the parent body is essentially the atrophy or interruption of a connection which has become functionless or nearly so, and it is the environment of the sex cell, i. e., the nutritive and respiratory environment, which has made the connection functionless. If this interpretation is correct, the isolation of the sex cell may be regarded as a physiological isolation resulting from direct local action on the cell.

The extrusion of the sex cells from the parent body is perhaps in its original, purely physiological significance a process of getting rid of waste material. The sex cells have completed their development and are approaching death from old age: any endocrine, or other functional relations to other parts of the body which they possess in earlier stages have reached a minimum and when they accumulate to a certain degree, or under the action of certain external stimuli, they are cast off. In the mammal, however, the fertilized egg enters into a new functional relation with the parent body and profound modification results. Here again, however, a change in the significance of these functional relations results in the separation of embryo and parent.

CHAPTER XI

IRRITABILITY, EXCITATION AND TRANSMISSION

The question of the significance of excitation and transmission as the primary correlative factor in organismic integration has already been touched upon in Chapter V and we have seen in later chapters that the axial physiological gradients, the physiological axes of individuals, exhibit primarily all the physiological characteristics of excitation-transmission gradients and that they may be determined by local or differential excitation or apparently by any environmental differential which gives rise to a persistent local differ-- ence in rate of fundamental metabolism (Chap. IX). In "The Origin and Development of the Nervous System" the various lines of evidence were brought together which indicate that the physiological conditions determining the structural and functional origin and development of the nervous system in the individual themselves originate in excitation and transmission. Certain aspects of the problem of excitation were considered in Chapter IV of that book, but for present purposes a somewhat more extended survey, particularly of the development of present conceptions of excitation, transmission and the more highly specialized conduction seems necessary.

THE PROBLEM OF THE NATURE OF EXCITATION AND TRANSMISSION

In the consideration in Chapter V of excitation and transmission as factors in physiological correlation, attention was called to the following characteristics of the excitation-transmission change in protoplasms: first, all living protoplasms are to some extent irritable or excitable and capable of transmission. Second, excitation is a dynamic change involving increased energy-liberation in the protoplasmic system. Third, it is initiated by the impact from without of some form of energy upon the protoplasm excited [1] and the relation between the exciting factor and the process of excitation is non-specific, in other words, the same excitatory changes may be induced by different forms of external energy. Fourth, transmission

---

[1] The question whether or to what extent "self-excitation" may occur and whether the so-called automatic tissues are really self-exciting is considered below (pp. 184–186).

results from the fact that an excited region is capable of inducing in some way excitation in adjoining regions within a certain distance. Fifth, in non-nervous transmission and in nervous transmission under certain conditions a decrement in intensity or energy, in short of physiological effectiveness, of the excitation very generally, if not always, occurs. In other words, the excitatory change loses in effectiveness in the course of its progress, so that finally at a greater or less distance from the point of origin, it is no longer effective in exciting further points and so transmission ceases. And finally, no specialized structure of any sort beyond that of a living protoplasm with limiting surface is necessary for the occurrence of excitation and transmission. The excitation itself makes the excited region different at least temporarily from unexcited regions and the transmission of excitation brings different and often widely distant regions into correlation. The action of the external exciting factor determines regional differences and relations of organismic character and magnitude in the protoplasm. In short, as pointed out in Chapter V and in "The Development of the Nervous System" (Chap. V) excitation and its transmission, apparently give rise to a temporary pattern and relation of the simplest and most primitive organismic character possible between regions or parts, and this pattern is in its simplest terms a physiological gradient. So far as determined, this gradient differs from the axial physiological gradients of axiate organisms chiefly as being less permanent and more immediately dependent on the action of the external factor. Apparently the excitation-transmission gradient and the physiological axis in its simplest terms are fundamentally similar or identical phenomena in living protoplasms. If this is actually the case, a knowledge of the nature of excitation and transmission is of fundamental importance for an adequate conception of the individual organism.

Unfortunately our knowledge of excitation and transmission is still very incomplete. Investigation has naturally been largely concerned with the most excitable tissues, nerve and muscle and with these tissues in their most highly specialized forms in the higher animals. Even in some of the recent works on general physiology, excitation and transmission are discussed primarily from the viewpoint of nerve and muscle physiology, and little attention is given to their significance for the behavior of living protoplasm in general. Certain features of the development of our conception of excitation and transmission are of interest here and are briefly discussed in the following paragraphs.

Earlier theories of excitation and transmission. — The complexity of the dynamic changes in living protoplasm and the difficulties involved in obtaining positive and exact knowledge of them and their relations to each other have made advance in this field slow, and this situation has favored the formulation of widely different hypotheses. With the development of physiology and the experimental method, the older metaphysical hypotheses of vital spirits and their flow through the nerves gave place to physical and chemical hypotheses, but even these differ widely.[1]

Galvani's discovery that excitation and transmission in nerves could be electrically induced led him to believe that the principle of electricity and of nervous function are the same. Since Galvani's time it has been abundantly demonstrated, on the one hand, that electric changes may bring about excitation, not merely in nerve but in other kinds of protoplasm, and on the other, that changes in electric potential are involved in excitation and transmission. The belief that the electric changes are in some way of fundamental importance in excitation and transmission and the hope of attaining a solution of the problem by investigation of these electrical phenomena and their experimental modifications has been responsible for the great development of electro-physiology during the latter part of the last century.[2] During this period widely different hypotheses concerning the origin and rôle of the electric changes in excitation were advanced. Originating perhaps in Du Bois Reymond's hypothesis of the electromotor molecule, the belief in the purely physical origin of the electric phenomena was widespread and appeared in various forms. On the basis of the experiments by Matteucci the conception of the nerve, or at least the medullated nerve, as made up of two different conductors, *i. e.*, the axis cylinder and the medullary sheath, between which electric polarization occurred, was developed in various publications by Hermann [3] and others. Boruttau

---

[1] Only a few of the more important points can be mentioned in the text. For any adequate appreciation of the various theories and the enormous bibliography of this very interesting chapter of the history of biology, the reader must refer to the discussions, general surveys and reviews of the subject which have been published from time to time: e. g., Hermann, '79; Biedermann, '96, '03; Hering, '79, '88, '99; Boruttau '01 b; Cremer, '09; Verworn, '06, '13, Chaps. V, VI; Bernstein, '12. References to the work of R. S. Lillie, Loeb, Tashiro, Mathews, Lapicque, Lucas, Adrian and others are given below. The discussions of excitation and transmission in the text-books of physiology are usually very largely concerned with the phenomena in nerves and muscles of the higher animals.

[2] For the theories and literature of this period see Biedermann, '96, '03; Bernstein, '12.

[3] See Hermann, '79, '99, and other references cited by Biedermann, '96, '03.

('00, '01 a, b, '02) and Hoorweg ('01) went so far as to maintain that between the point of original excitation and the end organ there was no transmission of excitation in any physiological sense, but merely of electrical changes. Various other authors also held that the process of transmission is something quite distinct from excitation, *i. e.*, that the excitatory change itself is not transmitted. Hermann, however, insisted that with electric polarization without excitation in a physiological sense a wave-like transmission could not occur. More recently, Bose ('02, '06, '07, '13) on the basis of extensive investigation of the electrical features of response in plants and in metals, maintains that excitation is fundamentally a molecular, a physical disturbance. Macallum ('11) has suggested that the electric phenomena in nerve may originate in surface tension changes.

But even during the period when these purely physical conceptions of excitation and transmission were very generally current, various physiologists called attention to the probable significance of "physiological factors," *i. e.*, factors characteristic of living protoplasm and including the chemical reactions of metabolism. Hermann in some of his earlier papers ('67 a, b) maintained that excitation of a nerve results from a sudden acceleration of metabolic processes. Later, however, he abandoned this purely chemical view as incomplete, but insisted on the importance of a "physiological *x*." Hering ('79, '88) also maintained that the electric phenomena of nerve and muscle result from changes in chemical function. Biedermann ('96), a pupil of Hering, adopted essentially this viewpoint and called it the Hermann-Hering theory.[1] Waller ('97, '03) maintained that metabolism was concerned in the electric phenomena of excitation and tramsmission. Bernstein ('99) and Hörmann ('99) developed the idea that irritable substance consists of chains of molecules surrounded by nutritive fluid. These molecular chains may take up certain atoms or atomic groups from the nutritive fluid and these are given off or broken down in functional metabolism and in excitation. According to Hörmann, transmission is a transmission of chemical reactions and is not necessarily associated with electric changes.

Later theories of excitation and transmission. — With the rapid development of physical chemistry toward the end of the nineteenth century, the application of its conceptions to the phenomena of excitation and transmission began. The theory of electrolytic dissociation with its definition of the ion as an atom or atomic group bearing pos-

[1] For a more extended account of these views see Hyman and Bellamy, '22.

itive or negative electrical charges, offered new possibilities of accounting for the electric phenomena characteristic of excitation and transmission. The rapid increase of knowledge concerning the properties of colloids in general and especially of semipermeable membranes has likewise afforded general ideas which have played an important part in the more recent development of our conceptions of these and many other physiological processes. Applications to the problem of excitation and transmission of some of these principles and conceptions of physical chemistry were soon made by Bernstein, Nernst, Loeb, Lapicque, Boruttau and many others. Loeb, for example, showed in a series of papers the important part played by ions in excitation and inhibition.[1] Nernst ('08) advanced a theory of electrical stimulation in terms of polarization effects in relation to a semipermeable membrane. Lapicque presented much experimental evidence in favor of the view that excitation is a process of polarization and also called particular attention to the chronological factor in excitation. He showed that an electric current of a certain intensity must act for a certain length of time to excite and on this basis he established a chronological coefficient which he called chronaxie. This coefficient differs in different nerves and muscles and with different conditions and this difference, heterochronism, is of great physiological importance. And finally, he maintained that all these features of excitation can be interpreted in terms of electrical polarization of semipermeable membranes.[2] This conception of excitation, like various others of this period,[3] is essentially electrolytic in character, but some physiologists maintained that the chemical reactions of metabolism play an essential part in the complex of changes which constitute excitation. Among the theories which belong to this group, that of Verworn ('13) asserts that excitation is fundamentally an acceleration in the rate of breakdown or protoplasmic molecules so labile that the excitatory process may be regarded as more or less explosive in character. Verworn also points out that the necessity of oxygen for the maintenance of irritability in aërobic organisms indicates that oxidation is a fundamental factor in the reaction. As regards transmission, he holds that the experimental evidence supports the view now generally

[1] See Loeb, '06, Chap. V and numerous special papers of earlier and later date.

[2] For Lapicque's conception of excitation as polarization see more particularly: L. Lapicque, '07 a, b, c, d, e, '08 c, '09 b; Lapicque et Petetin, '10. For "chronaxie" and heterochronism see L. Lapicque, '07 c, e, '08 a, b, '09 a; L. et M. Lapicque, '03, '12a, Lapicque et Legendre, '13.

[3] *E. g.*, Mathews, '01, '02, '03, '04, '05; MacDonald, '05; Lasareff, '18 and various others.

accepted, though opposed by some of the earlier authorities, that the excitation itself, not merely some electric or other change, is transmitted. Nevertheless, electric changes resulting from the decomposition of the labile molecules at one point are regarded by Verworn as the factors primarily concerned in inducing the decomposition at another point. If the colloid membranes of protoplasm are permeable to positive, and not to negative ions, the chemical decomposition at the point of primary excitation brings about changes in electric potential with flow of current, and this initiates the decomposition at another point. R. S. Lillie's theory considered below is somewhat similar to this as regards rôle of the electric current.

It is well known that excitation in organisms generally and in many organs is associated with increased respiratory exchange, and Tashiro has recently shown that excitation in the nerve fiber is accompanied by increase in CO_2 production [1] and various other authors have found that metabolism occurs in nerve and is increased during excitation.[2] Mathews ('15, pp. 584–593) also regards metabolism as a fundamental factor in nervous excitation.

Lillie's theory of excitation and transmission. — In the course of the last twelve years R. S. Lillie [3] has developed a general theory of excitation in terms of current physico-chemical conceptions and based on extensive experimental evidence. Because this theory represents the most recent generalization in this field of physiology, because it is not merely a speculative modification of earlier theories, but is based on various lines of experimental investigation, because it is concerned to some degree, not only with the highly specialized processes of nervous excitation and conduction, but with excitation and transmission in general, and finally, because it will serve very well as a point of departure for discussion of the relations

[1] Tashiro, '17 and earlier papers. Bayliss and Lucas have criticised Tashiro's conclusions, in part on the ground that Hill ('12) has been unable to discover any appreciable heat production associated with the nervous impulse. They suggest that the carbon dioxide may be dissolved in the tissues and that its increase on electric stimulation may be due to the rise in temperature. The demonstration by Riggs ('19) that chemical, as well as electrical stimulation is accompanied by increase in CO_2 appears to answer this objection. Moore ('19), using a colorimetric method, was unable to confirm certain of Tashiro's results, but Tashiro and Hendricks ('21) maintain that the colorimetric method is unsuitable because the nerve produces a volatile base, presumably ammonia, as well as CO_2. More recently Sheaff ('22) has determined the oxygen consumption of resting and stimulated nerve, the latter being two to four times the former.

[2] Thunberg, Skand. Arch. Physiol., XLIII, 1923 and papers there cited.

[3] R. S. Lillie, '09 a, b, c, '11, '13, '14, '15, '16 a, b, '17, '18, '19, '20 a, b, c, '22, '23; R. S. Lillie and E. N. Johnston, '19.

between excitation-transmission phenomena and physiological gradients, its chief points must be stated somewhat fully.

Various experimental data, as well as theoretical considerations, indicate that protoplasmic limiting surfaces, the plasma membranes, are the seat of electrical polarization, and the belief in the existence of such polarization is widespread among physiologists. Moreover, the so-called membrane theory of stimulation (Nernst, '08) has been very generally accepted. According to commonly accepted views the membrane in the unexcited condition acts as if it were permeable or reversible to certain or all positive ions and impermeable or less permeable to certain negative ions, which are present in higher concentration in the cell than outside. Consequently the unexcited

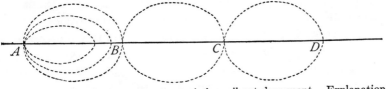

Fig. 144.—Diagram illustrating transmission wihout decrement. Explanation in text.

membrane is electropositive externally, electronegative internally. Proceeding on the basis of these conclusions, Lillie's experimental investigations have provided many new data in support of the view that excitation involves an increase in permeability to the negative ions and that consequently a more or less complete depolarization of the membrane is associated with excitation. Since the increase in permeability permits the negative ions to pass out, some or all of the positive charges on the outside of the membrane will be neutralized and the region of excitation will show externally an increased electronegativity (negative variation), which must be accompanied by an increased electropositivity internally.[1] These changes in electric potential determine electric currents between excited and unexcited regions, and Lillie agrees with certain of the earlier investigators in regarding the electric currents initiated by the excitation at one point as the means by which transmission of the excitation to adjoining regions is accomplished. The action of these currents is briefly as follows: since the excited region A (Fig. 144) is electro-

---

[1] According to recent work by Heilbrunn ('23), protoplasm, at least the protoplasm of certain animal eggs, bears a positive electric charge internally and a negative charge externally. If this is true for protoplasm in general, it appears that the electrical changes which have been found to be associated with excitation must involve an increase in the potential difference across the membrane.

negative externally and electropositive internally to an unexcited region B, the positive current must flow from A to B through the tissues and in the opposite direction through the external medium. Such a current must increase the external electronegativity and the internal electropositivity of all other parts within the range of effectiveness, AB, determined by strength of current and resistance. At the same time it must decrease the external negativity and the internal positivity at A. In other words, the electric currents produced by excitation at A bring about excitation at other points within a certain range, AB, and at the same time tend to reverse the state of excitation at A and to bring about repolarization of the membrane there. As points between A and B become excited they likewise become the source of electric currents, and if the excitation at these points is of the same degree or intensity as that at A these currents at B will excite points within the range BC and thus transmission to an indefinite distance without decrement may occur. Because of the existence of a refractory period following excitation, the excitation of B and of C cannot reëxcite A and by the time A has recovered from the refractory period the wave of transmitted excitation is so far distant that A is beyond the range of the currents arising from it.

This brief sketch will perhaps suffice to indicate the lines along which Lillie's interpretation of excitation and transmission proceeds. He has also made various suggestions concerning details of the process, but only certain of those need concern us here. In one of his earlier papers he says regarding permeability that the evidence indicates

"that the change in permeability associated with stimulation is not a direct effect due to merely physical changes in the protoplasmic surface layer, but is the consequence of a chemical reaction which alters the character of the surface film and temporarily deprives it of its normal semipermeable and electromotor properties, and that this chemical process may in a highly irritable tissue like nerve be initiated by any slight local decrease in polarization, provided the change is sufficiently rapid" (R. S. Lillie, '14, p. 443).

In various other later papers [1] he maintains that the chemical reaction involved in the increase in permeability is a metabolic reaction probably oxidative in nature. Whether this chemical reaction or some colloidal change or a change of some other sort is the primary effect of the depolarization Lillie does not attempt to say, but since the whole series is indissociable and mutually related, it makes little difference which factor we regard as primary and which as secondary.

[1] R. S. Lillie, '17, pp. 80–82; '18, p. 3; '19, p. 458; '22, p. 17.

It is not impossible that, at least in some organisms or tissues, the primary change may differ with different forms of energy as exciting factors.

This conception of excitation and transmission resembles that of Verworn and some others in insisting that a chemical reaction is a fundamental factor somewhere in the process. It is evident that according to such a theory the velocity of transmission of excitation is not the velocity of electric transmission, but a variable dependent upon the velocity of the chemical reactions and any other changes concerned in giving rise to the electric currents.

As we have seen, changes in permeability and in electric polarization of membranes are, according to Lillie, essential factors in excitation and transmission. If this is the case, it follows of course that excitation and transmission are phenomena of plasma membranes or of limiting surfaces in protoplasm. Such semipermeable membranes or limiting surfaces are commonly believed to constitute the external boundaries of all cells and protoplasms, but it may be pointed out that limiting surfaces or membranes must also exist between the colloid phases in the interior of protoplasm and the possibility exists that excitation-transmission phenomena, differing perhaps in certain respects from those occurring at the external limiting surfaces, may take place in the limiting surfaces of the continuous phase of the protoplasm. The assumption made by some that excitation and transmission are phenomena of external cellular or protoplasmic surfaces only, seems therefore unnecessary.

Lillie has devised inorganic models of excitation and transmission, consisting of iron wire, the excitation being the activation of the surface of the wire which has previously been passivated. The activation supposedly consists in the decomposition of a surface film previously formed by the action of strong nitric acid (R. S. Lillie, '18, '19). Excitation in such models may be brought about electrically or by other means, even mechanically, and the excitatory change is transmitted by means of the electric currents associated with the chemical change at any point. The velocity and range of transmission differ according to experimental conditions and can be controlled and modified. These models also show the refractory period following excitation and a gradual recovery of transmissivity (R. S. Lillie, '20).

The advance of our knowledge of the phenomena of excitation and transmission in general makes it more and more probable that they are very complex processes, involving, as Lillie maintains, both chemical reaction, probably the fundamental metabolic reactions, and physical changes. Various facts, such as the difference in rate of transmission in different protoplasms or in the same protoplasm under different conditions, e. g., at different temperatures, the relation between oxygen and excitability and between respiration and excitation, etc., indicate clearly that the electrical changes are closely associated with and dependent upon other changes, probably usually, if not always, chemical. And finally, the evidence points more and more definitely to the electric currents and their effects as the factors determining the progress or transmission of excitation from point to point. Lillie's theory takes all these and various other points into consideration and may therefore serve as a general foundation for the following discussion, but it may be pointed out that the interpretation of the physiological gradients and their significance for the organism in terms of excitation and transmission is not dependent on this particular theory of excitation nor upon any other, but is based primarily on experimental evidence from many different lines.

PRIMITIVE AND SPECIALIZED EXCITATION PROCESSES

Excitation and metabolism. — As already noted above, many of the earlier physiologists believed that metabolism is not concerned in nervous conduction, while others maintained that it is an essential factor. Certainly the natural conclusion from Tashiro's demonstration of increase in CO_2 production during stimulation in nerve is the one which he draws, viz., that oxidative metabolism is concerned in the process, but certain critics have questioned the correctness of his conclusions on various grounds, some of which are certainly not adequate (see pp. 178, 190). For example, Hill's failure to find appreciable heat production in nervous excitation has been regarded by some as conflicting with Tashiro's conclusions, since oxidation, if it occurs, ought to liberate heat. According to current views, however, oxidation is an essential factor in the production of light by living organisms, but no appreciable heat production has been observed in bioluminescence. Light production is unquestionably one form of excitatory change and if oxidation without heat production may occur in it, it seems possible that it may also occur in other forms of excitation.

In view of all the facts it appears improbable that any sort of excitation or transmission is possible in any sort of living protoplasm without at least some metabolic change at some stage of the process between its initiation and the attainment of the "resting" condition. A point to which I wish particularly to call attention, however, is that the processes of excitation and transmission are not necessarily exactly the same in character in all protoplasms and perhaps not even in the same protoplasm under different conditions. Whatever the nature of the processes in certain highly specialized tissues, it is a well-established fact that increase in rate of respiration is a characteristic feature of the more generalized and more primitive forms of excitation in living protoplasm. In short, it appears to be true, essentially as Verworn ('13, Chap. V) maintains, that excitation in general is primarily an acceleration in the rate of living, or in certain fundamental dynamic factors of life, and we may agree with Verworn on this point, even though we differ from him as regards what constitutes living.

Living in different protoplasms and even in different organs and tissues and in different stages of development of a single organism does not remain the same complex of changes. Factors in the complex which are closely associated in primitive protoplasm may be more or less independent in some highly specialized tissues and vice versa. In primitive protoplasm, for example, changes in permeability appear to be closely associated with changes in metabolic conditions, but in highly specialized membranes with definite physical structure, changes in permeability, at least to certain substances, probably occur with little, perhaps with no metabolic change. It is conceivable that in some forms of excitation physical changes in permeability, surface tension, etc., may be the primary factors and the metabolic changes may be merely incidents or results. In other forms the reverse may be the case. Moreover, excitations of different degree or intensities may differ in character: a weak excitation may bring about only the decomposition of certain molecules and certain physical changes, while a strong excitation may bring about also the breakdown of other molecules with formation of other products and the determination of other physical changes. Excitation and transmission undoubtedly differ in character, not only with differences in the protoplasms in which they occur, but also with differences in the environmental conditions. Nevertheless, in a broad sense, excitation, particularly in its more primitive forms, appears to be fundamentally an acceleration in rate of living.

Excitation in different protoplasms and in a particular protoplasm under different conditions differs also as regards the rate at which the acceleration occurs. In general the more primitive excitation processes are the slower, the more highly specialized the more rapid, nervous excitation being the most rapid of all. In fact, an important feature of the specialization of excitation consists in decrease in the latent period, *i. e.*, the time between the impact of the external factor and the excitation itself. The velocity with which the excitation rises to its maximum after initiation also increases in general with specialization. Evolution of the excitatory mechanisms and processes along these lines has been of fundamental importance in the evolution of structure and function in general. Without such evolution of excitation and its mechanisms, structural and functional evolution along other lines, particularly as regards animals, would have been very narrowly limited.

To sum up, the conception of excitation to which the facts point us is not that of a process *sui generis* superimposed on life by the impact of energy from without, but rather that of excitation as life itself accelerated by these impacts.

Rhythmicity, automaticity, self-excitation. — It is evident that in general excitation occurs as a response to action of a factor external to the protoplasm concerned, but the question whether any kind of protoplasm is capable of self-excitation requires some attention. At first glance many cases of rhythmic contraction of muscles suggest an "internal stimulus" or self-excitation. Such contractions have been observed in smooth, cardiac and skeletal muscle under various conditions in which nervous or other rhythmic excitation from without is excluded. For example, rhythmic contraction of smooth muscle fibers has been observed in tissue cultures by M. R. and W. H. Lewis ('17) and of skeletal muscle fibers by M. R. Lewis ('15). Wintrebert ('20) states that rhythmic contractions of the myotomes occur in certain fish embryos before nervous connections are established. These contractions pass both anteriorly and posteriorly from a myotome acting as pacemaker, but this function of pacemaker moves from myotome to myotome in the posterior direction as development advances. It is a familiar fact that heart muscle, completely isolated from nerve centers may contract rhythmically under a continuous stimulus such as a constant current. Biedermann, Loeb and others have observed rhythmic contraction of isolated skeletal muscle in certain salt solutions.[1] There is also considerable evidence indicating the presence of a rapid rhythm in at least some nervous stimuli. Various other organs, from cilia and flagella through different de-

[1] See, for example, Biedermann, '80; Loeb, '99 b, '06, pp. 120–140, also various special papers.

grees of motor specialization, show either rhythmic response to constant stimuli or rhythmic behavior in the apparent absence of external stimuli.

The usual interpretation of rhythmic response to constant stimuli is based on the existence of a refractory period. For a certain length of time after a response the organ is not excitable; then excitability gradually returns until the point is reached at which the constant stimulus initiates a new response, and so on. For those cases in which a constant stimulus of any kind is known to be present this interpretation appears to be satisfactory, but the question whether a stimulus of any kind, rhythmic or constant, is present in all cases of rhythmic activity remains. It has been maintained by certain authors that some such activities result from alternate accumulation and spontaneous breakdown of excitable material, i. e., that a real self-excitation occurs. This view, however, does not appear at present to have any adequate physico-chemical basis.

It may still appear difficult, however, to account for such cases as the rhythmic contractions of muscle fibers in tissue cultures or even of certain myotomes in embryos in the absence of nerves. But even in these cases there is the possibility of stimulation by mechanical tension. The Lewises state that the muscle fibers in their cultures appear to be under more or less tension and the cytoplasm is elastic. Moreover, stretching them often serves to initiate rhythmic contraction. In the case of the myotomes the tensions associated with growth may start the rhythm in a particular myotome at a certain stage. In a recent paper E. J. Carey ('21 b) has laid great stress on the importance of mechanical tension in determining, not only the development and differentation of muscle, but rhythmic response. He maintains that the stimulus to the heart beat is primarily the tension caused by the blood and that the continuation of the beat in the differentiated heart in the absence of blood results from the reciprocal tension of different muscle layers or regions. Carey does not discuss those cases in which heart beat begins in the absence of circulation, but if it is true that tension is the essential factor, the tensions associated with growth and development may be effective on the heart in the absence of blood, or fluid accumulating in the cavity of the heart may exert tension in the absence of circulation.

In the cases of muscles contracting rhythmically in salt solutions mechanical tension is not necessary and the stimulus must be chemical or electrolytic. Concerning the origin of rhythm in nervous discharge we know practically nothing beyond the fact that it is not directly dependent upon a rhythmic stimulation, but may occur even with a single stimulus. Given the original stimulation, the rhythm of the nervous impulse must result from conditions within the cell, but, so far as we know, impulses do not originate without a stimulus of some sort from without.[1] What appears to be spontaneity may be in some cases merely failure to recognize the exciting factor and the relation between this factor and the response may be so indirect that recognition is difficult.[2] As the facts stand at present there is no reason for assuming the occurrence of self-excitation. Spontaneity in the strict sense is far from being a demonstrated fact. One cell region, cell or cell group may of course excite another, but the original source of excitation and of the initiating energy is apparently always outside the region, cell or cell group excited. Transmission in all its forms from the primitive protoplasmic transmission to the highly specialized nervous conduction is such excitation of one region by energy transfer from without.

These conclusions of course raise the question whether, or to what extent life itself is fundamentally excitation, that is, whether it would not in the absence of the energy relations to the external world undergo gradual retardation and finally attain a static equilibrium. Doubtless so long as material exchange between a protoplasm and its environment occurred, certain chemical reactions would go on, but it is by no means certain that such reactions alone would constitute anything that we could recognize as life. Certainly without excitation nothing in the way of reaction or response to an environment could occur and to most biologists it is this capacity for response that distinguishes the living from the non-living.

DECREMENT, EXCITATION-TRANSMISSION GRADIENTS AND "ALL-OR-NONE" REACTION

The decrement in intensity, energy or in short effectiveness of excitation which is characteristic of many forms of transmission has been repeatedly discussed in earlier publications (Child, '15 b, Chaps. II, V, VI, '21, Chaps. IV, XII). This decrement apparently

[1] Some discussion of the rhythms of nervous discharge and their probable rôle in the analysis and correlation of neuromotor activities in higher animals will be found in Herrick's work ('24, Chap. IX).

[2] Herrick ('24, Chap. II) points out that automaticity, or spontaneity in the restricted sense of internally excited activity, seems to be an important factor in progressive evolution, especially in higher animals, leading up to trial-and-error reactions, active search for satisfying stimuli and the impulse toward self-satisfaction and self-realization in the psychological field.

resembles the decrement which we find in various forms of physical transmission, water waves, sound waves, etc. In general, the decrement in physiological transmission is more conspicuous in the more primitive forms of excitation, but we sometimes find that in the same protoplasm a marked decrement occurs in transmission of a weak excitation while in transmission of a strong excitation the decrement may be much less or is apparently absent.

In all cases where such a decrement is present an excitation-transmission gradient results, that is, the degree, intensity or energy of excitation is greatest at the point of origin and decreases from that to some more or less distant point where it becomes inappreciable or ineffective. That such gradients are of very general occurrence in the less highly specialized forms of excitation and transmission is well known. Among the lower invertebrates, for example, we frequently see that the muscular contraction or other effect of a local excitation gradually decreases with increasing distance from the point of original excitation and at a certain distance ceases. As yet we have no exact knowledge concerning the slope or steepness of such excitation-transmission gradients and their relations to different physiological and other conditions; while we have no certain direct measure of the strength, degree or intensity of excitation, there can be no doubt that in the less highly specialized forms the length of the gradient, *i. e.*, the effective range of transmission, very generally varies with the degree of the original excitation, as indicated by certain of its effects, and with the conductivity of the protoplasm, as determined first by its specific constitution and second by its physiological condition at the time (see for example Verworn '13, Chap. VI). On the other hand, it is commonly believed by physiologists that the specialized conduction process in the nerves of higher animals occurs normally without a decrement, *i. e.*, that its range is indefinite. But under certain conditions, *e. g.*, low temperature, partial anesthesia, a very distinct decrement is present, even in such nervous conduction (Verworn, '13, Chap. VI; Lucas and Adrian, '17). Moreover, even in rather primitive nervous systems such as the nerve net of certain cœlenterates slight excitations are transmitted with a decrement and are limited in range, but, as the experiments of Mayer ('06, '08, '16) and Harvey ('12) on the medusa *Cassiopea* show, a sufficiently intense excitation may be conducted in the nerve net for an indefinite distance. Briefly stated, the experiment demonstrating this fact consists in starting a wave of excitation in one direction around a ring of tissue cut from the umbrella of the medusa. Conduction of the excitation wave may continue for days or weeks until the tissue dies. In such a case the impulse passes through many cells and since the cells are essentially alike and excitable the impulse continues indefinitely. From such facts as these it appears that the presence or absence of a decrement in certain nerve paths may depend on degree or intensity of excitation.

Conduction without decrement in the nerve fiber is interpreted as resulting from the all-or-none type of reaction (Verworn, '13, Chap. VI; Lucas and Adrian, '17). According to the current conception, the all-or-none reaction is a reaction which is maximal for all strengths of stimulus above the threshold. In other words, the weakest stimulus which is capable of bringing about excitation at all brings about just as great or intense excitation as any stimulus of greater strength. In this sort of reaction the degree or intensity

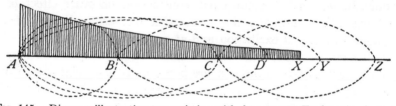

Fig. 145.—Diagram illustrating transmission with decrement. Explanation in text.

of excitation is entirely independent of strength of stimulus, except in so far as a certain minimum strength is necessary to bring about excitation. In protoplasms which show this all-or-none form of reaction the external exciting factor merely initiates the excitatory changes, as the electric spark initiates the explosion, and the further changes are determined by the potential energy of the protoplasmic or the explosive system.

At present only suggestions or surmises are possible by way of physiological interpretation of the differences between all-or-none and other types of reaction, but consideration of certain points is of some interest. In the first place, excitation of any point A (Fig. 145) of a living protoplasm supposedly always gives rise to an electrical gradient. Since resistance increases with distance, the strength of the electric current must decrease with increase in distance of the points between which it flows. The strength of current resulting from excitation of A decreases progressively through B, C, D, and it is evident that at a certain distance, X, from A, it will be so weak that it cannot bring about excitation of more distant points. The distance AX corresponds to the distances AB, CD, etc., in Figure 132, *i. e.*, it represents the range of physiological effectiveness of excitation of a given point A. If the excitatory change brought about at B, C, D and other points is proportional to, or varies with, the strength of the current between A and each such point, the result of excitation at A will be merely an excitation gradient extending from A to X. In Figure 145 this gradient is indicated in a purely diagrammatic way by the shaded portion of the figure, the slope being purely hypothetical. In such a case the range of transmission is nothing more than the range, AX, of physiological effectiveness of the electric current orginating from the excitation at A. This may perhaps be regarded as the simplest and most primitive form of excitation gradient. Its length may vary widely according to the electric change at A and the resistance interposed between A and other points. In protoplasms which are but little specialized, *e. g.*, the very simple organisms and early stages of development, and perhaps in some cases with weak excitation, physiological transmission may perhaps be little or nothing more than such an excitation gradient determined directly by the electrical gradient resulting from the original excitation.

Between such primitive transmission and the all-or-none type of conduction without decrement intermediate transmission forms are at least theoretically possible and probably occur. If, for example, excitation of the point B (Fig. 145) by the current originating at A gives rise to a sufficiently strong electric current to be effective over the range BY, the total range of transmission will be extended to Y. And if this current arising at B increases the excitation at C the current arising at C may extend the range of transmission to a still farther point Z. As the range of transmission extends farther, the decrement of course becomes less steep, until finally the all-or-none type of transmission may be attained. From this viewpoint the differences between the primitive excitation gradient and all-or-none conduction depend upon the differences in what happens at the various points B, C, etc., which are excited by the current. If the current brings about changes more or less proportional to its strength a decrement results, but if any strength of current above a minimum determines maximum excitation, the all-or-none type of conduction results. In this latter case, assuming that the electric current resulting from excitation at A, is effective at all points between A and X, all these points will develop a maximal excitation and all will give rise to electric currents of the same strength as those arising at A. That is, excitation of A will be followed by maximal excitation of the region AX and this in turn by maximal excitation of a region of equal length from X onward and so on indefinitely (Fig. 144). Nevertheless, as noted elsewhere (Child, '21 a), transmission may show a decrement even though it is of the all-or-none type. If the path of such transmission, e. g., the nerve fiber, is already a physiological gradient of such character that the maximal excitation decreases in strength in a certain direction, transmission in that direction will show a decrement and, if the path were long enough, might conceivably attain a limit. In short, the all-or-none type of reaction does not necessarily mean absence of decrement in transmission.

Certain chemical aspects of the specialization of excitation. — As regards the differences in the nature of the excitatory changes which underlie the differences in transmission, we have no positive knowledge. Protoplasms in general undoubtedly contain molecules of very different degrees of lability and from the facts at hand it appears probable that in the more primitive processes of excitation different molecules or atomic groups may be concerned in the same protoplasm, according to intensity of energy of stimulus and condition of the protoplasm. A weak excitation may perhaps involve oxidation of only certain molecules or groups and the velocity of this reaction and the electric changes will determine a characteristic rate of transmission and decrement. A stronger stimulus may determine the decomposition of other molecules in addition to those susceptible to the weaker stimulus and the rate of transmission and the decrement may be different in this case. In the maximal excitation all the molecules capable of reacting at all under the conditions are concerned and it is apparently demonstrated that, at least in some protoplasms, such excitation is transmitted without decrement, while submaximal excitations, or those below a certain level, are transmitted with decrement (see pp. 187–188). Frequently also we observe differences in rate of transmission with different degrees of excitation in the protoplasm. In the ctenophore plate row, for example, as in various other conducting paths, the stronger excitation is transmitted more rapidly than the weaker (Child, '21 a, p. 219). In terms of an electrochemical theory such differences in rate of transmission mean at least in part differences in the velocity of the chemical reactions concerned.

The specialization of excitable tissues, reaching its highest degrees in certain organs of special sense, in nerve and in muscle, appears in general to involve as an important factor a specialization of the physico-chemical constitution of the irritable substratum of the tissue concerned. In the different sense organs such specialization is in different directions according to the form of energy to which reaction occurs most readily. In nerve and muscle specialization toward the all-or-none form of reaction occurs and in so far as chemical factors are concerned in such specialization, they must include an increase in uniformity of chemical constitution of the excitable substratum and increase in lability, such that any energy transfer above a minimum sets the whole mechanism in action as the spark does the powder. But of course we do not know whether this lability and apparent uniformity of constitution is actually chemical in nature.

It is an interesting fact that in low temperature or in partial anesthesia the nerve fiber, which normally shows the all-or-none reaction transmits with a rather steep decrement. Whether or not chemical factors are concerned in this change, it appears to consist in a return to the primitive type of transmission with a decrement, perhaps to the primitive excitation gradient determined directly by the strength of electric current. But as already noted even the normal nerve fiber may conceivably represent a gradient in lability or in other features of constitution determined in its development and it may react according to the all-or-none law and nevertheless show a decrement.

The possibility must also be noted that in the course of evolution different factors of the excitation process may play the chief parts in different protoplasms or tissues. In the more primitive protoplasms, for example, excitation appears to be rather closely associated with the fundamental metabolic reactions and to involve a relatively large amount of chemical reaction, at least in many cases. In striated muscle, on the other hand, the oxidative reactions appear to be in large part, if not wholly, an incident or result of the excitation process in the stricter sense. Forms of physiological excitation without chemical reaction are conceivable, though whether excitation actually occurs in living protoplasm without any chemical reaction may be doubted. The very close relations existing in protoplasm between physical conditions and chemical changes leave little room for doubt that the two sorts of change are very generally, if not always, associated.

EXCITATION AND TRANSMISSION IN RELATION TO THE BEHAVIOR OF ORGANISMS

We have seen that excitation appears to be fundamentally an acceleration in the rate of the changes which are concerned in living protoplasm with the liberation of energy. According to current theories it is a change ocurring in relation to protoplasmic membranes or limiting surfaces, but probably we shall not know exactly what constitutes excitation in protoplasm until we know what constitutes life. But whatever the nature of excitation, living protoplasm is able to transmit it to a greater or less degree. Transmission consists essentially of excitation of one point or region by the excitatory changes occurring in another and when such transmission follows definite morphological paths such as nerves, it is generally known as conduction. This possibility of excitation of one part or region of protoplasm by another is of fundamental significance in relation to the rôle which excitation plays in the life of organisms. Transmission makes possible the extension to the whole cell, cell mass or organism of the excitatory change initiated by the external factor at some particular point. In Chapters IV and V it was pointed out that a relation of dominance and subordination is a characteristic feature of organismic pattern and that excitation and its transmission constitute the physiological basis of this relation and the primary factor in the integration of the individual organism out of a specific protoplasm, a cell or a cell mass. According to this conception, excitation and its transmission constitute the physiological basis, the starting point, of the organism as a whole. Excitation determines physiological differences in different regions or parts, i. e., the more excited and the less excited, and transmission determines an actual physiological relation between them of such character that the more excited part brings about excitatory changes in other parts and so dominates them. The presence or absence of decrement in transmission and the consequent limited or unlimited range of dominance are merely features of different protoplasmic constitutions, or perhaps in some cases, of different intensities or degrees of excitation and as such have been fully considered in another place (Child, '21 a, Chaps. V, XII, XIII). In the more primitive protoplasms these factors determine how large a mass of protoplasm or cells of a particular constitution can be integrated into an organism, a whole. In the higher animals, however, the size of the individual is limited rather by the cessation of growth with the progress of differentiation, while the range of dominance may be indefinite, at least in certain nervous structures (p. 170).

Excitation and its transmission, then, make possible a change in the life of a mass of protoplasm, a cell or a cell mass as a whole in consequence of the local action of an external factor upon some part of it. Such a change is what we call physiological reaction or response and this in turn is the physiological basis of what we commonly call behavior, *i. e.*, excito-motor behavior in living organisms. Behavior in this sense is fundamentally an ordered and integrated change, reaction or response occurring in relation to local action of an external energy factor. No one except the vitalist doubts that behavior is physiologically a consequence of the irritability of protoplasm and that excitation of the irritable protoplasm and the transmission of such excitation are the primary factors in each such reaction or response. The ability to react or behave as a whole is a fundamental physiological characteristic of the living organism and it is obvious that the material relations between the individual and the external world are affected by, and in large measure dependent upon, its behavior. In "The Origin and Development of the Nervous System" I have considered the various lines of evidence which indicate that the nervous system, the organ of behavior *par excellence* in all animals except the simplest, develops in the individual on the physiological basis of an excitation-transmission gradient or gradients. Moreover, its intimate relation to the primary factors in the integration of the organism is indicated by its extremely early differentiation preceding that of other definitive organs. The whole development of the nervous system is a development of mechanisms of excitation and transmission and of relations between them. Of course the particular type of these mechanisms and of their relations in any particular organism is primarily a matter of the hereditary constitution and potentialities of the protoplasm constituting the organism, but in the development of the individual certain physiological conditions are necessary for the realization of the hereditary potentialities. As I have endeavored to show, these physiological conditions originate in the physiological gradients which are not independent of external factors, but represent the result of the differential action of such factors on the protoplasm. The facts force us to the conclusion that such physiological gradients are primarily excitation-transmission gradients. If this is true the physiological basis of the behavior of the individual organism and of the organism itself as a pattern and integration is the same. From this viewpoint the individual organism the "organism as a whole" is not as Morgan ('19, p. 241) puts it, "the collective action of the genes," but rather the collective *reaction* of the genes to the differential action of environment. We may say then that pattern and development, as well as the function of the individual organism, represent the behavior of the germ plasm in a given environment. Or more briefly, the individual organism represents a behavior pattern in a specific protoplasm. It is doubtless evident to the reader that the whole course of the argument of preceding chapters has been concerned with the development of this purely physiological conception of the individual, but the following chapter is an attempt to make the viewpoint still more clear by a summing up, a synthesis of the data which underlie the conception.

CHAPTER XII

THE INDIVIDUAL AS A BEHAVIOR PATTERN IN A
SPECIFIC PROTOPLASM

In the preceding chapters attention has been called to various aspects of the relation between the individual organism and environment. That the individual as a pattern in a specific protoplasm has no significance except in relation to environment was pointed out in Chapter II. Chapter III was concerned chiefly with showing on the one hand the impossibility of accounting for the individual in terms of purely predeterministic conceptions and on the other the necessity for a clear distinction between the potentialities of the hereditary mechanism and the realization of certain of those potentialities in an individual. The following chapters (IV–IX) constitute essentially a consideration of the general physiology of organismic pattern, *i. e.*, of the individual or "organism as a whole," as distinguished from the hereditary substratum out of which it develops. This consideration has led us to the conception of the physiological gradient as the basis, the starting point of the order or pattern and of the integrating mechanism of the individual organism. As I have endeavored to show, the conception of the physiological gradient has developed from, and is supported by, many different lines of experimental and observational evidence. Moreover, it is not in conflict with any data of investigation, but only with certain speculative predeterministic and vitalistic hypotheses.

It now remains to consider the relation between the more or less permanent physiological gradients and the phenomena of excitation and transmission and to determine whether the facts justify us in regarding the individual organism as a behavior pattern in a specific protoplasm.

THE OCCURRENCE AND SIGNIFICANCE OF EXCITATION GRADIENTS

As we have seen, excitation in its more primitive forms is very generally, if not always, transmitted with a decrement in energy or intensity, or, since we do not know its nature, but only its effects, we may call it a decrement in physiological effectiveness. Consequently the more primitive phenomena of transmission in living protoplasms usually appear as excitation-transmission gradients with a certain range and limit of effectiveness. This range of effectiveness may vary widely with the degree or intensity of the primary excitatory change and with the physiological state, that is, the irritability and conductivity of the protoplasm concerned. According to the electrochemical theories of excitation, such a decrement results primarily from the fact that electrical resistance increases with distance, and in the simplest forms of transmission the decrement may be little or nothing more than the electric decrement due to resistance (pp. 188–189). Only in the all-or-none type of reaction is transmission without a decrement possible, but even here the decrement is not necessarily absent (pp. 186–191). The electric gradient is of course present in the wave-like conduction of the nerve impulse, even though no decrement in height or steepness of the wave occurs. At each level of the electric gradient above the threshold maximal excitation occurs. But the excitation does not reach the maximum instantaneously. The facts at hand indicate that after a brief latent period the excitatory change begins as a minimal change and requires a certain length of time to attain the maximum. The advancing front of the excitation wave is then always an excitation gradient from maximum excitation at the summit to minimum excitation at the point where excitation is just beginning. This gradient of the wave front is then a gradient in degree of excitation and therefore analogous in a way to the gradient in degree of excitation characteristic of the more primitive forms of transmission, but its relation to the electrical gradient is not necessarily the same as that of the latter. Moreover, the gradient of the wave front of the nerve impulse is not a stationary gradient but advances, and any given point occupies successively every level from the low to the high end and from the high to the low end of the descending gradient which follows the maximum. Even in the transmission of the nerve impulse, then a quantitative gradient appears in the wave-like form of the impulse, or at least of the electrical changes associated with it. This gradient, however, is apparently not simply an expression of resistance, but may include other factors, such as velocity of reaction at any point of the nerve. In short, the nerve impulse is an advancing gradient followed by reversal while the primitive gradient is stationary and may or may not be reversible.

The chief point in this discussion is that a quantitative gradient in physiological condition, unquestionably involving both chemical and physical factors, is a very general, if not universal characteristic of the protoplasmic transmission of excitation. Even in the highly specialized nerve fiber of higher animals the electrical gradient is present as in the primitive form of transmission and is undoubtedly associated with an excitation gradient. In the most primitive forms of transmission the gradient is stationary and may persist and become a basis for differentiation. In the nerve fiber it is the advancing front of the wave-like impulse and undergoes rapid reversal. According to an electrochemical theory of excitation the existence of such gradients depends first upon the increase of electrical resistance with distance, and second, on the fact that the changes concerned in excitation at any given point are not instantaneous, but proceed with a certain velocity.

Moreover, even if the nerve fibers of higher animals conduct impulses without any decrement so that the changes involved are the same in velocity and amount at all levels of the fiber there is good reason to believe, as Lucas ('17) has pointed out, that certain regions of the reflex arc, such as the neuro-muscular junctions and probably the synapses between individual neurons, are regions in which a decrement occurs. If we accept the views which I have advanced elsewhere (Child '21 a) concerning the relations between the origin and development of the nervous system and the general axial gradients of the body we must expect to find quantitative differences as regards excitation in the neurons of different levels of an axis. In general, the neurons developing at the higher levels of an axial gradient may be expected to show a greater irritability, $i.\ e.$, a lower threshold, and probably also a higher excitation maximum than those of lower levels. According to this view the reflex arc as a whole originates physiologically in an excitation-transmission gradient, which in turn is an expression of a more or less permanent physiological gradient of the body (Child, '21 a, Chaps. XII, XIII).

The significance of excitation-transmission gradients in the behavior of the original organism can scarcely be overemphasized. In the simpler organisms, both animals and plants, such gradients determine the degree and extent of integration following a particular excitation. In such forms the reaction following a slight excitation is more or less local and disappears at a certain distance from the point of primary excitation, while the reaction to a stronger excitation extends to greater distances and may involve the whole body. In hydra or the sea anemone a slight excitation of a single tentacle tip brings about contraction of only the distal region of the tentacle or of the whole tentacle, without affecting other tentacles or other regions of the body, while a stronger excitation is followed by contraction of a number or all of the tentacles and perhaps of the whole body. The behavior of the simpler animals shows everywhere such differences in extent and complexity of reaction correlated with differences in degree of excitation. It is probable that excitation-transmission gradients play a part in determining the different behavior patterns exhibited in the motor reactions of such forms as the starfish (see pp. 65–66). Certainly the differences in behavior of the different arms must be correlated with differences in degree of excitation.

Even the behavior of higher animals indicates that in the nervous system as a whole somewhat similar relations must exist. For example, the summation in the reflex arc of impulses individually too weak to be effective suggests the existence somewhere in the arc of a region of decrement (pp. 195–197). Again a local excitation of a sense organ may at first give rise to a simple reflex action involving only certain nerve paths and certain muscles or other effectors. But with continuation of the excitation other nerve paths are affected, other effectors are involved and sooner or later the whole organism may be involved in the reaction. The familiar experiment of local excitation of the hind leg of a decapitated frog by mechanical, chemical or other means affords a good illustration of this point. The first reaction is the relatively simple reflex directed toward removal of the source of excitation, but if this is not effective and the excitation continues, other reflex arcs become involved until finally a large part of the skeletal muscular system may take part in the reaction (Herrick, '24, Chaps. XVII to XIX).

These few illustrations will perhaps suffice to indicate that excitation-transmission gradients are certainly of fundamental importance in neuromotor behavior. As regards the higher animals the situation is of course very complex, but even here it is difficult to go very far in a physiological interpretation of behavior without postulating the existence of such gradients in some form or in certain parts of the nervous system. But we may go further than this and assert, I believe, without exaggeration that the excitation-transmission gradient is a factor of fundamental importance in the reactions of living protoplasms to their environment. Apparently it is the most primitive and most generalized form of reaction of protoplasm and therefore the physiological basis of the integrative behavior of living things.

THE REVERSIBILITY OF EXCITATION

The question whether or not excitation is completely reversible has been touched upon elsewhere (Child, '21 a, pp. 82–85), but its im-

portance for the present purpose makes necessary some further discussion at this time.   We are accustomed to regard excitation as a
temporary change followed by recovery, *i. e.*, by return to the condition preceding excitation.

It is of course true that the organism, the muscle or the nerve persists apparently unchanged as regards its more conspicuous aspects
after a period of excitation.   There are, however, many facts which
indicate clearly enough that even in the so-called irritable tissues,
muscle and nerve, some of the changes concerned in or associated
with excitation are not, under ordinary conditions of individual life,
completely reversible.   In muscle, for example, frequent excitation,
if not carried to the point of exhaustion, brings about growth, *i. e.*,
functional hypertrophy, and other changes in the muscle, while lack
of excitation after a certain stage of development results in atrophy
and disappearance of the muscular tissue.   In the earlier developmental stages the intrinsic rate of metabolism is apparently high
enough to maintain the muscular structure without external excitation, but as the tissue grows older and its intrinsic rate of metabolism
decreases, the increase in rate associated with excitation is necessary
for its continued existence and may bring about hypertrophy in it.
The change in form, the contraction of the muscle which is an expression of the excitation, is of course completely reversible, but under
ordinary conditions the process of excitation as a whole is certainly
not rapidly completely reversible.   But changes in condition may
bring about more or less complete reversal of these effects of excitation in muscle which are commonly more or less persistent.   The
hypertrophy resulting from a period of activity may disappear during a following period of inactivity and after injury muscle cells may
undergo more or less dedifferentation.   In spite of such changes as
these, it is true that under ordinary conditions certain of the changes
associated with excitation are more or less persistent.

As regards the effects of excitation on the nervous tissues the facts
are equally clear.   Memory, the possibility of learning, the development of habit, all show clearly enough that excitation brings about
exceedingly persistent changes somewhere in the nervous system.
Moreover, the changes in form, size and protoplasmic structure of
nerve cells in relation to excitation, fatigue and recovery are also
effects of excitation which are much less readily reversible than the
dynamic changes immediately concerned in the process.   Probably
excitation is as nearly completely reversible in the nerve fiber as
anywhere, but it may at least be questioned whether even here the

passage of excitation does not leave some more or less persistent effect beyond that of the brief refractory period. It is highly probable that excitation is necessary for the maintenance of the fully developed nerve fiber, as it is for muscle, and that the absence of excitation is a factor in the degeneration following separation of the nerve fiber from the cell body. But whatever the situation as regards the nerve fiber, it is certain that in nervous tissue in general certain effects of excitation may be highly persistent.

Turning to the question of the persistence of effects of excitation and transmission in protoplasms generally, it is evident that, from the viewpoint of this book, this question is closely connected with the question of the origin and nature of the physiological gradients. Postponing general discussion to the following section, certain facts may be noted here, viz., that in certain plants polarity, in certain others symmetry is usually determined by light (pp. 58, 115), that polarity may be electrically determined in certain animals (pp. 111, 115), and that in general the physiological gradients which represent physiological axes in their simplest known terms apparently originate as reactions to differentials in external factors which alter primarily the rate of living. In the following section we shall see how closely such gradients are related physiologically to excitation-transmission gradients.

There are of course great differences in the permanency of the record, *i. e.*, the degree of irreversibility of the effects of excitation in different protoplasms. In some simple forms, *e. g.*, *Amœba*, they apparently are very largely and very rapidly reversible under ordinary conditions, but one of the features of progressive evolution is an increase in the persistence and stability of such protoplasmic records, and this stability or irreversibility attains the most striking manifestations in the phenomena of memory in the higher animals and man (Herrick, '24, Chaps. V, XX).

THE PHYSIOLOGICAL AXIAL GRADIENTS IN RELATION TO EXCITATION-TRANSMISSION GRADIENTS

It was shown in Chapter VII that physiological axes and directions in which pattern and order arise in individual development appear in their simplest known terms and in the earliest stages as quantitative gradients in physiological condition. Although various theories of polarity and symmetry postulate a stereochemical or other molecular structure and orientation as the basis of these phenomena, there is no actual evidence that such structure and orientation exists in protoplasm generally, in eggs or in the early stages of embryonic development. According to the evidence, physiological axes in their simplest terms and their earliest distinguishable stages are physiological gradients.

In Chapter VIII it was shown that these gradients are fundamental factors in axiate localization and differentiation, that when they are obliterated experimentally, axiate differentiation fails to occur and that when new gradients are experimentally established they determine new and corresponding axial relations.

Such gradients exhibit in general the same physiological characteristics as excitation-transmission gradients except for the fact that they are more or less persistent according to the nature of the protoplasm in which they appear. They involve differences in rate of the fundamental metabolic reactions, and differences in electric potential similar to those observed in excitation and transmission, and in many cases differences in permeability of membranes have been demonstrated at different levels of these gradients and such differences are probably present in all.

In Chapter IX evidence was presented to show that the physiological gradients, even though in some cases they persist from one generation of individuals to another, are not inherent in protoplasm, but originate in a reaction of protoplasm to a local or differential impact upon it of an external factor. Moreover, this relation between the protoplasmic reaction which gives rise to the gradient and the external factor is not specific, qualitative or material in nature, but rather quantitative and dynamic.

From all these facts only one conclusion appears possible: the physiological gradient, which according to the evidence at hand, represents the physiological axis in its simplest terms, exhibits essentially the same dynamic characteristics as the excitation-transmission gradient and originates, like the latter, as a reaction or response to a local or differential action from without. The facts indicate also that the essential feature of such action is not its specific character, but its quantitative effect upon the rate of dynamic change in the protoplasmic system. This statement may appear at first glance to conflict with some of the evidence presented in Chapter IX. For example, it was pointed out there (pp. 117–119), that differences in oxygen supply or accessibility or differences of exposure permitting different rates of CO_2 discharge are probably in many cases essential or important factors in determining new axial gradients. The objection may be raised that such relations between protoplasm and environment are material and qualitative in that they involve specific chemical substances. This is of course true but it is equally true that these relations also possess a quantitative and dynamic aspect. Within certain limits the supply or accessibility of oxygen is an essential factor in determining the rate of fundamental protoplasmic activities, in other words, the rate of living. In general, decrease in oxygen supply below a certain level retards, and increase accelerates the rate of living. Similarly the accumulation of CO_2 in protoplasm above a certain limit retards and increase of its rate of discharge accelerates the rate of living. As regards some of the specialized mechanisms of higher animals and as regards anærobic organisms these statements require qualification, or may not be true, but, so far as we know, they hold good for the less highly specialized ærobic protoplasms, and it is in such protoplasms, if anywhere, that these conditions are effective in determining new axial gradients. It has never been maintained that axial gradients may not be determined and established by material relations between protoplasm and environment, but it is maintained that the essential factor of such relations as regards gradient determination, is not their specific material character, but their quantitative dynamic effect upon the protoplasm. There is then as regards this point no conflict between evidence and conclusion.

Again, it may be pointed out that axial gradients are normally or usually determined in different ways in different protoplasms, in some cases by light, in some probably by oxygen, in some perhaps by gravity, etc. This is true, but this means only that the normal or usual factor is the factor to which the protoplasm is normally or usually subjected, or which is most effective under natural conditions. In experiment the gradients may be determined by other factors than those which are normally effective. In the egg of the alga, *Fucus*, for example, the gradient is usually determined by differential illumination (pp. 58–61) but as Hurd ('19, '20) has shown, polarities, *i. e.*, the gradients of eggs lying close together are determined with reference to each other. In such cases a material relation perhaps to oxygen or CO_2 is apparently the effective factor instead of light. In hydroids the axial gradients may be determined by difference in exposure to water, oxygen or CO_2 or both, being probably the effective factors, but as Lund ('21) has found, the gradients may also be determined by the electric current. Under certain experimental conditions the polar gradient in the sea anemone, *Harenactis*, may be determined by local injury (pp. 119–121), and while it is not known how the gradient is normally determined it is certainly in some other way than this. And finally, it has been shown that axial gradients may be altered in the same directions or even obliterated by many different chemical agents without relation to the chemical constitution of such agents (pp. 104–107). In the light of the evidence the only possible conclusion seems to be that any external factor which is able to alter the rate of the fundamental changes concerned in the life of a protoplasm may be effective in determining, altering or obliterating the axial gradient or gradients in the protoplasm.

Summing up, the important conclusions from this brief review are these: The physiological and axial gradients are primarily quantitative gradients in specific protoplasms; they represent physiological axes and directions of order and pattern in development, in their simplest known terms; they show all the physiological characteristics of excitation-transmission gradients except that they are usually more persistent than the latter. They originate through the local or differential action, continued for a certain length of time, of external factors which alter the rate of changes fundamentally concerned in life. In short, whatever the character of the determining factor in a particular protoplasm or under particular conditions, the physiological gradients apparently constitute essentially more or less fixed or permanent excitation-transmission gradients and become the basis of the further local and regional differences which constitute axiate development.

If these conclusions are correct, the chief difference between the axial gradient and the excitation-transmission gradient is the relative fixity or permanency of the former as compared with the latter. In a particular protoplasm this difference is undoubtedly dependent upon the difference in the period of local or differential exposure to the external factor in the two cases. An excitation-transmission gradient may arise from a momentary or very brief exposure, but the determination of a physiological gradient requires a relatively long time. We have as yet few exact data on this point, but in the case of the *Fucus* egg, for example, it is known that the differential illumination must continue for at least several hours, the length of time being dependent within certain limits on intensity and on wave length (Winkler, '00 b, Hurd, '20). In hydroids the period of differential exposure to water (oxygen or CO_2) has not been determined, but is at least several hours. As regards animal eggs we have no data, but the period may be days or perhaps weeks if the local action or differential is slight.

So far as we can determine, protoplasmic changes involved in the brief or momentary excitation of protoplasm may be rapidly and completely reversible, though it is evident that some effects, however slight, may persist for a longer or shorter time, even in such cases. But it is also evident that with the continued, or frequently repeated local, or differential action of the external factor the persistent or irreversible changes in the protoplasm become appreciable. These changes are in general such as to perpetuate the gradient determined by the external factor. Just what they are physicochemically is not known, but biologically they constitute an equilibration, a regulation in the protoplasmic system, initiated by the external factor. Since the continued local or differential action of the external factor constitutes an alteration in the conditions to which the protoplasm is subjected, the equilibration in the protoplasmic system results in altered conditions in that system, that is, in the gradual determination of a gradation in physiological condition, involving both structural and dynamic features. In other words, the local or differential action of the external factor gradually develops a more or less permanent record in the protoplasm and this record constitutes the beginnings of the physiological axes and of axiate pattern.

The permanence of such record differs very greatly in different protoplasms. In *Amœba* each pseudopod is a gradient for the time being (Hyman, '17), but does not become a permanent axis, though in the *"limax"* forms (Fig. 13), it may persist for a considerable period. In such cases the lack of physical and probably of chemical stability in the protoplasm determines that each new gradient is sooner or later obliterated by another or others.

In axiate organisms, however, such gradients, having passed what may be called the critical point in their development, become the protoplasmic foundations of physiological axes and directions of order. Moreover, they not only persist as real regional physiological differences after the external factors which determined them have ceased to act, but they undergo a progressive development until they attain a certain steepness or slope dependent upon the hereditary constitution of the protoplasm in which they appear. Experimentally we find that the physiological differences, at different levels as indicated by susceptibility, permanganate reduction, permeability, etc., are in general slight in earlier stages of development and undergo increase up to a certain point. This means that after a physiological gradient is once established, its later slope or steepness and so its length, and in fact all its physiological characteristics are dependent primarily on the constitution of the protoplasm in which it exists and only secondarily on external factors. The physio- logical gradients of different species must differ in certain respects as the protoplasms differ, and in a particular protoplasm very differ- ent external differentials may give rise to gradients which are similar. When once the physiological differential has become per- sistent in the protoplasm, the protoplasmic constitution is the primary factor in determining further changes.

This viewpoint eliminates the difficulties involved in accounting for the high degree of constancy in individual development within the species in terms of physiological gradients determined by exter- nal factors variable in degree or different in kind. The external fac- tor initiates, and the hereditary constitution of the protoplasm de- termines the general course of development of the physiological gradient.

There is then, I think, no escape from the conclusion that the axial gradient is essentially an excitation-transmission gradient which has become more or less persistent through the occurrence of irrever- sible or slowly reversible protoplasmic changes. If such gradients represent the foundations in specific protoplasms of the pattern of the individual, this pattern is fundamentally an excitation-transmission pattern, originating in a reaction to an external factor. Such reac- tion is as truly behavior as the growth reactions of a plant or the motor reactions of *Paramœcium*, an insect or a human being. It differs in character from these reactions because the mechanism is different. The gradient involves no mechanism beyond the proto- plasmic mechanism, but the other reactions mentioned involve or- ganismic mechanisms of various degrees of development and com- plication (Herrick, '23, Chap. XIX). The various lines of evidence point to the conclusion suggested in Chapter V, viz., that excitation and its transmission are the primary factors of organismic integra- tion in protoplasm. We know that excitation and transmission con- stitute the physiological basis of organismic excito-motor behavior (Chap. XI). If this is true, the physiological origin of the organism as an individual and of excito-motor behavior is the same. In view of the facts, the assertion that the individual organism represents a behavior pattern in a protoplasm of specific hereditary constitution is not a fanciful speculation, but a conclusion based on many differ- ent lines of experimental and observational evidence and involving no assumptions not based on such evidence.

PHYSIOLOGICAL DOMINANCE AND SUBORDINATION IN RELATION TO
EXCITATION AND TRANSMISSION

It is perhaps necessary to repeat here that physiological dominance
or control is a relation of organismic magnitude. That is to say, it
consists not in a relation between individual molecules, colloid particles or any other single component parts of the protoplasmic system,
but rather in the control of one region, cell or cell mass by another.
In fact, physiological dominance and subordination are relations
between parts each of which constitutes a living protoplasmic system
with all the complexity of constitution and of physico-chemical
relations among its parts that the word "living" implies.

The physiological basis of dominance. — In an excitation-transmission gradient the region of primary excitation exercises a certain
dominance or control over other levels of the gradient, simply because its excitation initiates the gradient and constitutes the primary
factor in determining for the time being the physiological condition
of other regions within the gradient. As already suggested (pp. 49–
52) this is apparently the most primitive sort of physiological correlation, i. e., correlation of organismic magnitude, between different
regions of a mass of protoplasm or of cells. The physiological differences at the different levels of the gradient which make dominance
and subordination possible are not preëxistent differences, but arise
through the excitation itself and through its transmission. The facts
indicate that the primary excitation and the differences in condition
at the different levels of the gradient are fundamentally quantitative
changes, and finally the relation between the external factor which
gives rise to excitation and the excitation itself is primarily quantitative, not specific or qualitative. If these conclusions are correct,
the physiological relation of dominance and subordination characteristic of an excitation-transmission gradient is a relation resulting
from differences in rate of living which are initiated by the local or
differential action from without and further determined by transmission. If we agree that all protoplasms are irritable or excitable,
it is evident that all protoplasms subjected to the action of external
factors are capable of giving rise to this relation of dominance and
subordination.

Moreover, there can be no question that this relation is organismic
in character (pp. 51–52) since it originates in physiological differences
between regions and cells and constitutes, at least for the time being,
a more or less definite physiological relation between them. Physio-

logical differences between different regions and cells are the characteristic features of every individual organism. In their absence the
individual organism does not exist.

According to this view, physiological dominance or control appears
in its most primitive form in excitation and transmission. These
processes afford a basis for physiological correlation and control
even in the complete absence of any definite channels or other means
of transportative or material correlation between the parts concerned,
and this relation of dominance and subordination is the most general
physiological relation between regions and parts in the individual
(Chap. IV). It constitutes the basis of "wholeness," i. e., the capacity
for integrated harmonious action of parts. Granting the correctness
of the argument, we cannot escape the conclusion that physiological
integration and the wholeness of the individual originate in excitation
and transmission. This does not necessarily mean that all individual
organisms arise directly and only through excitation and its transmission. Specific material or chemical relations between protoplasm
and environment may conceivably give rise to local or regional differences and relations in the protoplasm, and such differences and relations may become the basis of an individual organism (see pp. 53–
55). Even though the external factor in such a case is a specific
substance, its effect on protoplasmic condition is often as a whole
quantitative rather than specific, e. g., in case of many nutritive
substances, and in any case quantitative effects constituting excitation or inhibition, as well as qualitative effects, are involved. Un-
prejudiced survey of the evidence indicates that the quantitative
changes in living protoplasm are far more important in initiating
individual pattern and integration than any specific, qualitative
factors (Chaps. VII–IX). The latter unquestionably affect the course
of differentiation, but at present there is no reason to believe that
any individual organism originates in specific material differences
without excitatory factors.

Dominance in the axial gradients. — In Chapter X evidence was
presented to show that dominance and subordination are characteristic features of physiological axial gradients. The high end of the
gradient is the dominant region. The degree and range of dominance
depend on various factors. According to the preceding section of
the present chapter, however the physiological gradient arises, it
is essentially an excitation-transmission gradient more or less permanently fixed through the accumulation of relatively stable changes
in the protoplasm.

It follows that dominance and subordination in the physiological axis are derived from the dominance and subordination of the excitation-transmission gradient. The high end of a physiological gradient differs from, and acts upon other levels in the same way as the region of primary excitation in an excitation gradient. The appearance of qualitative differences at different levels of an axial gradient affords a basis for specific material relations, "chemical correlation" between these levels, and out of these relations another sort of dominance and subordination may arise (pp. 44–47). But even in such cases, if the gradient persists, excitation-transmission relations may still persist in it. In any case the development of the individual consists, not only in the qualitative differentiations of different regions and parts, and the establishment of specific chemical relations between them, but also in the development of the dynamic relations of excitation and transmission. In the higher animals we see these two sorts of dominance, nervous and chemical, side by side, both highly developed and in some cases affording to some extent a double control of the same organ. According to the views advanced here, nervous dominance develops out of the more general and fundamental factor in physiological integration, while chemical dominance by means of hormones or other substances is of secondary origin (see Chap. V), though unquestionably of great importance, particularly among the higher forms.

Nervous dominance. — In "The Origin and Development of the Nervous System" attention was particularly called to the very intimate physiological relation of nervous structure and function to the axial gradients and the relations of dominance and subordination characteristic of them. We find that the central nervous system is definitely localized at the higher levels of the chief axial gradients and the later complications arising in it appear to correspond to the complications in the gradients during the course of development. The inference is that the nervous system in the individual develops out of the more primitive excitation-transmission relations characteristic of the gradients and that the functional relations of dominance and subordination in the nervous system originate physiologically in the more primitive dominance and subordination of the gradients. Morphologically the nervous system represents the further progress of differentiation of the higher levels of the gradients beyond the stage of quantitative differences. This conception enables us to recognize a physiological continuity between the primitive excitation-transmission gradient and the nervous system, and between the behavior of protoplasm in general in response to local or differential action of an external factor and the nervous mechanisms and phenomena of behavior in the higher organisms (Herrick, '24, Chaps. XVIII, XIX).

The early localization and differentiation of the nervous system and its function as an organ of integration and of relation to the external world appear, in the light of this conception, as a physiological consequence of the establishment of physiological gradients in protoplasms: that is to say, where the nervous system develops at all it constitutes a fundamental aspect of the development and differentiation of physiological gradients.

The fact that nervous systems do not appear at all in some organisms and attain very different degrees of differentiation and complexity in others depends of course primarily on the differences in hereditary constitution of the different protoplasms. In some protoplasms differentiation in relation to the gradients is not permanent enough, or does not proceed far enough, to give rise to definite nervous structure and function. In such forms the gradients, the integration dependent upon them and the behavior of the organism all remain relatively simple and primitive, as, for example, in the plants. At the other extreme are the higher animals in which the nervous system is the first definitive organ to become morphologically distinguishable and in which it attains a high degree of permanency and complexity of structure and function. Such differences result primarily from differences in protoplasmic constitution which are hereditary. The physiological gradients are merely the factors which determine the realization as an individual organism of the hereditary potentialities of each particular protoplasm. The development of nervous structure and function in any particular organism represents certain aspects of behavior in the presence of certain physiological conditions, viz., the axial gradients, and in every case such behavior takes place in a protoplasmic system possessing a certain hereditary constitution. This constitution plays an essential part in determining the character of the behavior and of the record which behavior leaves in the protoplasm and therefore in determining the course and result of development in each particular case.

To sum up: the available facts force the inference that the simple excitation-transmission gradient is the physiological basis of the relation of dominance and subordination which constitutes the integrating factor in the individual organism. Such dominance represents the action upon other regions of the region most affected in a dynamic way by an external factor. This primitive excitatory reaction and the resulting transmissive relation constitute the physiological basis of the mechanisms of control which develop in each particular kind of organism. Dominance does not arise autonomously at the beginning, or in the course of development, but results from a reaction of the protoplasmic system to an external factor. The primitive dominance, arising momentarily in an excitation gradient, the dominance of the growing tip of the plant in development, of the apical region in a hydroid, of the head in *Planaria*, etc., of the receptor end of the reflex arc and of the brain in the behavior of man, all apparently originate in and develop from physiological gradients. If true, that means that they all result from the behavior of a protoplasm under certain conditions. But as the mechanisms differ with the constitution of different protoplasms and different stages of development the results differ, and we have at the one extreme the evanescent excitation and transmission and at the other the dominance of the brain.

HEREDITY AND THE INDIVIDUAL

In earlier chapters attention has been called repeatedly to the relation between heredity and the individual which this physiological conception of the individual involves, but at the risk of some repetition, it is desirable to bring together here and summarize briefly the chief points in this relation. In the first place, this conception recognizes physiological continuity from the simple excitation gradient in protoplasm to the structural and functional relations of the higher animals. Every individual represents a special case of realization of certain hereditary potentialities and in any one individual only a small part of the potentialities are realized. When we bear these facts in mind, it is perfectly evident that the hereditary mechanism alone cannot account for all the special cases of realization, no two of which are exactly alike. Moreover, if we accept Morgan's conclusion that "every cell inherits the whole germ plasm" (see pp. 22–26), it is obvious that heredity alone cannot account for the fact that in development different cells and cell groups become different. Biological theory sometimes seems to regard the hereditary mechanism as if it were autonomous. Roux's often repeated assertion that the earlier stages of development are determined by heredity, the later stages by function, seems to regard the hereditary mechanism as working autonomously in the earlier stages. According to Weismann the distribution of the determinants during development is accomplished entirely by the mechanisms of heredity working independently of environment and the belief that hereditary mechanisms work autonomously apparently persists up to the present time (see pp. 21, 221). Even the most extreme predeterministic conceptions must of course admit the existence of certain respiratory and nutritive relations between the developing individual and the external world, but these are regarded as primarily sources of energy for the hereditary mechanism. Roux recognizes such factors as "realization factors" but apparently does not regard them as essential in determining individual pattern.

It seems that something more than this is necessary to account for the facts. In *Planaria*, as in many other forms, cells at all levels of the body are capable of giving rise to heads, posterior ends or any other region of the body, but in any particular planarian the cells of each level actually give rise only to a certain region. Evidently it is not the hereditary mechanism of those cells, but their environment, *i. e.*, their relations to other cells or parts, or to the external world, which determines what they shall do in any particular case. Consequently, although they are all primarily alike as regards hereditary constitution, they give rise to different regions and organs in the individual, and in isolated pieces they react to the altered environment by altering their behavior. Moreover, it has been shown in earlier chapters that physiological axes of polarity and symmetry may be experimentally altered and obliterated and that new axes may be determined in many different ways. Preformistic theory has usually endeavored to account for such facts as these by the assumption that polarity and symmetry are inherent in protoplasm, but can be affected or altered by external factors. At present, however, there is no convincing evidence in support of this view and much against it (pp. 25–29).

Again, the preformist maintains that the high degree of constancy of axiate pattern in each species cannot be accounted for, if polarity and symmetry are not inherent, but determined by environment. The development of the experimental method is showing us that this "constancy" is itself related to the conditions under which development of the individual occurs. As soon as we alter these beyond a certain limit, the constancy disappears. Apparently this relative constancy in development under normal conditions results chiefly from two factors: in the first place, the protoplasmic systems are products of very long periods of evolution and have attained a dynamic equilibrium or condition which under the range of conditions standardized as normal is relatively constant; and second, in the course of evolution the conditions under which the gametes arise and under which the individual develops have become increasingly constant, *i. e.*, have undergone progressive standardization (see pp. 222, 223).

In the excitatory reaction of protoplasm an external factor initiates, but the nature of the protoplasm is the primary factor in determining the character and further course of the reaction. In the case of a nerve fiber we know that the same effect may be determined by electrical, chemical, thermal, or mechanical energy and over a wide range of quantity or intensity for each form of energy. And as regards protoplasm in general we know that excitation is not dependent on any specific action of an external factor, but rather on a sufficient intensity, or perhaps in some cases, amount, of energy transfer. As regards the axial gradient we have seen that as soon as the external factor has brought its development to a certain point, the protoplasmic constitution becomes the chief factor in determining its further development. In a particular protoplasm similar gradients may result from widely different environmental relations, because, as in other reactions, so here the external factor merely initiates and the protoplasmic constitution determines the further course of events. As a matter of fact, the relative constancy and uniformity of so-called normal development and form present no difficulties to the conception of the individual as a reaction, a behavior pattern, in a specific protoplasm. On the other hand, the ease with which axial relations may be altered, obliterated or determined anew, does constitute a real difficulty for the preformistic conception. If a particular protoplasm possesses an inherent fundamentally bilateral "intimate" or molecular structure, the fact that such structure can be, so far as we can determine, completely obliterated by simply exposing the egg or embryo to certain concentrations of many different inhibiting agents (pp. 83, 104) is certainly remarkable and inexplicable. We should expect such inherent structure to be one of the most stable and persistent characteristics of protoplasm, but as a matter of fact polarity and symmetry are readily altered, obliterated or determined in the simpler organisms and the earlier stages of development.

Leaving out of account the speculative assumptions of preformistic theory and considering the evidence as it stands, the only possible conclusion seems to be that the individual organism as a pattern, an order, a physiological whole, originates in a reaction of a specific protoplasm to certain environmental factors. There is no conflict between this conception and modern theories of heredity, except in so far as some of those theories attempt to interpret the individual in terms of heredity alone. But when we recognize the fact that heredity has to do with potentialities and the individual pattern with realization of some of those potentialities under certain conditions, the theories of heredity and the gradient conception are not in conflict, but supplement each other.

Even the interpretation of inheritance in Mendelian terms does not account for the individual. It accounts merely for the distribution of certain differences in different individuals. For the realization of the different potentialities segregated into different germ cells, environmental factors are always necessary. Here as elsewhere, the individual represents the behavior of a specific protoplasm in reaction to certain environmental factors.

The gradient is merely the most generalized, the most primitive form of organismic behavior of a living protoplasm and if it persists long enough, it becomes the basis of later changes, some more or less permanent, others evanescent. Such changes constitute development, function, behavior of the individual. The gradient pattern constitutes the pattern, the order, the individuality in which the realization of the heredity potentialities occurs. That the gradients persist and so are hereditary in certain processes of agamic reproduction means merely that environmental relations are not such as to alter or obliterate them, but such persistence is in no sense Lamarckian inheritance.

The conception of the individual as a behavior pattern in a specific protoplasm is, in short, a purely physiological conception having to do with the realization of hereditary potentialities in the form of individuals. It is not in conflict with the facts of inheritance nor with the essential points of current theories of heredity, but accepts the hereditary potentialities as given in some form and attempts to account for the development of individuals from them. It is a theory of development and is therefore not primarily concerned with the problems of heredity, though the light which it throws on development may at some time be reflected to some extent upon those problems.

CHAPTER XIII

REGULATION OF PATTERN IN ORGANISMS

REGULATORY ACTIVITIES IN GENERAL

Regulation of function. — Investigation of the functional activities of organisms, particularly the higher animals and man, could not proceed very far without becoming aware of the existence of various mechanisms and processes which serve to control, order and adjust the various activities to varying conditions in such manner as to maintain the physiological unity and harmony of the organism in the changing environment to which it is subjected. Through such mechanisms and processes the activities of organisms are "regulated" within certain limits, and physiologists have very naturally come to call them regulatory mechanisms and processes. We know more or less concerning many such mechanisms in organisms, *e. g.*, the mechanism of the regulation of heat production and heat loss in the warm-blooded animals, of respiration, of blood flow and blood volume, of neutrality in the blood and tissues, of blood sugar, of the heart beat, of various digestive functions, of various internal secretions, of the transport of water, salts and carbohydrates in plants, and so on.

Our knowledge of even the simplest of such mechanisms is far from complete, but it is evident that with the progress of evolution their number and variety and the complexity of interrelation between them have increased, until in the higher animals and man they are far beyond the present range of scientific analysis. These mechanisms of functional regulation are mechanisms of physiological correlation, involving the transmission of excitation, or in some cases, of purely mechanical effects, or the mass transportation of substance, or in many cases, all of these factors. In general terms these mechanisms may be said to represent the rôle of physiological correlation in maintaining the organism as a functional whole.

Regulation of form and structure. — With the development of the experimental method and its application to the phenomena of individual development, it became evident that the capacity for regulation or adjustment appears, not only in the special functional activities of organisms, but in the development of form and structure. The ability of the plant body to react to altered conditions by the development of new individuals or parts from other parts has long been known and it was demonstrated some fifty years ago that in certain of the simpler plants, every cell, or almost every cell, even though normally giving rise to only a small part of an individual plant, is nevertheless capable of giving rise to a complete new individual.

The systematic and analytic application of experimental methods to the development of animals occurred somewhat later, but as investigation along these lines developed, it was soon discovered that in the normal development of an individual only a part, often a small part of the hereditary potentialities inherent in any cell or cell group was realized. When the cell or cell group was subjected to conditions different from those which acted upon it in the normal or usual course of development, the reaction often showed that it possessed potentialities which did not appear at all under the normal conditions. It was discovered, for example, that in many species the two cells resulting from the first division of the egg, and in some forms even the first four or eight cells, or even smaller portions, were each capable when isolated from each other of giving rise to a complete embryo or larva. Moreover, although it has long been known that many animals were capable of regenerating missing parts, more extended investigation along these lines brought to light potentialities of isolated pieces, particularly in the simpler animals, which had been hitherto unsuspected. It was found that in many forms, *e. g.*, hydroids, various turbellaria, etc., even small pieces of the body from any, or almost any region were able by a process of reconstitution to give rise to complete individuals.

REGULATION AND THE NORMAL

The earlier workers in these fields, particularly the zoölogists, were much impressed by the fact that although the course of events in the reconstitution of a new whole from a part was in many respects different from the course of events in embryonic development, the final result was, nevertheless, within a wide range of experimental conditions, an individual essentially identical with the individuals of the species developing in the usual way. In such cases, then, although the course of developmental events was "abnormal," the result as regards form and structure was "normal." The only possible inference from such facts is that reaction and adjustment of some sort to altered conditions may occur in the development of form and structure as well as in the special functional activities of fully developed individuals. On this basis developed the general biological conception of regulation.

Definition of regulation. — In the development and formulation of this conception Roux and Driesch have perhaps played the most important parts.[1] According to Roux regulation has a physico-chemical basis and is dependent upon physiological correlation, but his interpretation is in terms of a preformistic theory of heredity and is to a large extent formal, rather than directly physiological. Driesch, on the other hand, postulates a non-mechanistic principle, to which he applies the Aristotelian term "entelechy," as the basis of regulation and regards it as involving a purpose or end to be attained. In the conception of regulation as defined by these authors the idea of the normal plays an important part. For example, according to Driesch "regulation is a process or a change in a process occurring in the living organism by means of which a disturbance of any sort of its preëxisting ' normal ' condition is wholly or in part, directly or indirectly compensated and the ' normal ' condition, or at least an approximation to it, reëstablished" (Driesch, '01, p. 92). Again, according to Roux, "regulation is the complete or incomplete compensation of disturbances, that is, the return or approach of the disturbed organism to the type or norm" (Roux, '12, p. 339).

In both these definitions it is implied that the "normal" condition is internally determined and independent of external disturbances. This conception of the normal is the logical consequence of the views of these authors. For Roux the normal organism is determined solely by heredity, although he is forced to recognize certain environmental factors as playing a part in the realization of hereditary potentialities. For Driesch the entelechy is the determining factor and physico-chemical constitution and conditions are merely means which it uses. For both, the action of external factors, except those essential to life, is always "disturbance" or alteration of the norm and regulation is the return or approach to it. Although Roux emphatically rejects the vitalistic viewpoint, his conception like other pre-deterministic conceptions of the organism involves a vitalistic or dualistic implication in that the hereditary mechanism is conceived as fundamentally autonomous in its relation to the individual organism.

[1] See, for example, Roux, '95, index under "Selbstregulation-mechanismus," "Regulatorische Funktionen," "Entwickelung," also '05; Driesch, '01, '08, and various special papers.

REGULATION AS EQUILIBRATION

From the strictly physiological viewpoint it appears impossible to maintain any such distinction between normal and abnormal, disturbed, or altered organisms. At all stages of its existence the organism is in relation to external factors of some sort and these factors are always subject to change. Life apparently consists in a succession of disturbances and alterations by external factors and in the reactions to them, and there is abundant reason to believe that in the absence of such disturbances and alterations life would soon cease and static equilibrium would sooner or later supervene.

It is evident, however, that protoplasms and organisms are within certain limits complex dynamic equilibrating systems. We mean by this that more or less complex internal alterations, compensations, reversals of former processes, etc., occur in relation to each other, in the living system following action upon it of an external factor, with the result that the system either approaches more or less closely its previous condition or progresses toward an altered equilibrium. Within certain limits the changes are such that life continues, and the order and integration which constitute the individual persist either with or without appreciable alteration. This capacity for equilibration depends primarily on the physiological interrelation or correlation of the various activities. In consequence of this cor- relation the effect of disturbance by an external factor is not limited to the part directly affected, but is determined to a greater or less extent by the whole. Through physiological correlation with other parts, the change in the part directly affected may be more or less completely inhibited, compensated, neutralized, or otherwise oblit- erated and the organism may approach, or practically attain its pre- vious condition, or the disturbance may modify the whole organism so that, instead of approaching its previous condition, it attains a new condition. Evidently in all cases in which life continues after such disturbance some sort and degree of equilibration must occur in the living system. Physiological equilibrium does not necessarily consist in return or approach to a preëxisting or normal condition, but may involve persistent alteration of the living system. In fact, it is at least a pertinent question whether the condition of a living organism is ever exactly the same after the action upon it of an ex- ternal factor as it was before. It is impossible to answer the ques- tion on the basis of evidence, but it becomes more and more evident, as our knowledge of organisms advances, that the reactions to ex-

ternal factors very commonly consist in more or less permanent alteration of the organism in some way, rather than in a return to the
preëxisting condition. Moreover, if we regard the organism as a
physico-chemical system, it seems certain that we must answer the
question in the negative.

From this physiological standpoint the normal condition appears,
not as a condition independent of external factors, but rather as the
range of conditions determined in a particular organism, species or
group by the range of quantity, intensity and kind of external actions to which it is ordinarily subjected in its natural environment.
In other words, the normal is nothing more than the usual, as standardized in the course of evolution. Normal individuals of the same
species, variety, or race may differ from each other, both as regards
hereditary potentialities and the alterations determined by external factors, and as a matter of fact no two of them are alike.

What then becomes of the conception of regulation as a return
or approach to the normal? It seems clear that the regulatory mechanisms are mechanisms of dynamic equilibration and that regulation
is in general dynamic equilibration of some degree and some sort, in
reaction to a disturbance. But if it is true that an organism is never
the same after action of an external factor as it was before, every
equilibration is, strictly speaking, an alteration, and every regulation
is to some extent a modification, rather than a return to a pre-
existing condition.

The point of chief importance in this general discussion is that
the conception of the normal and that of regulation, like any other
abstractions, merely serve the purpose of calling attention to certain similarities, while ignoring certain differences in a number of
individual cases viewed from a certain standpoint. The persistence
and continuity of the individual organism in a changing environment is unquestionably a fact of great interest and significance and,
observing that in general organisms of the same species are much
alike, we reach the conception of the normal. Similarly, when we
investigate the physiological conditions on which their maintenance
and persistence is based, we see that when these are disturbed by
external factors they commonly react in a way that appears to be
useful in that it makes maintenance possible. The reaction may
be a compensation of the disturbance, an escape from it by locomotion, or some other reaction, but the effect in general is some
sort and degree of equilibration of the system as a whole. On this
basis we attain the idea of regulation as a useful reaction. Both

these conceptions are convenient and valuable, but when we view living organisms in certain other aspects, we see variation instead of a normal, and equilibration and modification instead of regulation as a return to normal (*Cf.* Herrick, '24, chap. XX).

The broader conception of regulation as equilibration is more satisfactory from the physiological standpoint, because it does away with the difficulties inherent in the conception of regulation as fundamentally a useful and apparently purposive process, involving an approach or return to normal. Much stress has been laid upon the apparently useful or purposive character of regulatory processes. In the mutilated animal, for example, missing parts may be replaced or at least healing of the wound occurs. In the mutilated plant removal of a part may be followed by development of new, or modification of old parts in other regions of the body. In the sea urchin and various other forms isolated blastomeres or portions of the embryo, within certain limits of size and region, develop into complete larvæ. In all such cases the regulatory process appears to be useful.

Functional regulations, *i. e.*, regulations of special function in mature organisms, show similar characteristics. In the mammal a rise in internal temperature brings into play mechanisms which tend to decrease the internal temperature; life in high altitudes brings about increased production of red blood corpuscles; similarly in motor reactions, the organism encountering unfavorable or injurious conditions commonly moves away, and the useful reflexes, such as the withdrawal of a part from painful stimulation, the closure of the eyelid in excessive light, etc., are familiar to all.

The wide range, great variety and remarkable delicacy of the useful and apparently purposive regulatory or equilibratory mechanisms in organisms has often tended to obscure the fact that there is also a great group of reactions to disturbance which do not tend toward restoration of the normal and which are neither useful nor purposive. Many interesting cases of this sort are found in the developmental reactions of isolated pieces. Under certain conditions isolated pieces of hydroids, planarians, etc., give rise to partial individuals, biaxial heads, headless forms, etc. Pieces which give these "abnormal" results are not necessarily any smaller or otherwise different from pieces which give rise to "normal" animals. In fact, it can often be determined experimentally whether a piece shall give a normal or an abnormal result.[1]   Many of these abnormal forms are incapable of continued existence because of absence of essential parts, such as mouth, certain sense organs, organs of attachment, etc.   It is also possible to alter and control by means of experimental conditions the proportions and relations of organs and parts and so to produce forms which are extremely abnormal in various respects and often incapable of continued development, or even of continued existence.[1]

Similarly the special functional regulatory mechanisms, under conditions outside the normal range, may work in such a way as to alter, injure, or even destroy the organism.   A case in point is the ability of the organism to acquire tolerance to drugs or other toxic substances.   The development of tolerance may lead to habit-formation and the desire for larger and larger quantities.   Shelford ('18) has shown that fishes rapidly establish a preference for water containing certain toxic substances, e. g., alcohol, cocaine, etc., but to carbon dioxide, which apparently has physiological action resembling in certain respects that of alcohol and cocaine, they are persistently negative (Shelford and Allee, '14).   The interpretation suggested is that since fishes may be exposed more or less frequently within the range of "normal" environment to carbon dioxide in toxic concentration, evolution has had time to act by natural selection or otherwise in developing the negative useful reaction.   Alcohol and cocaine, on the other hand, being outside the range of the normal environment, the reaction of the fishes to them occurs independently of useful or injurious results.   Similarly the moth singes its wings or even kills itself in the flame to which it is attracted.   The mechanisms of heat regulation, neutrality regulation, blood sugar regulation, etc., in man may work under certain conditions of disease or experiment in very different manner from the normal and injury or death may result.

All these cases obviously involve equilibration in the organism, but they are equilibrations to unusual or abnormal conditions, i. e., conditions more or less outside the range standardized by evolution. The point which I wish to emphasize is that the useful, apparently purposive regulations are not a fundamentally different category of reactions from these injurious or destructive reactions, but that both belong physiologically in the same category of equilibration processes. The useful regulation is an equilibration process of significance to the

[1] See, for example, Figures 85–89, 93–100, 112–116; also Child, '07, a, c, d, '11 c, '12 a, '16 b, '20 a, '21 c.
[2] See Figures 48–57, 76–81, 117–121; also Child, '16 d, '17 d; Stockard, '07, '09, '10, '11, '21; Bellamy, '19, '22.

organism in its relations to environment. Once present as a potentiality of a particular protoplasm, such a reaction may of course become a factor in evolution, *i. e.*, the protoplasm possessing it may be maintained or favored by natural selection and so the reaction may in time be regarded as an adaption, but the equilibration process itself is a matter of the physico-chemical constitution of the protoplasm and its reaction to a certain range of environment.

The useless, injurious, or non-adaptive equilibrations are usually, if not always, reaction to conditions outside the standardized range of the normal, *e. g.*, the reaction to habit-forming drugs, the reaction of the moth to the flame, the development of biaxial or partial forms from isolated pieces and of abnormal forms under experimental conditions. Physiologically these are as truly equilibrations as the useful reactions, but whether we call them regulatory or not depends on whether we regard regulation as simply equilibration or as equilibration which is useful to the organism.

REGULATION IN DEVELOPMENT

Normal development and heredity. — It may appear, and in fact has often been asserted that the course of development in its earlier stages is, so far as its "typical" or "normal" features are concerned, independent of external factors and determined by heredity (pp. 215–219). That is to say, up to a certain point at which functional relation to the external world begins, the individual organism represents primarily the working out of a scheme, order, or pattern predetermined by heredity. This typical hereditary course of events may be modified by external factors which transcend the normal range, but within the normal range the external factors play no essential part, except in making possible the continuation of life. This typical or normal course of development unmodified by external factors results in the normal individual and regulation represents the return or approach to normal when modification does occur. According to this preformistic conception, the development of the individual represents primarily the construction of certain mechanisms through internal factors, and only when this construction is completed, or has attained a certain stage, does function begin. Regulation is a sort of repair process, through which the hereditary mechanism obliterates or compensates more or less completely the accidental action of external factors. The biologists of the Roux-Weismann school, and particularly Roux, have made much of this distinction between the typical or normal as predetermined and the regulatory as essentially the result of accident, and have attempted in various ways to reconcile it with the facts of developmental physiology.

Actually, however, it becomes more and more evident that life is largely, if not wholly made up of accidents. The constancy and uniformity of normal development in nature, results, as already noted, from the fact that a certain degree of standardization has occurred in the course of evolution as regards the range of such accidents to which the developing individual is likely to be exposed. This has been accomplished in various ways, e. g., through position of the gonads, through conditions under which fertilization occurs, through the formation of enveloping membranes, jelly, or capsules about the developing eggs, through the selection of certain localities for egg deposition, through care of the young, viviparity, etc. But these various provisions do not eliminate external factors; they merely tend to limit the variation in range, in other words, to standardize their action.

The gamete and the developing embryo are acted upon by, and react to factors external to themselves at all periods of their existence and whatever mechanisms or structures are present at any time are functioning. Material exchange is always going on and we know that excitation by various forms of energy and the transmission of such excitation may occur in these stages as well as in the fully developed individual. We know also that even within the range of the normal many differences between individuals result from differences in external conditions within the standardized range. And finally, we know that when we subject these stages to external conditions outside the standard range, i. e., "abnormal" conditions, reaction of some sort, with equilibration leading either to a normal or an abnormal result, or destruction of the system and death may result. In fact, we can find no evidence for the hereditary predetermination of a normal or typical course of development, except in so far as each protoplasm possesses a certain hereditary constitution and as the conditions under which the individual develops are more or less exactly determined or standardized by the hereditary mechanisms of the parent and the species. The hereditary constitution of the protoplasm determines certain possibilities which are realized only in relation to external factors, and the hereditary mechanism of the parent or species, as noted above, determines position of gonads, method of egg deposition, etc. So far predetermination occurs, but such predetermination is indirect and physiological, rather than direct, that is, it determines, on the one hand, the possibilities of reaction and on the other, the range of conditions likely to be met.

From this viewpoint development is not fundamentally different from the so-called functional later stages. Mechanism and function of some sort are present at all stages and the mechanism and function at any stage constitute the structural and physiological basis for what follows, but what actually does follow in a particular case is determined by the mechanism functioning in relation to particular conditions. Adjustment, equilibration, is going on at all stages, but the sort and degree of equilibration at any stage is determined by the mechanisms characteristic of that stage and the conditions to which it is subjected. In the earlier stages of development and in the simpler organisms equilibrations involving the larger features of form and structure are in general more extensive and more readily induced than in later stages and in the higher forms, because in the former function is less narrowly and exactly limited by morphological structure than in the latter. Except as regards the earliest stages, which are really stages of dedifferentiation and disappearance of gamete and zygote structure (Child, '15 b, Chaps. XIII-XV), we find that in general processes of structural differentiation are more conspicuous features of the earlier than of the later stages of development. The larger, more general features of structure appear first and the details are, so to speak, filled in later. As structure develops, it determines and limits function more and more definitely, therefore its stability increases and the specialized functions of organs are dependent upon its existence but both structure and function of some sort are present at all stages.

Development as regulation. — It is evident from what has been said that development itself may be regarded as a complex regulation resulting from the action of various factors. Among these fertilization is usually essential, but various others, *e. g.*, the isolation of the gametes from the parent body, the altered nutritive and respiratory conditions, the physico-chemical constitution of the external medium to which the developing individual is exposed, or its relation to the parent body, may be concerned in determining the course and results of development, according to the species. Assuming that the normal hereditary constitution of the protoplasm is present, whether the course and result of development are what we know as normal depends simply upon what I have called the standardization of these environmental conditions through the hereditary mechanisms of the species, *i. e.*, the determination in one way or another, and to a greater or less degree through heredity, of the conditions to which the developing individual shall be subjected. With the progress of evolution this standardization becomes in general more complete, that is, the parent plays a more and more important part in determining the conditions which its developing offspring shall meet, and the regulatory mechanisms of the protoplasms become more delicate and varied. Normal development of a normal protoplasm is then a complex series of regulations or equilibrations to conditions within a standard range and abnormal development is a similar reaction to conditions transcending this range. Certain abnormalities, however, are hereditary and in such case must have a certain basis in the protoplasmic constitution. With these we are not concerned here except to point out that the experimimental work of recent years in genetics has shown that at least some such hereditary abnormalities originate in the action of abnormal factors upon the reproductive cells at some time. Such cases are equilibrations with persistent effect and it is a pertinent question which has no necessary connection with Lamarckian theory, whether all existing hereditary characteristics of organisms are not in the final analysis of such origin.

Physiological gradients as regulatory mechanisms. — The conception of the physiological gradients and their significance in individual development is merely an attempt based on many lines of evidence to throw some light on the physiological character of the general regulatory mechanisms and processes which underlie development. The mechanism of excitation and transmission and the excitation-transmission gradient are regulatory mechanisms of fundamental significance in life, and the establishment of a more or less permanent physiological gradient as the basis of a physiological axis is a further regulatory modification of the protoplasm in reaction to an external differential. As already pointed out (pp. 133–137), once the gradient is established in a protoplasm, it tends under ordinary conditions to attain a certain height, slope and length characteristic for such protoplasm and changing as the condition of the protoplasm changes. The further course of developmental events in relation to it consists in a complex series of regulations involving form, structure, constitution and function of the various parts concerned. These represent the reactions of the hereditary constitution of each particular protoplasm to the physiological gradients established in that protoplasm and within the range of normal development they approach the condition characteristic of the mature normal individual of the species. From this viewpoint the physiological gradient is merely the primary regulatory mechanism in the development of the axiate individual and probably also in the development of the surface-interior organism (pp. 93–94).

Under conditions outside the standard or normal range the course of development and the end attained may be altered in one way or another. Such alterations appear in the development of new individuals from isolated blastomeres of an embryo or from isolated pieces of the body of a mature individual. In *Planaria*, for example, the course and results of the development of isolated pieces differ widely according to age, nutrition, and physiological condition of the animals from which the pieces are taken and also according to size of piece, region of body represented, temperature and chemical constitution of the external medium (Child,' 11 b, c, d, '12 a, '14 e, '16 b, '20 a, '21 c). Moreover, the work of many investigators has demonstrated that the course and results of embryonic development may be very greatly altered by changes in environmental factors, and I have endeavored to show that changes in the gradients are fundamental factors in such alterations (Child, '16 d, '17 d, '21 c). It has been shown further that physiological gradients can be obliterated and new gradients established experimentally (see Chaps. VIII, IX) with corresponding changes in the course and results of development. All such changes represent regulations or equilibrations of the protoplasmic system to the conditions to which it is subjected. The fact that many of them differ widely from the normal means merely that under different conditions different equilibria are attained or approached.

The relation of dominance and subordination between regions and parts of the organism, which is the most general and primitive sort of physiological relation in the organism is, as I have pointed out, primarily an expression of a physiological gradient and therefore a feature of the regulatory mechanism which that gradient represents (see Chapter X).

As regards the special functions of the organs of the individual at any stage, we recognize clearly that the unity and integration of the individual are maintained by the interrelation and equilibration of such function, in short, by regulation. The various regulatory mechanisms of the physiologists, *e. g.*, mechanisms regulating transport of water, salts and carbohydrates in plants, blood-flow, respiration, heat production, heat loss, secretion, excretion, neutrality, etc., are cases in point. But as noted above, under conditions transcending the normal range, the working of these mechanisms is altered and may lead to abnormal results, or even to death. Here as elsewhere the normal represents merely a certain range of constitution and conditions more or less standardized by evolution and heredity. The physiological unity of the organism is in fact dependent upon the existence of regulatory mechanisms of one kind or another and the evidence indicates that the general basis of such mechanisms is on the one hand the hereditary constitution of each particular protoplasm which determines the character of its reaction to any conditions and, on the other, the primary regulatory mechanism of the individual organism, the physiological gradient. The fact that each protoplasm possesses a certain hereditary constitution implies the potential existence in it of certain protoplasmic regulatory mechanisms of physical and chemical character, but only as these are integrated and ordered on a large scale by the establishment of a differential of some sort, involving different molar regions of the protoplasm do they become of organismic significance (pp. 6–12, 43). The physiological gradient represents, I believe, the most general and primitive form of such differential and therefore constitutes the primary organismic regulatory mechanism. The gradient or gradients established in a protoplasm initiate a series of regulations involving form, structure and function, and these constitute development. The structure of any given moment or stage is a factor in determining and limiting the character of the function occurring in it and the function of any given moment alters the structure in which it occurs.

We are accustomed to speak of development as ending with maturity. Actually of course, development never ends while life continues, for structural and functional equilibrations are always going on and leaving their records in the protoplasm. So far as its developmental aspects are concerned, then, life may be regarded as a continuous series of regulations, or in the words of Spencer as "continuous adjustment of internal relations to external relations."

EXCITO-MOTOR BEHAVIOR AS REGULATION

In the past biologists have often drawn a sharp distinction between development as a process of construction of a machine and behavior as the functioning or working of the machine after construction is completed. But if the position taken in the preceding section is correct, development represents behavior as truly as any activities of the mature organism, and we have to distinguish not between development and behavior, but between different aspects and phases of developmental and other forms of behavior.

In the excito-motor group of behavior phenomena, motor changes in position in space are a conspicuous feature. These may consist of locomotion of the organism as a whole, of movement of some organ or part through change in direction, rate or character of growth, contraction, etc., or of movements of substances in consequence of excitatory changes in permeability of membranes, etc., *e. g.*, in secretion. Since such behavior is usually the most conspicuous feature of the reaction of organisms to environment in the more advanced stages of development, we may for convenience distinguish it as excito-motor behavior from developmental behavior. From the present viewpoint, however, such behavior is essentially one aspect or form of developmental behavior, characteristic of the more advanced stages after morphological mechanisms have differentiated, and developmental behavior in general is merely one aspect of life. Life itself, in so far as it consists in reaction or response is behavior (Chaps. I, XII, XIV). Jennings says for example:

"Behavior is merely a collective name for the most obvious and most easily studied of the processes of the organism, and it is clear that these processes are closely connected with, and are indeed outgrowths from the more recondite internal processes." (Jennings '06, p. 339).

Moreover, if behavior means reaction or response to some external factor we are forced to conclude that behavior occurs, not only in living organisms, but in all non-living things. In short the universe considered as a series of changes causally determined by the relations between its constituent parts is behavior.

But, employing the term for the present in its common biological sense as referring primarily to excito-motor reactions, it is evident that in the behavior of living organisms the capacities of the individual for adjustment, equilibration or regulation are even more conspicuous and striking factors than in its other activities. In general, behavior appears to be directed toward the end of adjustment and the most delicate, most rapid and most complete adjustments are accomplished in this way. That is to say, behavior generally, though not always, leads to results which are useful to the organism in one way or another and enable it to exist, to maintain itself, to propagate its kind and particularly in the higher, more strictly psychic forms of behavior to profit by past experience and to act more or less intelligently when brought into relation to new collocations of external factors.

Even the simpler organisms behave, in general, in ways that favor their maintenance. In the absence of food, activities appear which tend to provide it. Motile forms in a region of insufficient oxygen attempt to escape. Forms normally living in darkness or weak light tend to move away from strong light, those needing light move from darkness or weak light into stronger. All such reactions are not only physiologically speaking equilibrations, but are also regulations in the stricter sense that they are useful. In fact, as Jennings puts it, "behavior is adjustment or regulation" (Jennings, '05 b, p. 474).

As in other fields of biological activity, so in the behavior of organisms in the stricter sense, we do, however, find many reactions which are not useful, and which may even be injurious or lead to death. The preference of fishes for water containing certain injurious drugs (p. 220), the reaction of the moth to the flame, are cases in point. Again, the reactions of which the organism is capable may not suffice to meet the conditions to which it is exposed and death results in spite of them. In water with low oxygen content, for example, *Planaria* shows first a distinct negative reaction to gravity. Such a reaction would ordinarily bring it toward the water surface and into levels of higher oxygen content, but in a closed vessel without air the reaction, although useless, occurs. In general such reactions are observed under external conditions well outside the standardized range which we call normal, in other words, under conditions to which the evolutionary process of standardization has not been applied. Physiologically they are of the same character as the useful forms of behavior, but they are not useful and may be injurious or deadly. The regulatory mechanisms are at work, but are inadequate, and any equilibrium attained or approached is so far from the normal as to be useless or injurious. In some cases of this sort the reaction of the organism undergoes modification in the course of time and a useful reaction takes the place of the original useless or injurious reaction, but in other cases no useful reaction is possible and injury or death is inevitable.

These cases of useless or injurious behavior, like the useless or injurious forms occurring under certain conditions in the regulation of form and development (pp. 219–220) are of interest as showing something of the limitations of organismic mechanisms, but they do not alter the fact that in the main the behavior of organisms is both equilibratory and useful, *i. e.*, regulatory in the stricter sense.

The potentialities of behavior of each organism are of course given in the hereditary constitution of its protoplasm in what Jennings terms its action system, in its simplest terms, but the actual behavior pattern is realized only in behavior, *i. e.*, in the reaction of this protoplasm to external factors. As already pointed out, this does not mean that light is essential to the development of the behavior mechanisms in which the eye is concerned, or sound to those involving the ear. It means merely what I have endeavored to show in the preceding section, viz., that protoplasm is not autonomous and that the individual from its beginning represents a series of reactions to external factors of a particular protoplasm with certain potentialities. The behavior of the mature organism represents merely the most advanced and most conspicuous features of this reaction series and is dependent upon the various reactions of earlier stages. In his discussion of regulation in behavior and in other fields Jennings ('06 a, Chap. XXI) reaches essentially this conclusion.

As regards the methods by which regulation is accomplished through behavior, it is evident that they must depend on the nature of the behavior mechanisms present in each organism. Moreover, if it is true that behavior in the ordinary biological sense is an expression of the structural and functional mechanisms which make up the organism, it is also evident that the behavior mechanisms present in any case must depend upon the fundamental pattern of the organism concerned. In most plants, for example, in the absence of special motor mechanisms, behavior reactions are usually accomplished through growth, turgor changes, etc., while in motile organisms movement of the organism is commonly concerned in such reactions. In Chapter VI it was pointed out that an organism without a permanent physiological axis must necessarily accomplish its behavior reactions in ways different from those which are characteristic of axiate organisms. Again, the method by which the result is accomplished must differ in certain respects in radial and in bilateral animals. And going one step farther it is also clear that the method of reaction must depend upon the degree to which permanent structural and functional mechanisms have developed in relation to the general organismic pattern.

A brief consideration of the simpler forms of motor behavior will serve to show something of their regulatory character, and of their dependence upon the kind and degree of development of organismic pattern and its mechanisms.

REACTION BY TRIAL AND TROPISM

The question whether there is a fundamental or primitive mechanism or method of motor behavior in motile organisms is one of very great interest, and in attempts to answer this question two widely different conceptions have arisen. One of these, the theory of reaction by trial and error or, as commonly known at present, the theory of trial, was formulated and developed with reference to the behavior of the simpler organisms by Jennings, the other, the theory of tropisms, with reference to motor reactions of animals, by Loeb.[1]

Trial and error reaction.— The work of Jennings has made the conception of reaction by trial so familiar that only a restatement of it is necessary: First, definite internal processes, *e. g.*, respiration, digestion, transmission of excitation, often internal motor activity, etc., are occurring in organisms, and their sum total constitutes the physiological state of the organism at any given moment. Second, interference with these processes determines changes in behavior and varied movements result because motility is a feature of the action system of the organism. Third, these movements are purely random movements not directed with respect to the disturbance, but they subject the organism to different conditions and among these conditions some one may relieve the disturbance of the physiological state and then the changes in behavior cease. In short, the organism, excited by some external factor, moves about at random until it happens upon an environment in which the excitation no longer occurs.

According to this conception any orientation of the organism or of its direction of movement with respect to the external factor is purely a matter of chance and results from the fact that the organism, when disturbed, performs varied movements, some one of which may happen to bring it into a definite position or direction of movement with respect to the external factor and if this relieves the disturbance it continues. Although we need not suppose that in the simple organisms the disturbance constitutes pain and its removal pleasure, it is evident that the theory of reaction by trial as the fundamental behavior pattern leads us, as we enter the field of more strictly psychic behavior, to a pleasure-pain psychology.

The tropism theory. — The term tropism has been variously and loosely employed. Some regard as a tropism any reaction in which

[1] Only a few references to the extensive bibliography relating to these two theories and their relative importance need be given here. For statements of the trial-and-error theory the experimental data on which it is based and discussion of the tropism theory from Jennings' viewpoint see Jennings, '04, '05, '06, '08, '09, '10. The theory of tropisms and the data bearing upon it have been dealt with in many special papers by Loeb and others and in the following general works (Loeb, '90, '99 a, '06, '12, '16 b, '18 d). For other discussions of these theories in relation to behavior see Torrey, '07; Holmes, '11, '16; Mast, '11; Ritter, '19.

orientation of the body or of direction of movement with respect to the external factor occurs, whether by trial and error or otherwise. Others reserve the name "tropism" for those reactions in which direct, immediate, or "forced" orientation occurs in consequence of a-symmetric action of the external factor upon an organism with some sort of axiate organization. Both Webster's New International and the Standard Dictionaries define tropism as the inherent or innate tendency of organisms to react in a definite manner to an external stimulus. Loeb, who is chiefly responsible for the theory of tropisms as applied to motor reactions, apparently regards a tropism as a forced orientation of an organism based upon a symmetrical mechanism of some sort, i. e., a reaction directly determined through the agency of some known or postulated physiological mechanism in consequence of the unequal action of the external factor upon the two sides of the unoriented body (Loeb, '18 d). In the case of the motile animal with its axis at an angle to the direction of action of the external factor, the unequal action of this factor upon the side of the body turned toward, and that turned away from it, forces the organism directly to change its position or direction of movement until both sides are affected alike, that is, until it is moving either directly toward, or directly away from the source of the external action. Some organisms are positively, others negatively tropic to particular factors and often the tropism characteristic of particular conditions is reversible under others. The growth reactions of the plants leading to orientation with respect to external factors and known as tropisms constituted the starting point of Loeb's theory of tropisms as applied to motile organisms, and Loeb considers the tropism as the fundamental form of reaction of the motile organism. The theory has been repeatedly and severely criticised and many of the criticisms remain unanswered.

Jennings extends the conception of tropism to any reaction in which orientation occurs, whether directly or by trial. According to this view of the tropism, it is not the most primitive form of excito-motor behavior, but results, either from trial, or from the presence of a specialized mechanism which permits immediate orientation. In an animal such as an insect with bilaterally localized sensory and motor organs, e. g., eyes and appendages, a tropic reaction must involve at least a highly complex reflex mechanism and if such a mechanism exists, the tropism in the insect is certainly far from being a primitive form of reaction.

The two reaction patterns contrasted. — It is obvious that the trial-and-error method of reaction to any particular factor depends on the absence of mechanisms which provide for immediate, direct, or in the higher animals and man, conscious and intelligent orientation. The tropism theory, on the other hand, postulates the existence in all reacting organisms of a mechanism so related to the action of external factors that it makes possible direct or forced orientation. In short, although Loeb holds that the tropism itself is not regulatory, adaptive or useful, it is evident that the mechanisms postulated as the basis of the tropisms imply a far greater degree of evolutionary standardization, *i. e.*, of adaptation, than do the mechanisms of trial and error.

In the case of *Amœba* the interpretation of directed movement, *e. g.*, with respect to light, in terms of Loeb's theory of tropisms requires the postulation of a photoreceptor mechanism of remarkable delicacy and one in which the chemical or other action of light is very directly related to amœboid movement. If such a mechanism exists, it is certainly a regulatory mechanism, useful to the animal, and therefore a feature in evolutionary standardization, that is, an adaptation. Again, in the tropic orientation of axiate organisms, an axiate pattern must be present, and Loeb ('18 d) apparently regards symmetry as an essential factor in tropic behavior. In fact, it seems evident that the tropisms, as conceived by Loeb, require a greater degree of development of organismic pattern and mechanism than do the trial reactions. If pure tropisms exist they certainly represent a more advanced stage in the development of behavior than the trial reactions.

Obviously both methods of reaction, so far as they are really different, represent processes of regulation or equilibration. Whether the reaction is by trial or tropic, it normally represents an approach toward an equilibrium after disturbance of the previously existing condition. Obviously also both sorts of reaction represent a result, an expression of the structural and functional mechanisms which make up the organismic pattern and which are themselves a consequence of developmental behavior.

Attention may be briefly called to the relation between the motor reactions and the axial gradients which I have called the primary, regulatory and behavior mechanisms of the organism as an individual. The anaxiate *Amœba* does not turn its body about in orientation but develops a temporary regional differential, in other words, it acquires a new temporary behavior pattern of axiate character (see pp. 57–59). In the axiate organism this pattern is already established and has determined various mechanisms, and radial or bilateral pattern and mechanisms are also present. Fixity and complexity of mechanism are far advanced in these forms, but, as pointed out in Chap. VI, even such organisms may develop new excito-motor behavior patterns, either for the time being, or as a more or less permanent habit. These new patterns apparently originate, like the axial gradients, in regional differentials in activity, determined by some factor external to the protoplasm concerned. If they persist for any considerable length of time, they may become important factors in further reactions.

REFLEX BEHAVIOR

Reflex action, as the term is commonly used, implies the presence of a more or less differentiated sensory apparatus of some sort, the receptor, a differentiated nervous path, the conductor, and a differentiated motor or other organ as the effector, Herrick ('22, Chap. IV and '24, Chap. XVII), and various other authorities also include a central nervous organ, the adjustor, in the reflex mechanism. The reflex arc is then a rather highly specialized structural and functional mechanism which accomplishes a definite reaction of a particular kind involving certain definite organs. Reflex behavior is in general conspicuously and immediately regulatory in character. The burned or pricked finger is reflexly withdrawn from the source of disturbance. Irritation of the eye by intense light, by dust, etc., brings about closure of the lid and increased secretion of the lachrymal glands. Reflex equilibration of the body follows disturbance of normal position and so on. Consciousness, intelligence, reason are not concerned in such reactions. In nature, however, the reflex arc is not usually if ever, an independent reaction system but is correlated with other arcs. In the nervous systems of the higher animals and man these correlations and combinations constitute an apparatus of regulation, or of equilibration of almost inconceivable complexity, delicacy and range of action (Herrick, '24, Chaps. XVII, XIX).

It is a self-evident fact that the reflex arcs and the reflex behavior of any organism are dependent upon the course of development in that organism. They are consequences and expressions of all that has gone before. The receptor and effector connections of each reflex arc, the interrelations of different arcs, whatever their adaptive evolutionary significance, must all have a physiological basis in the developmental processes and are evidently outgrowths of the general organismic pattern. In fact, the physiological continuity in the individual between the physiological or metabolic gradient and the reflex arc is evident (Child, '21 a, Chap. XIII). The physiological gradient is the general physiological foundation on which the reflex arc develops. If we consider development in its functional, rather than in its structural aspects, it appears that the gradient is the primitive and generalized excitation arc out of which the various reflex arcs develop by specialization of function and differentiation of structure. In short, the physiology of development of the reflex arc has its starting point in the excitability of protoplasm, the differential action of environmental factors upon it and the resulting physiological gradient or gradients.

It is perhaps necessary to emphasize again the fact that this continuity with which we are concerned here is strictly physiological continuity in individual development, not hereditary continuity. The possibilities of reflex pattern in any particular protoplasm are of course given in the hereditary constitution of that protoplasm, but the actual reflex pattern appears only in the development of the individual, i. e., as a behavior pattern in the broad sense in that protoplasm. And the evidence indicates that the physiological gradient is the primary mechanism of organismic integration, equilibration and regulation. If it is true, as I have endeavored to show, that the physiological gradient in each case represents the behavior of a protoplasm of a certain hereditary constitution in response to an external differential, it becomes clear at once that this behavior is the physiological factor which initiates the realization of the hereditary possibilities, that is to say, the development of the germ plasm into individual organisms. From the physiological viewpoint, then, the reflex arcs and the reflex behavior of any particular organism, like other characteristics of the individual, are determined by this primary behavior and from the viewpoint of heredity, by the hereditary constitution of the protoplasm. Here, as elsewhere, heredity determines the possibilities in each case and behavior in the broad sense determines the realization of possibilities in each individual.

Elsewhere (Child, '21a) I have maintained that it is impossible to account physiologically for the origin and development of the nervous system except in some such terms as these. If the individual is not from the beginning of its development a behavior pattern we cannot escape some form of dualism or vitalism. The reflex is the unit reaction (Sherrington) or the physiological unit (Parker) on which nervous function and integration are built up, and if physiological continuity between the reflex and the primitive behavior of protoplasm, as shown in the gradients resulting from differential excitation, does not exist, the problems of the origin and development of the nervous system and of reflex behavior must, I believe, be regarded as metaphysical rather than scientific problems.

The relations between reflex, trial and error, and tropic behavior require brief consideration. Trial reactions and tropisms occur both in organisms without and those with structurally differentiated nervous systems. In the former there are, strictly speaking, no reflex arcs, but temporary or permanent excitation arcs or excitation gradients may be present and so be factors in the reactions. In forms possessing nervous systems, reflex arcs may play a part in both trial reactions and in tropisms. The behavior of the decapitated frog when a drop of acid or other irritating substance is placed on one hind leg and the other held is a beautiful case of reflex trial reaction. Failure to remove the source of irritation by reflex movements of the other leg is followed by various other movements, until, if the irritation is sufficient, the greater part of the muscular system of the animal is involved. In organisms with bilateral sense organs and a nervous system a tropic orientation must depend upon a reflex mechanism. In fact, tropisms in general, at least in animals, are often regarded as reflex behavior.

Summing up, the reflex, strictly speaking, is a specialized behavior pattern depending on the presence of certain morphological mechanisms; but it is physiologically a development from the primary organismic behavior mechanism, the excitation gradient. Both trial and error reactions and tropisms are integration patterns of the behavior mechanisms present in the organisms concerned and in organisms possessing reflex arcs either trial reaction or tropism may consist of reflexes. The question of the rôle of the reflex are in conscious intelligent behavior of man and the higher animals is outside the limits of this consideration (see the concluding chapters of Herrick, '24).

REGULATION IN ITS HISTORICAL ASPECTS

While regulation is in physiological terms equilibration accomplished in one way or another, from the viewpoint of evolution it is in general adaptive. The protoplasmic constitution which makes possible certain equilibrations favoring maintenance of the system in response to external disturbance is able to survive and persist under conditions which determine the destruction of some other protoplasm that does not possess the same possibilities of equilibration. The latter protoplasm, on the other hand, may be able to undergo equilibration to certain other disturbing conditions which destroy the former. Different protoplasmic constitutions present different possibilities of equilibration and every change in protoplasmic constitution provides new possibilities. The mechanisms of equilibration are the physicochemical changes which make up life in their interactions and interrelations. In the organism all the mechanisms of physiological correlation are concerned. Whatever value we may assign to natural selection with respect to morphological characters, we cannot deny its importance with respect to these mechanisms of equilibration. Its action is inevitable. A protoplasm or organism which cannot equilibrate under certain conditions in such a way as to persist perishes, while one which is able to equilibrate survives. Going one step farther it is evident that in the course of evolution the useless or injurious equilibrations must in the main disappear, since the organisms in which they occur must be more or less rapidly weeded out.

If the conception of the individual organism which has been developed in the preceding chapters and elsewhere (Child, '15 c, '21 a) in some measure approximates the truth, we are forced to the conclusion that evolution is primarily concerned, not with morphological characters, but with these physiological mechanisms of equilibration and integration. In other words, the organism has evolved primarily, not as a morphological structure, but as a behavior mechanism in the broadest sense. The morphological features are secondary products of the behavior mechanism.

Evolution, as suggested at various points in this chapter, has been a process of standardization, of the behavior mechanisms of organisms, and through these behavior mechanisms, of the conditions which they are likely to meet in nature. In this way we attain again the conception of the normal in organisms and the normal in environmental factors. Within the range of these norms the mechanisms of behavior, that is, of equilibration or regulation, are in the main useful or adaptive; they tend toward persistence of the individual or maintenance of the species, or often both. Such adaptation is not dependent upon some mysterious purposive character of the mechanisms of equilibration, but appears to be primarily a matter of selection of protoplasmic constitutions, of action systems with their mechanisms.

It is difficult not to believe that the natural selection of mechanisms of equilibration or regulation is an important factor in evolution but its action does not exclude or conflict with the action of various other factors. Changes in protoplasmic constitution may conceivably occur suddenly as mutations, or gradually as lesser variations. Certain courses of change may be inherent in certain protoplasmic constitutions. A secular senescence (Child, '15 b, pp. 193–4,) or more or less irreversible differentiation may occur in the evolutionary history of a protoplasm, and, as Herrick ('20) has pointed out, may appear as an orthogenesis.

Whatever the factors of evolution, there can be little doubt that it is primarily concerned with mechanisms of equilibration, integration or regulation, in short with behavior mechanisms in the broad sense. Morphological characters are the products or the records in protoplasm of the action of the behavior mechanisms and so are of secondary importance. If this is true the organism, not only in its life as an individual, from the beginning of development on, but in its evolution, is fundamentally a system of behavior mechanisms. Evolution has standardized for every species both these mechanisms and the range of conditions to which they are likely to be exposed. The result is on the one hand what we call the normal in nature and on the other the capacities of the organism for "return to normal," "adjustment of internal relations to external relations," or regulation.

CONCLUSION

This chapter is a consideration of certain aspects of life as a series of equilibrations or regulations. The mechanisms of the living organism are from the beginning on behavior mechanisms, and excito-motor behavior is not something distinct from these mechanisms and superadded at some stage, but it is the outgrowth, the consequence, and for the individual the culmination of organismic integration and the most advanced expression of organismic pattern. The physiological gradient as the primary behavior mechanism of axiate type and the primary factor of axiate pattern and integration constitutes the general physiological foundation on which the axiate behavior patterns are built up. From this viewpoint life is, physiologically speaking, behavior, equilibration, regulation, and evolution is a process of standardization of the behavior mechanisms of protoplasms and of the range of environmental conditions to which they are likely to be subjected.

In an earlier discussion of regulation (Child, '11 f) attention was called to the analogy in certain respects between the living organism and the flowing stream. Both are within a certain range equilibrating systems and in both structure and function are similarly interrelated. The stream like the organism is always approaching equilibrium, but if it attains equilibrium it ceases to flow and is "dead."

From the morphology of its banks and channel we can determine that such a "dead stream" was once a flowing stream, but this morphology is merely the record of its past activity. As the stream flows structural and functional equilibration, in short, regulation, is always taking place and always making the stream different in some way from what it was previously. We cannot, I believe, adequately conceive the living organism except as such a system in which equilibration between the parts and between the whole and its environment is continuously going on and continuously changing the organism. We are forced to believe that the organism is not left absolutely unchanged by anything that has any relation to it. Life is change, modification, progression.

We reach the conclusion then that the organism does not, strictly speaking, represent the maintenence of a certain equilibrium, in spite of external disturbance, but rather a continuous alteration and equilibration in reaction to external factors. It is not a "closed system" maintaining itself against the rest of the world, but a system open at every point and in continuous and necessary relation to environment and the same is true for its parts in their relations with each other. Only through the fact that it is an open system are development and evolution possible. Evolution is a process of standardization of the potentialities of behavior, of regulation, and of its mechanisms and through this means, of the environmental conditions to which the individual is likely to be subjected.

CHAPTER XIV

MODIFIABILITY OF PATTERN IN GENERAL

Even though we accept the conclusion of the preceding chapter that life is a series of modifications of protoplasmic and organismic patterns, it is evident that both in the individual and in evolution different components and features of pattern exhibit different degrees of fixity or modifiability. This is particularly true for excito-motor behavior, but it is also true for development, and for the structural and functional mechanisms of the mature organisms. Moreover, different species show wide differences in modifiability of pattern. In some, even the more fundamental components of pattern may be readily and greatly modified, while in others they are fixed or stable to a high degree. Again the stability of a particular component of pattern may differ widely at different stages of development. It may be readily modifiable at one stage and highly stable at another.

It is evident that our interpretation of fixity and modifiability must depend upon our conception of organismic pattern in general (see particularly Chaps. III, XII, XIII). Preformistic theories, for example, lead us to a conception of a normal pattern, which is predetermined and innate, that is to say inherited, while modifications of that pattern represent effects of individual reactions to environmental factors. From the physiological viewpoint, however, the normal pattern is no more and no less preformed, predetermined, or hereditary than any modifications or abnormal patterns. All organismic patterns are hereditary in that they represent potentialities of a certain protoplasmic constitution. On the other hand, the evidence forces us to the conclusion that all are likewise behavior patterns, that is, their realization is not an autonomous action of a protoplasm, but the reaction of a protoplasm of specific constitution to an environment. If this is true, fixity and modifiability of pattern are to be interpreted physiologically, not in terms of a predetermined normal and departures from it, but rather in terms of the physicochemical constitution of each particular protoplasm and the effects of external factors upon it. The normal in any field of biology represents merely a certain range of pattern among the potentialities of the protoplasmic system, and its significance is not physiological but evolutionary. Physiologically it represents merely the realization of certain possibilities of the system in relation to certain conditions, but from the evolutionary viewpoint it represents a standardization of both the protoplasmic system and the conditions to which it is subjected (Chap. XIII).

Moreover, a distinction is to be made between the modifiability of pattern in organisms through the direct action of external factors and the modifiability through internal factors, changes in physiological state (Jennings). In the case of excito-motor behavior modifiability through changes in external factors is so obvious and characteristic that it is commonly taken for granted and the student of animal behavior is chiefly concerned with modifiability in its relation to internal physiological conditions or physiological states. Physiological states do not, however, arise or change autonomously so far as we know, but in the final analysis are related to external factors. To the "behaviorist" the point of chief interest is of course the modifiability of behavior by experience, the ability of the organism to learn, and it is evident that such learning can occur only when some sort of record or effect of a previous reaction to an external factor persists in the protoplasm (Herrick, '24, Chap. XX).

MODIFIABILITY OF DEVELOPMENTAL PATTERN

Development as modification— The development of the individual is itself a series of modifications of pattern (see Chap. XIII). Moreover, if the physiological conception of organismic pattern is correct, protoplasm does not give rise autonomously to such pattern, but only as it is modified by external factors. According to the conception of the physiological gradient, organismic pattern originates in the local or differential alteration in rate of the fundamental physiological activities of protoplasm by some external factor. Such alteration amounts essentially to local or differential excitation or inhibition. This of course constitutes a modification of the preëxisting pattern, and if this modification persists, it becomes the basis of a physiological axis and of the developmental changes occurring in relation to that axis. New gradients arising in particular regions during the course of development initiate new series of modifications and the appearance of local qualitative differences affords a basis for chemical or transportative correlation and so for further modifications. In fact, this process of development of an individual from an egg, a spore, an isolated piece, or any other reproductive element, involves a modifiability so great that many biologists are still not quite able to accept the evidence of their senses, even when reinforced by the experimental method. They find it necessary or desirable to postulate at least the rudiments of the pattern as a property of the germ plasm, but they either ignore the problem of the origin of this primary pattern or offer only speculative solutions of it. Physiologically considered, the development of individual pattern is the realization of new patterns out of the potentialities of preëxisting patterns through behavior. In the development of the social institution which we call a state new patterns, new mechanisms, which existed only as potentialities of the system, *i. e.*, as ideas, or possible ideas in the minds of men, become real working patterns and mechanisms. We are accustomed to say that the human mind has "created" these new patterns and mechanisms. In the development of organisms an essentially similar "creation" occurs and there is no reason so far to believe that Driesch's entelechy or Bergson's *élan vital* is any more necessary for such creation than for the creation of a new chemical compound out of the reacting substances, or for the creation of the features involved in the development and differentiation of a flowing stream and its banks and bed.

Under the usual standardized range of conditions the order and course of the modifications constituting development are relatively constant in each particular protoplasm and from this fact the idea has arisen of the normal in development as something fixed or predetermined, at least to a relatively high degree (pp. 215–219). From this viewpoint, modifiability represents the capacity of the organism to depart from this fixed or predetermined course of events in reaction to external factors. The normal may include a certain range of modifiability, but beyond this, modifiability leads to "abnormal" results. In the preceding chapter I attempted to show that the real significance of the normal in biology is not physiological but historical or evolutionary. Physiologically normal and abnormal represent merely different degrees or ranges of modification and may be determined by different energies, intensities, or periods of action of the same factor.

Changes in modifiability with progress of development. — When we examine modifiability or developmental pattern more closely we see that it is apparently related in certain ways to stage of development of the individual and of evolution of the species or group. These relations may be briefly stated as follows: modifiability of the morphological pattern and of the special functional expression of each structural mechanism decreases in general with the progress of development and of evolution. By this statement we mean merely

that the range of external conditions under which these features of
pattern persist, increases during development and evolution. If
development and evolution are equilibrations following disturbances,
this progressive stabilization of pattern is to be expected. Specifically
it must result from physical and chemical changes which are irreversible or only in part reversible under ordinary conditions. The accumulation of relatively stable molecules provides a more or less permanent structural basis for functional stability, and functional stability tends in its turn still further to increase structural stability.
Considering, for example, the primary factor of axiate pattern, the
"polar" gradient, we see that a simple organism like *Amœba* may
acquire such a gradient or axis temporarily as a result of an external
differential (pp. 57–59), but the nature of the *Amœba* protoplasm
is such that the gradient disappears soon after the external factor
ceases to act. In the egg of *Fucus*, however, differential exposure
to light for a few hours determines a gradient which becomes the
basis of the axiate pattern of the plant (pp. 58–61). Similarly in
the hydroids we see gradients determined by external differentials
persisting after the external factor has ceased to act and becoming a
permanent or relatively permanent basis of pattern (pp. 115–123).
Even in the fully developed hydroid, however, the stability of this
fundamental factor in the pattern, viz., polarity, is not very great,
i. e., is dependent on a relatively narrow range of conditions. Old
gradients may be obliterated and new gradients, and so new polarities,
may be experimentally determined in various ways (pp. 119, 123). In
Planaria, where a greater degree of differentiation has occurred in
relation to the axial gradients, with a nervous system of well-defined
axiate pattern as its primary characteristic, the experimental obliteration of preëxisting axial gradients and the establishment of new
gradients requires much more extreme conditions. In many of the
higher animals we are able at present to obliterate the major axial
gradients and determine new ones only in the earlier stages of development or not at all.

Again, the experimental alteration of slope of the axial gradient
through differential susceptibility and the resulting alterations of
form are brought about by less extreme conditions in the earlier stages
of development and in the simpler organisms than in later stages and
more highly differentiated forms (pp. 101–109). In the sea urchin, for
example, a certain degree of differential inhibition applied during the
early stages may greatly reduce or obliterate polarity as well as bilaterality, while the same degree of inhibition at a later stage may reduce

or obliterate bilaterality while polarity still persists (Child, '16 d), and at still later stages may have but little effect on either polarity or bilaterality.

As regards form-regulation, the reconstitution of individuals from isolated pieces, the regeneration of appendages, organs or tissues, we find in general that the simpler organisms are more capable of modifications along this line than the more highly specialized. In many plants every cell or almost every cell is capable of giving rise to a new individual. Among sponges and hydroids very small fragments are capable of forming complete new individuals (H. V. Wilson, '07, '11 b). Among the Turbellaria limitations in this reconstitutional capacity occur. In some species, e. g. *Planaria*, some cells at all levels of the body are sufficiently modifiable to give rise either to a head or a posterior end according as they lie at the anterior or posterior end of an isolated piece. In other forms such as *Dendrocœlum* (F. R. Lillie, '01) only the cells of the more anterior body levels are able to develop new heads, and in most of the rhabdocœls and the polyclads levels posterior to, or more than a very short distance posterior to the cephalic ganglia do not give rise to new heads, but all levels are capable of giving rise to posterior parts. Among the aquatic oligochetes a very similar antero-posterior decrease in modifiability of pattern in the regulation of pieces occurs (Hyman, '16 a). In the later stages of development of the arthropods and vertebrates no cells of any level of the body are able under any known conditions to give rise to a new head, though appendages and various minor parts are regenerated in arthropods and the lower vertebrates, and tissue regeneration occurs even in the mammals and man.

Similarly the range and frequency of "abnormal" forms in form regulation are much greater in the simpler than in the more complex animals. With the determination of new gradients the occurrence of biaxial and multiaxial forms ("axial heteromorphosis") is readily controlled experimentally in the hydroids (pp. 116–118). Among the flatworms and oligochetes biaxial forms are of less general occurrence and in other groups can be produced only in the earlier stages of development if at all. In the adult *Planaria* a series of different degrees of differential inhibition of head-development can be determined experimentally in a great variety of ways (Child, '21 c). In fishes and amphibia somewhat similar modifications can be experimentally determined in early developmental stages, but not later (Stockard, '07, '09, '10, '11, '21; Bellamy, '19).

So-called self-differentiation and mosaic development. — Many of the special problems of the physiology of development are simply different aspects of this general problem of modifiability of pattern. The apparent self-differentiation (Roux) or independence of certain parts, the correlative differentiation or dependence of others, the "mosaic" character of the early developmental stages of the annelids and mollusks and certain other forms (pp. 146, 244) and the plasticity of the early stages of echinoderms, medusæ, etc., all represent widely different degrees of modifiability either of different parts of the same embryo or of different species.

In the discussion of mosaic development in Chapter X, it was pointed out that development is not always a mosaic of independent or self-differentiating parts, as the earlier preformistic theories assumed, but that very different degrees of independence or dependence of parts appear, according to species, stage of development and region of body. According to the theory of qualitative nuclear division which postulated the distribution of different determinants or other hereditary entities to different nuclei in early development, development must always be a mosaic. As the advance of knowledge forced the abandonment of this theory, the theory of "formative substances" definitely localized in the cytoplasm and distributed to different cells took its place. But the attempts to interpret mosaic development in terms of such "formative substances" localized in different regions of the egg was practically abandoned when it was shown that the localization and distribution of the supposed formative substances might be very greatly altered without altering polarity or the course of development and differentiation (F. R. Lillie, '08). These facts made it clear that at least many of the supposed formative substances were first of all the products rather than causes of differentiation and that we must account for their presence rather than use them to account for development.

In general the facts show that the stability of organismic pattern in the egg at the beginning of embryonic development differs widely, not only in different species but as regards different regions of the body. While we know practically nothing as yet concerning the physico-chemical basis of this stability in any particular case, its relations with the physiological gradients are evident (Chap. X). In some protoplasms, e. g., annelids and mollusks, the gradients determine a relatively stable pattern before cleavage begins, while in others, such as the sea urchin egg, the changes brought about by the presence of a gradient or gradients are much less stable and may even be completely obliterated experimentally (pp. 104–107). In general, also, so-called self-differentiation and correlative differentiation are expressions of conditions existing at different levels of a physiological gradient. The high end of a gradient, the dominant region, is the most nearly self-differentiating, or independent of any body level (see Chap. X, also Child, '21 a, Chap. VII) and the degree of dependence increases as we go down the gradient.

According to this view "mosaic" development and "self-differentiation" are merely consequences of stability or fixity of certain features of organismic pattern in eggs and early developmental stages of certain forms. It makes little difference whether we say that the annelid egg has developed a greater degree of specialization than the sea urchin egg along the gradient at the beginning of embryonic development, or that the constitution of the annelid protoplasm determines that the differences at different levels of the gradient when once established are much less readily reversible than in the sea urchin egg.

As long as development proceeds without extensive alteration of gradients and patterns the differentiation of different parts becomes in general increasingly independent or mosaic-like, but in the annelid the apparent mosaic character of early stages concerns the larval rather than the adult organs, and disappears more or less completely with metamorphosis and the development of the trunk region.

DEVELOPMENTAL MODIFIABILITY IN RELATION TO PHYSIOLOGICAL GRADIENTS AND OTHER FACTORS

It has long been recognized by students of evolution that in general characteristics of early phylogenetic origin are less modifiable than those of later origin. Similarly, in the development of the individual, it is evident that under the usual range of conditions, the larger more general features of organismic pattern which appear earlier in development are less modifiable than the details of pattern which appear later, and polarity and symmetry, the most general features of organismic pattern are the most stable of all. If we are able to modify polarity and symmetry we modify the whole pattern of the organism (Chaps. VIII, IX). As regards the individual, these differences in modifiability are expressions of the fact that the primary physiological gradients once established, are the most stable, the least modifiable features of organismic pattern, because such gradients are the record in protoplasm of the most generalized form of reaction which underlies all other organismic behavior. Only in so far as the primary gradients persist in a protoplasm is any further development of organismic pattern possible. Returning again to *Amœba* and *Fucus* (pp. 57–61), we see that in *Amœba* each pseudopod is for the time being a gradient, or the whole body may become temporarily axiate, but the gradients constituting such patterns are completely reversible and therefore do not become the starting point of differentiation. In *Fucus*, on the other hand, the gradient determined by the illumination differential persists and constitutes the basis of the whole axiate pattern of the plant.

Going one step further, it is also true in general that the fixity or modifiability of the other components of organismic pattern depends upon their relation to the primary gradients. The more general features of pattern more directly and closely related to the general axial gradients are more stable than the minor features, appearing at later stages and representing more remote relations to the primary gradients. For example, the localization, course of development and general pattern of the central nervous system, all of which are very closely related to the primary gradients (Child, '21 a) are much more stable features of pattern than the relations between different reflex arcs and neuron paths. Even in man these latter vary widely as regards different individuals and are highly modifiable. Again, the bilateral arrangement of appendages on the body is less readily modifiable than the structure and symmetry of the single appendge.

In animals we also find that the components of pattern which represent higher levels of a gradient are less readily modifiable into those representing low levels than the reverse. In *Planaria*, for example, it has never been possible to transform a head into any other region of the body, but any other level may transform into a head. Somewhat similar relations exist in other animals in which isolated pieces from the lower levels give rise to new complete individuals, *e. g.*, hydroids, many flatworms and annelids.

These examples serve to illustrate what appears to be a fact of very general, if not of universal significance in the development of organismic pattern, viz., that there is a relation between the stability of the components of organismic pattern and the metabolic rate of the region or developmental stage in which they arise. In general those pattern components determined in the earlier stages of development and at the higher levels of a gradient are more stable than those determined at later stages and lower levels. The rate of metabolism is in general higher in earlier stages of development from the beginning of morphogenesis on, than in later stages (Child, '15 b) and is also higher at higher levels of the gradient than at lower. In many organisms there are regressive stages in development, as in the atrophy and loss of larval organs in nemerteans, echinoderms, polychetes, insects, etc. In such cases previously existing gradients may disappear and be replaced by others and under the altered conditions the stability of pattern of the earlier stages may also disappear and new relations of stability be built up with the new gradients. Evidently the stability of any pattern component, structural or functional, can persist only so long as the more general components of pattern on which its existence depends are stable.

In a particular environment a certain organismic pattern may appear highly stable, but experimental changes in environment may show that even its most general features are readily modifiable by many factors. This is strikingly true in the case of the sea urchin. The normal pluteus presents a very definite, highly constant pattern, but through experimental conditions affecting the height, slope, etc., of the gradients, this pattern is modifiable to such an extent that if we did not know the origin of the forms thus produced, we should never recognize them as belonging to the same species, or in the more extreme cases, to the same class, or perhaps even the same phylum as the normal larvæ (Child, '16 d, also pp. 83, 84 ,106).

If we consider the development of the individual as a dynamic equilibration (Chap. XIII), we see that modifiability of organismic pattern follows in general the same laws as modifiability of pattern in other dynamic systems. In the flowing stream the more general, larger features of pattern are more stable than the details and the morphological features determined at a high rate of flow are more stable than those determined at a low rate of flow. Whatever future investigation may teach us concerning the particular physical and chemical conditions concerned in the development of the organism, its similarity in many respects to non-living dynamic systems is, I believe, highly significant.

When we turn to phylogeny we find, in so far as we can analyze the evidence, that the same general laws hold as for the individual. As I have suggested in earlier publications (Child, '11 f, '15 b, pp. 266–270), evolution, as well as individual development, appears to be an equilibration process, that is, the course of evolution has been in general a progressive fixation or stabilization of mechanisms composing organismic pattern. We do not know whether the rate of metabolism has undergone a general decrease during evolution, as it does during individual development and senescence, but if the "biogenetic law" that ontogeny repeats phylogeny means anything, it must mean that individual development and evolution represent changes in protoplasm which are similar in general character and course, but of very different period. If the individual organism represents the behavior of a particular cell or cell mass in a particular environment, evolution represents the behavior of protoplasm in general in environment in general, or more specifically, the behavior of the primordium or substratum which we call in abstract terms the "germ plasm," and on which the pattern of the individual organism is superimposed. There is in fact some ground for the assertion that the pattern of the individual organism represents primarily, or in large measure, the behavior pattern of the cytoplasm, and the evolutionary pattern primarily the behavior pattern of the nucleus. To conceive evolution as behavior and the patterns of the various phyla, classes, etc., as behavior patterns, does not by any means require the adoption of Lamarckian views. The behavior of the "germ plasm" in relation to its environment rather than the behavior of each individual organism may be the significant factor in evolution.

DEVELOPMENT, MEMORY AND LEARNING BY EXPERIENCE

At the beginning of this chapter it was noted that to the student of animal behavior modifiability usually means the possibility of alteration of behavior under identical external conditions through changes in physiological condition or state of the organism. Modification in this sense, i. e., learning by experience, occurs when traces, records, or effects of a previous reaction are more or less irreversible and persist after the external factor determining them has ceased to act and so become factors in altering the course of subsequent reactions.

The biologist ordinarily thinks of development as something very different from such modification of behavior by experience, but from time to time the idea that the basis of heredity and development is fundamentally similar to memory has been advanced. More than forty years ago Hering ('76), in his highly suggestive paper "On Memory as a General Function of Organized Substance" advanced this idea in general form. Later Semon ('04 and later works) developed the idea in great detail, but in Lamarckian terms. Various other suggestions along the same line have also been made. Manifestly this mnemic conception of heredity is not necessarily Lamarckian. Even if heredity is protoplasmic memory, it is not necessarily memory of the characteristics acquired by the parent individual or earlier ancestors, but may be merely memory of the reactions of the germ plasm to its environment.

The present purpose is to call attention briefly to certain physiological features of individual development as they appear from a non-Lamarckian mnemic viewpoint. If the physiological axial gradient originates primarily as a reaction to an external differential, its persistence after the external differential has ceased to act, makes it a factor in modifying all subsequent reactions of the individual. What else is the gradient determined by light in the *Fucus* egg than a physiological memory of the differential exposure to light? And is it not true in a general physiological sense that through the experience of differential exposure to light the organism of *Fucus* learns to behave as an axiate organism? *Amœba*, on the other hand, may also learn to behave in an axiate manner (Figs. 13, 14), but here the protoplasmic memory is short and the axiate pattern usually persists only a short time.

Not only the primary axial gradients, but their later alterations and the new gradients of parts, organs or cells, may also be regarded as protoplasmic memories of environmental differentials of some sort. Viewed in this way the whole course of development is a process of physiological learning, beginning with the simple experience of differential exposure to an external factor, and undergoing one modification after another, as new experiences in the life of the organism or of its parts in relation to each other occur. Memory and learning in the narrower, psychological sense represent that part of the general developmental learning process which concerns the minute pattern of certain regions of the nervous system in advanced stages of development, particularly in the higher animals. There is no evidence of any fundamental physiological difference between the general protoplasmic memory as expressed in physiological gradients and their effects and the higher forms of memory characteristic of the central nervous system.

To sum up: the development of the individual may be regarded as the expression of a general protoplasmic memory, and experiment shows us that developmental behavior is modifiable by experience. Such modification or learning is going on at all times from the differential exposure which determines the primary axial gradient, to the end of life. To the objection that interpretation of a series of phenomena such as development in terms of a less known series serves no useful purpose, it may be replied that, although we know more in certain respects about individual development than about memory in the strict sense, yet in certain other respects we know more about memory than we do about development. To interpret development in terms of memory and learning is simply to identify certain characteristics of development with certain characteristics of memory and learning, and such identification is one step in a process of synthesis.

CHAPTER XV

MODIFIABILITY OF EXCITO–MOTOR BEHAVIOR IN RELATION TO GENERAL ORGANISMIC PATTERN

If we accept the viewpoint of preceding chapters that organismic pattern is a behavior pattern from the beginning, it is evident that the behavior of an organism in the narrower sense, as comprising fundamentally the excito-motor and closely related reactions, constitutes the most highly integrated, the most highly regulatory and in general the most highly reversible expressions of the pattern in relation to environmental factors. Some fifteen years ago Jennings ('06) suggested that the laws of this behavior are the same as those governing the other aspects of life, and the present book is in large measure an attempt to show that the experimental investigation of recent years supports and confirms this conclusion.[1]

EXCITO-MOTOR BEHAVIOR AS THE HIGHEST DEGREE OF ORGANISMIC INTEGRATION

All processes of equilibration or regulation are expressions of the integrative aspects of pattern, that is, of the correlative factors which make the organism physiologically a whole. But in excito-motor behavior the integrative aspects appear more clearly than in any other activity of life. Nowhere is the wholeness of the organism so conspicuous as in this field. The relative fixity or modifiability of such behavior must therefore depend in larger measure upon the fixity or modifiability of the integrative mechanisms of organismic pattern than upon any other feature of pattern. Moreover, the dynamic integrative or correlative mechanisms are much more important in this behavior than the transportative mechanisms (see Chap. V). Of the dynamic mechanisms, those of excitation and transmission are the most effective means of integration.

Modification of excito-motor behavior must mean change of some sort, either temporary or permanent, in the integration pattern and particularly in the integration of excitation and transmission. Such change may be determined in various ways, not only by preceding

[1] See also Herrick's discussion of modifiability of behavior from the neurological viewpoint; Herrick, '24, Chaps. XIX, XX.

excitation-transmission patterns, but also by change in the chemical or transportative factors of correlation, e. g., in amount or character of the internal secretion of the thyroid, the gonads, etc., by the complex changes associated with the satisfaction of hunger by food, or of thirst by water, by fatigue, bacterial intoxication and many other conditions. Even in such cases, however, the mechanisms of excitation and transmission are involved, for it is the effect of the chemical changes on these mechanisms which brings about the modification of excito-motor behavior. Frequently also, the chemical change is the result of a preceding modification of the excitation-transmission pattern. For example, the sight or smell of food determines a modification of behavior, viz., feeding, and fatigue is the result of other preceding modifications, usually in large part excito-motor. With the progress of differentiation and the increase in complexity of the organism, both in individual development and in evolution, the possibilities of physiological correlation increase and with such increase the possibilities of modification of correlative factors become greater, even though the general morphological and functional pattern of the organism is relatively very stable. Because of the physiological character and rôle of excitation and transmission in organisms, the possibilities of modification are greater for these than for any other correlative factors and, the higher the development of the nervous system, the greater these possibilities. From these facts it is evident that at least certain features of organismic behavior pattern may become more varied, more plastic and more modifiable, both in the course of individual development and of evolution, even though the general structural and functional pattern becomes at the same time more and more stable.

MODIFIABILITY AND GENERAL ORGANISMIC PATTERN

Students of behavior, particularly of animal behavior, have usually drawn a more or less sharp distinction between fixed and modifiable forms or patterns of behavior in the individual organism. This distinction is useful but somewhat arbitrary, since all degrees of fixity and modifiability of behavior exist and these characteristics also depend upon various conditions. The fixed type is often said to be innate or inherited. This does not mean that the behavior pattern itself persists through reproduction, but merely that it represents a potentiality of the protoplasmic constitution which under normal conditions (see Chap. XIII) is always realized as a feature of the organismic pattern. All the modifications of behavior in the individual are just as truly potentialities of the protoplasmic action system, *i. e.*, just as truly hereditary, as the fixed behavior patterns, but they are not realized in all individuals of the species. For the realization of a particular modification, the coincidence of a particular physiological state and a particular complex of environmental factors is necessary, and the degree of specificity of the physiological state and of the environmental complex differs widely, both as regards different organisms and different reactions in the same organism. In *Amœba* and *Paramœcium*, for example, certain modifications of behavior occur whenever an exciting factor acts for a certain length of time. Similarly, in man certain modifications of behavior appear under almost any sufficiently intense or long continued excitation. In *Amœba* and *Paramœcium*, however, the modifications of behavior are very few and simple and general in character, *i. e.*, essentially the same for a wide range of environmental complexes, while in man modifiability is practically unlimited. Some modifications of behavior in man are features of daily life, but others may be realized only once in a lifetime or only once in many generations.

In the preceding chapter it was noted that fixity and modifiability of the developmental and morphological aspects of organismic pattern depend upon their relation to the fundamental factors of the pattern. The more general, more primitive features of pattern, those which are more directly related to the primary gradients, are the more fixed and stable, while the details, the features of later origin, are more modifiable. If it is true that excito-motor behavior is merely the most conspicuous and highly integrated expression of organismic pattern and that the same laws hold for it as for the other features of this pattern, we must expect to find a similar relation between fixity and modifiability of excito-motor mechanisms and components and the fundamental or primary factors of pattern. That is to say, the mechanisms of the more firmly fixed or stable behavior patterns must be more closely or directly associated with the primary factors of organismic pattern, the physiological gradients, than the mechanisms of the more highly modifiable patterns.

In one sense the mechanisms of excito-motor behavior might be said to comprise all the mechanisms of the body, but the special mechanism of such behavior is transmissive correlation. In the development and evolution of the organism, we see transmissive correlation first becoming more or less fixed as physiological gradients, then undergoing further structural fixation with the origin of the nervous system. In the higher animals and man the individual nervous mechanisms, the neurons, the reflex arcs, possess a high degree of fixity both morphologically and physiologically, and modifiability is a matter of the integration or linking up of particular mechanisms into a particular excitation-transmission pattern. The complexity of nervous structure, the specialization of excitatory and transmissive processes, the significance of physiological condition of the synapse or of other parts of the neuron in determining the course of transmission, all make possible an increase in the modifiability of excito-motor patterns, with an increasing morphological fixity of the mechanisms concerned (Herrick, '24, Chaps. XVIII, XIX). In fact the excito-motor patterns of the higher animals and man are physiologically less dependent upon the fundamental factors of organismic pattern than any other feature of the individual. That this is true will appear more clearly in the following sections.

MODIFIABILITY AND THE PRIMITIVE MECHANISMS OF EXCITATION AND TRANSMISSION

The mechanisms of excitation and transmission, with which we are primarily concerned in the behavior of the organism as a whole, appear in various forms. The simplest and most primitive is apparently the excitation-transmission gradient in protoplasm (see Chap. XI). This in its simplest form is temporary and evanescent: it may arise at any point in relation to local or differential excitation and may soon disappear and be replaced by another. In an organism with gradient patterns of this temporary and shifting character the gradients themselves, the fundamental factors of axiate pattern, are directly concerned in the modifications of behavior.

In the case of *Amœba*, for example, motor behavior is a direct expression of physiological gradients. Each pseudopod is for the time being such a gradient (Hyman, '17) and in those cases in which the whole body is temporarily a single gradient, the *Amœba* is temporarily an axiate animal (pp. 57–59). We do not hesitate to call these different patterns of *Amœba* behavior patterns, but the gradients of the pseudopods or of the whole body differ from the physiological axes of axiate animals only in their instability. The motor behavior pattern of *Amœba* is in fact a gradient pattern and all modifications of motor behavior, *e. g.*, localization and development or reduction and disappearance of single pseudopods, as well as the initiation, change in direction, or cessation of directed locomotion of the whole animal represent modifications of the gradient pattern.

Actually *Amœba* constitutes a direct demonstration of the fundamental identity of axiate pattern and behavior pattern. Axiate pattern in *Amœba* is a behavior pattern in the strict sense, arising in response to the differential action of external factors, and rapidly reversible. Conversely the behavior of *Amœba* always involves the development, persistence or disappearance of axiate pattern, and the only modifications of behavior possible are made up of modifications in the localization, length, steepness and persistence of the gradients.

The development of a persistent axial gradient, a physiological polarity and symmetry, even in the absence of a definite nervous system, determines a relation of dominance and subordination (Chaps. X, XII), and the organism behaves primarily as an axiate organism, although surface-interior pattern may still play a part even in axiate organisms, in determining behavior. As long as axial gradients persist they constitute a relatively stable basis for behavior and we find that the most firmly fixed elements or types of behavior pattern are very directly associated with such gradients. For example, the precedence of the apical end or head in locomotion is a direct expression of an axial gradient. It has been determined experimentally that when the apico-basal gradient is obliterated through differential susceptibility, *e. g.*, in the sea urchin blastulæ (Child, '16 d), or in hydroid planulæ (see pp. 83, 106), definite orientation of the body is no longer possible. Under such experimental conditions the fundamental mechanism or pattern on which this highly stable feature of axiate behavior, viz., precedence of the apical end, depends, has been destroyed. Similarly, the integration or coördination of bilateral or radial organs is very closely associated with the axial gradients and disappears when they are obliterated.

In axiate organisms modifications of behavior occur in general with reference to the axiate pattern, that is, they are modifications of axiate behavior. To take a few simple illustrations, local excitation of some part may affect the speed of definitely directed locomotion, *e. g.*, in a creeping earthworm. Unequal excitation of the two sides of the body may partially or wholly obliterate for the moment the symmetry pattern and induce asymmetric behavior as in the case of a tropistic orientation according to Loeb (see pp. 230–231). Again, in the quiescent condition basal or posterior regions of the body may be for the time being more or less physiologically isolated and show a greater or less degree of independence, while excitation of the dominant region may bring them under control. Such relations appear in various flatworms and oligochetes (see pp. 153–156).

MODIFIABILITY IN RELATION TO DIFFERENTIATION OF THE
NERVOUS SYSTEM

With the development of the nervous system in animals the axiate character of the behavior pattern becomes in general still more stable. The very close physiological relations between the central nervous system and the axial gradients have been considered elsewhere (Child, '21 a). Reflex arcs arise with definite, functionally irreversible paths, all related in some definite way to the fundamental axiate pattern and there are many facts which indicate that a physiological gradient is the foundation on which each reflex arc develops (Child, '21 a, Chap. XIII). Evidently the actual development of a reflex arc is possible only when the gradient is to a certain degree fixed and stable. In fact, the single reflex arc, so far as such a thing exists, is to a high degree fixed and stereotyped in structure and function because it is an expression of the more general and more stable factors in organismic pattern and particularly in the pattern of the nervous system (Herrick, '24, Chaps. VIII, IX, XVII).

In the actual behavior of organisms, however, reflex arcs do not function singly and separately, but there is always some degree of integration, and it is in this integration of reflex arcs that the modifiability chiefly appears. From the appearence of the nervous system on through evolution and development the modifiability of behavior depends primarily upon the integration pattern in the nervous system and the changes of which it is capable. The structure of the neuron, its sensitiveness and delicacy of reaction during development to certain factors in its environment, perhaps electrical (Child, '21 a, Chap. XI), the alterations in physiological state of the synapse and doubtless also of dendrites and other portions of the cell body, and perhaps of axons, provide a basis for almost infinite complexity, variety and modifiability of excito-motor behavior.

Certain features of nervous function and structure are not only of fundamental importance for the modifiability of behavior in the higher animals and man, but are of very great interest, both from the physiological and the historical viewpoint. The invertebrate nervous system, even in its highest development in the insects, does not permit any very high degree of modifiability of behavior, and we must interpret the fixity of behavior in these forms as meaning that, even in their minuter details, nervous structure and functional correlation are determined with a high degree of fixity in individual development in relation to the general pattern of the species, *i. e.*, in the final analysis the physiological gradients and their modifications in that particular protoplasm. (Herrick, '24, Chap. XI). In the invertebrate the axiate pattern appears to be predominant throughout the nervous system and the behavior therefore consists of relatively rigid reflexes and reflex complexes.

In the course of vertebrate evolution, however, a new factor in behavior makes its appearance (Herrick, '24, Chapters XVII–XXI). A portion of the central nervous system becomes, so to speak, emancipated, or physiologically isolated to a greater or less degree, from the relatively rigid determining action of the general axial gradients in the body. This portion is, or becomes the cerebral cortex. In the arrangement of its neurons the cortex shows predominantly a surface-interior pattern with only slight and very general axiate features. The consequence of this pattern is that structural and functional relations are physiologically determined to a large extent by local factors which vary from moment to moment. Histological investigation has shown that the morphological connections of one region of the cortex with others are exceedingly complex and not the more or less uniformly directed connections characteristic of axiate pattern.

The cortex seems, in fact, to be to some extent what we may call a superaxiate region. It arises from the higher levels of the chief body gradient, i. e., broadly speaking, from the dominant region of the individual, and as it is superaxiate in position and structure, so it is superdominant in function. Judging from behavior, the relations of dominance and subordination within the cortex are not definite and fixed, but shift from moment to moment, according to the impulses coming in and the physiological state of the various cells.

According to this view, the cortex really represents a new form or phase of organismic integration. The gradient pattern is fundamentally an autocratic pattern. The dominant region controls other regions but is relatively independent of them. In the higher vertebrates, however, the development of excitation and transmission in the nervous system have made it possible for the lower levels of a gradient to affect the dominant region and the origin and development of the cortex are undoubtedly associated in some way with this situation. The cortex functions as a deliberative assembly, a parliament in a representative form of goverment. That is to say, the efferent impulses finally emerging from it are determined, not simply by its immediate relations to environment, as in the dominant region of a physiological gradient, but rather by the sum total of afferent impulses reaching it from lower centers and through these from all parts of the body, and by its own physiological state as determined by past activities and their records in the cells as functional alteration, memory, etc. (*cf.* Herrick, '24 at the end of Chap. XVII).

We may say then that in the higher vertebrates the gradient pattern of organization is undergoing modification from the autocratic form of dominance or control characteristic of the simple gradient toward the democratic form with representative government, with all its plasticity, modifiability and uncertainty of result in any particular case (see Chap. XVII). In this development of the cortex as a super-axiate pattern with an inconceivable number of individual neuron axes, but only slightly developed general axiation, lies the physiological and morphological foundation of the modifiability of excito-motor behavior in the higher vertebrates and man. The physiological problem of the origin of the cortex has been touched upon elsewhere (Child, '21 a, pp. 261–7), and since at present nothing more than speculation along these lines is possible, no further discussion is necessary here.

MODIFIABILITY IN RELATION TO PHYSIOLOGICAL STATE

Thus far we have been concerned chiefly with the mechanisms and components of behavior of excito-motor character, rather than with the integrated behavior of the organism as a whole. Any particular type of reaction of an organism to an external factor involves the integration of various mechanisms, and the character of the reaction as a whole depends on the integration pattern in each particular case. The question is, then, to what extent and how is the integration pattern of the various forms or types of behavior modifiable? That this pattern is modifiable through differences in the direct action of external factors is demonstrated by universal everyday experience. The excito-motor pattern determined by the sight of food in a hungry dog is different from that determined by the sight of his master or of a stranger. The behaviorist usually takes such modifiability for granted and concerns himself more particularly with modifiability of the behavior pattern through internal changes without change in the external factor.

When, for example, an individual organism changes its reaction to an external factor acting continuously without change, or when the separate reactions to interrupted or repeated identical actions of an external factor differ, or finally, when different individuals of the same species behave differently with respect to the same external factor, we say that the behavior is modifiable. Such modifiability evidently depends primarily upon changes in what Jennings has called the physiological state of the organism. The occurrence of modification of behavior in this way in man and the higher animals has long been a familiar fact, and the studies of Jennings and others have made it clear that in the simpler forms, even in the protozoa, some degree of such modifiability exists.[1] At present, however, we are primarily concerned, not with a general discussion, but rather with the question of the relation of this sort of modifiability and of physiological state on which it depends, to organismic pattern in general.

Physiological state.— Physiological state represents the sum total of the physiological factors which determine the excito-motor integration pattern at any particular moment. As Jennings has pointed out, many factors may be concerned in determining physiological state. Among such factors, for example, the persistent effects of previous reactions, such as altered· irritability, morphological alteration in pattern, memory, etc., the effect of different excitations occurring simultaneously, metabolic condition as determined by nutrition, respiratory, endocrine and other factors, physiological age and other periodicities, in short all factors, external or internal, which affect the organism.

In the simpler organisms the range of changes in physiological state is relatively narrow, because the instability, *i. e.*, the high degree of reversibility of the protoplasmic substratum permits only a relatively slight chemical and morphological differentiation representing the more general and constant factors in developmental behavior. Both transportative and dynamic correlation must remain simple in such organisms, and the transitory excito-motor reactions leave little or no persistent effect or record upon the protoplasm, or one which is soon obliterated by the reversal of the changes determining it. Memory in such organisms is, in short, a generalized protoplasmic function and but slightly developed. The excito-motor behavior of these organisms must of necessity be relatively simple and stereotyped in character, though, as will appear below, a certain degree of modifiability of behavior in relation to physiological state is possible, even in such forms.

As chemical and structural differentiation become more stable and general organismic pattern therefore becomes more complex, the possibilities of modification of physiological state increase. Particularly with respect to the nervous system is this the case. The mor-

[1] See for example Jennings, '06, particularly Chaps. X–XII, XVI–XVIII, and numerous references there given; also later works on animal behavior.

phological pattern of the nervous system, from the general anatomi-
cal features down to the hypothetical structural substratum of
memory, constitutes the most stable and least reversible structure
in the body. At the same time, the large number of neurons, the
branching of dentrite and axon, making possible great complexity of
relation between neurons, the relations of nervous organs to environment and to other organs, the complexity of the processes of excitation and transmission, their sensitiveness to mechanical, thermal,
chemical and electrical factors, all these, as well as chemical correlative factors, hormones, products of metabolism of the organism, of
bacteria, etc., play parts in determining that physiological state in the
nervous system is more labile than in any other organ. For similar
reasons physiological state in the cerebral cortex is more labile than
in any other part of the nervous system.

Summing up, we may say that physiological state at any given moment represents the process or stage of regulation or equilibration or
"adjustment of internal relations to external relations" which is occurring at that particular moment. It is, in fact, nothing else than life in a
particular individual at a particular time. If this is true, excito-
motor behavior, as the most highly integrated expression of organismic
pattern, is the most adequate and complete expression of the process
of living in a protoplasm. As regards this point, this general physiological conception leads us to the same conclusions as our observations
of, and relations with our fellow-men and animals.

Trial and error behavior. — Modifiability of physiological state
is an essential factor in trial and error behavior. It is the modification
of physiological state that determines the successive changes in reaction from which selection is made. According to Jennings, the changes
in physiological state result from the continuance of the disturbance
and must go on until some reaction determined by them brings relief,
or until the disturbing factor ceases to act. The trial form of behavior
occurs when the pattern of the organism does not include any behavior mechanism which gives directly an effective reaction in the
special case in question. As expressions of modifications of physiological state the successive changes in reaction really represent changes
in the integration pattern and the successful trial constitutes the
effective integration. It is often possible to observe the progressive
development of the new integration. In the anaxiate *Amœba*, for
example, the reaction to an external factor may consist first in the
formation of several pseudopodia, often in various directions, but
with continuation of the external action the animal may develop

temporarily a more or less clearly marked axiate pattern which has a definite relation to the external factor (Figs. 12–15); see also Jennings, '04, '06, Chap. I). This relation is such that the *Amœba* finally moves more or less directly away from — or toward — the source of disturbance. In such cases the change in physiological state is chiefly or wholly the progressive integration toward an axiate pattern which is more or less definitely referable to the localization or direction of action of the external factor.

In axiate forms the axiate pattern is of course already present, but adjustment to the special case may be necessary. In the case of *Paramœcium* the axiate pattern does not enable the animal to orient itself directly and at once with reference to the external factor act-

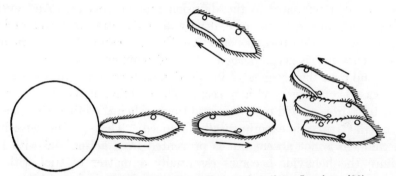

Fig. 146.—The avoiding reaction of *Paramecium* (from Jennings, '99).

ing upon it (Jennings, '06, Chaps. III–VI). It can only repeat the characteristic avoiding reaction, consisting of backward movement, for a short time, followed by forward movement at an angle to the original direction (Fig. 146), until an adjustment of the pattern to the particular case occurs, *i. e.*, the reaction is effective, or until fatigue, death, cessation of the exciting action or some other change terminates the reaction.

Certain observations indicate, however, that even in *Paramœcium* a modification of the avoiding reaction through change in physiological state by repetition may occur under certain conditions, *i. e.*, *Paramœcium* may learn by experience (Stevenson Smith, '08; Day and Bentley, '11). According to these authors a *Paramœcium* confined in a capillary tube so narrow that the characteristic spiral course cannot be followed in swimming, advances in the tube with a rotational movement about the long axis and when the end of the tube is reached, reverses the direction of this movement several times. Thus far the behavior is of the usual sort, altered only by the limited diameter of the tube. But it is not effective in bringing about adjustment and sooner or later the animal turns itself about in the tube by a new sort of reaction, consisting of a bending of the oral end, followed by sudden jerking movements (Fig. 147). Since this sort of reaction is unknown in unconfined locomotion, it is evident that the physiological state and so the reaction pattern have been modified by experience.

FIG. 147.—Modification of behavior of *Paramecium* in capillary tube (from Stevenson Smith, '08).

The flatworm, *Planaria dorotocephala*, in reacting to a chemical factor, *e. g.*, extractives diffusing from food, usually lifts its head and moves it from side to side before orientation of the direction of locomotion with reference to the diffusion gradient occurs. And even when it has begun to advance, it may alter direction more than once before the reaction becomes effective, that is, before the adjustment, the orientation, is accomplished. In trial reactions in the higher animals and man the progressive integration with reference to the particular case is often very clearly seen. The reaction of the decapitated frog to a drop of acid placed on one thigh, when the other leg is held, is a trial reaction experimentally induced. That is, the effective mechanism is not absent but is prevented from acting and with its failure the behavior becomes essentially a matter of trial with a progressive integration of the reflex arcs of the body with special reference to the local excitation. Evidently the excitation, at first local in the nervous system, spreads, involving one region after another until the whole body is more or less integrated, whether effectively or not. In trial behavior in man the progressive development of the new integration appears even more clearly. In attempts to learn a new complex coördination, *e. g.*, riding a bicycle, skating, the first failures lead to greater efforts, the use of other muscles, changes in posture, etc., and gradually the new behavior pattern develops out of the complex.

As Jennings has shown, such new integration patterns may often persist for a time even in unicellular animals, but usually disappear rapidly in these and in the simpler multicellular animals. The "physiological memory" of these organisms is rudimentary, the axial and symmetry gradients being the chief records and even these are not very stable. Apparently the possibilities of development of persistent records in the protoplasm reach or approach their limits with the differentiation in relation to these gradients, and the effects of new differentials and integrations are either rapidly reversible, or, if the action of the external factor is sufficient in degree or duration, they may obliterate the old gradients and determine new ones. In such forms the ability to learn, to acquire habits, goes but little beyond the most general habit of all, *i. e.*, the axial gradient, and more or less differentiation in relation to it.

With the increase in stability of protoplasmic records of behavior which is an essential feature of evolution, the possibility of persistence of the new effective integration in a trial reaction increases, *i. e.*, the ability to learn and acquire new habits increases. The gradual recording in the protoplasm of the new integration corresponds to Jennings' law of resolution of physiological states: The resolution of one physiological state into another becomes easier and more rapid after it has taken place a number of times (Jennings, '06, p. 291). The simpler organisms are what they are because the protoplasmic records of behavior reactions and integrations are to a large extent readily reversible and the more persistent features of such records are of very general character and, so far as organismic integration is concerned, rudimentary. In such forms excito-motor behavior must consist primarily of few and simple stereotyped components and the trial form of reaction must be predominant, with rudimentary and short-lived memory. Modifiability of pattern, whether morphological or excito-motor, by the persistence of protoplasmic records, *i. e.*, by learning, must therefore also be slight and rudimentary.

Tropisms. — The tropism in Loeb's sense (pp. 230–231) postulates the presence of an effective integration pattern, a pattern which gives the effective reaction directly. According to Jennings' conception of a tropism (Jennings, '06, Chap. XIV, '08, '09, '10), such a pattern is not necessarily predetermined or inherited, but may have developed in the individual as the result of successful trial behavior and the tropism may represent the working of the new integration thus developed. Undoubtedly some reaction patterns which approach more or less closely the form of a tropism are characteristic features of the normal organismic pattern of the species and definitely related to the axial gradients, and are therefore what we commonly distinguish as inherited from the patterns acquired by the individual during its life. Other patterns of this sort are doubtless developed in the individual on a trial foundation. The important point for present purposes is that the tropism requires the existence of a behavior mechanism or pattern already adjusted to the particular case. The orientation of the body of a swimming crustacean or a flying insect with reference to light requires a complex polar-bilateral reflex, or excito-motor mechanism of some sort. Granting this, we must conclude that tropisms are not the most general and primitive form of excito-motor behavior, or else we must follow Loeb in assuming that such a mechanism exists in all motile organisms, but the evidence is strongly against such an assumption. The tropism in motile organisms obviously postulates a relatively high degree of organismic integration and the evidence does not indicate that such a degree of integration exists in the simpler organisms.

From its very definite and direct relations to polar-symmetrical pattern in general we should expect the tropism to be a relatively stable or fixed excito-motor pattern, particularly in those cases in which it is a normal characteristic of the species and not acquired by the individual. So far as such tropisms actually exist, their stability is evident. Modification in minor respects, *e. g.*, in latent period, speed of reaction, etc., may result from alterations in physiological state, but the tropism as a whole remains a relatively fixed pattern. The reversal of direction of a tropic reaction does not represent a modification in the sense of a new integration, but may result from the change of excitation to inhibition, or *vice versa*, with quantitative change in the external factor, or in the critical point between excitation and inhibition in the physiological mechanism. The tropism as Loeb conceives it, affords no room for memory or learning. The mechanism must be stable, essentially unalterable in the individual and polar-symmetrical in character. If pure tropisms in this strict sense exist, they must obviously be very direct expressions of the fundamental features of organismic pattern, the physiological gradients, and are modifiable in any fundamental way only as these are so modifiable.

Instinctive behavior. — The instinctive forms of excito-motor behavior likewise represent highly stable, in common biological parlance, hereditary patterns (Herrick, '24, Chap. XI). These behavior patterns are among those determined in the individual by the hereditary protoplasmic constitution and the normal or standard range of environmental factors (pp. 211, 222). They represent complex integrations of significance in the life of the individual and so apparently adaptive. In general, however, this instinctive pattern remains merely a potentiality in the behavior of the individual until a particular physiological state arises, either by the attainment of a certain stage of development or by a particular configuration of environmental factors, and determines its realization as an actual reaction pattern.   In most, if not in all cases, the environmental configuration plays some part in initiating the actual integration of the instinct pattern into a reaction.   The sensory impression aroused in the well-fed squirrel by the nut apparently sets going the storage instinct and it may be that other factors effective at a certain season of the year start an instinctive search for nuts.   The sight, sound or odor of the opposite sex initiates the integration of the sex instinct pattern and so on.   In short, the component mechanisms of instinctive behavior are normal features of organismic pattern, but there is no reason to believe that their integration into a particular excito-motor behavior pattern occurs autonomously or spontaneously.   Apparently, like other behavior patterns, it requires for realization the action of an environmental factor—in the case of instinct usually a more or less specific complex.   As in the case of other features of organismic pattern, even the primary axial gradients or a plasma membrane, the potentiality of the pattern is given in the hereditary constitution of the protoplasm, but the action of some external factor or complex is necessary for its realization as an actual pattern in an individual organism.

Intelligent behavior. — The instinct, as a relatively stable pattern, is unquestionably represented by a more or less definite, relatively stable structural basis of some sort in the nervous system, but the integration of this pattern is to some extent modifiable, chiefly through conscious intelligence.   The degree of modifiability of instinct varies in general with the development and dominance of intelligent behavior in the individual.   In the insects excito-motor behavior is, so far as we can judge, very largely instinctive and based on the mechanisms of a polar-bilateral nervous system.   Since the polar-bilateral pattern is highly stable in these forms, even those minuter details of it which represent the mechanisms of instinct are relatively fixed.   In the higher vertebrates, on the other hand, the development of the cerebral cortex represents a considerable degree of physiological isolation from, or obliteration of, the general axial gradients in a part of the nervous system (pp. 257–258).   In consequence of this unique position of the cortex, it constitutes a mechanism for highly plastic and modifiable excito-motor behavior patterns.   The absence of a fixed dominance in any one region provides a basis for patterns of the deliberative, intelligent type.   And finally, the development of the cortex from the anterior region of the nervous system makes it a region of superdominance.   Even many of the more stable features of the polar-symmetrical excito-motor patterns of the lower levels of the gradients, *e. g.*, the reflex and instinctive complexes, may undergo more or less modification under the superdominance of intelligence, of which the physiological pattern exists primarily in the cortex.[1]

[1] Compare Herrick's discussion of the physiological characteristics of the cerebral cortex ('24, at the close of Chap. XVII).

CHAPTER XVI

THE BIOLOGICAL FOUNDATIONS OF SOCIAL
INTEGRATION

In the preceding chapters I have tried to show that the individual organism represents fundamentally a behavior pattern, *i. e.*, the behavior of a specific protoplasm in a certain environment. The development of the individual from the stage of the simple quantitative gradient to the mature organism, of whatever species, represents the modification of behavior resulting from establishment of the primary pattern and the changes which this brings about in the protoplasm. This conception of the organism as fundamentally a dynamic integration of behavior pattern in a specific protoplasm seems to throw light upon various fields of biology, which from other viewpoints have remained more or less obscure. Probably no one doubts that social integrations, patterns, institutions are fundamentally integrations of the behavior of living organisms in certain environments. If both the individual organism and human society represent behavior integrations of living systems, a comparison between them from this viewpoint should prove of interest.

Sociology and its problems are very often outlined in terms of human beings solely, but as a matter of fact various social patterns are found among various organisms in various degrees of development, from rudimentary and evanescent integration to highly stable and complex organizations. The fact that these integrations are based wholly or largely on instinctive, rather than on intelligent behavior does not make them any the less social in character, at least to the biologist. Social integration in man could not have been primitively an intelligent, fully self-conscious integration, but was unquestionably, in large measure, instinctive. Indeed it is a pertinent question whether many of the more primitive and evanescent types of social integration among human beings at the present day, *e. g.*, crowds, mobs, boys' gangs, etc., are not to a considerable extent instinctive rather than intelligent. If instinctive behavior does play any considerable part in them, they appear to be very similar or essentially identical with many social integrations among animals. It appears to the biologist that the attempts so often made by sociologists to define and consider social problems in terms of man alone are responsible for at least certain features of the vagueness, uncertainty and difference of opinion, particularly as regards social origins. The delimitation of the subject to the human species makes any adequate interpretation of social origins practically impossible. If man is a product of evolution, the foundations of human society lie, not in the human race, but in other organisms. It is certain that human society represents the highest order or plane of integration upon our planet. If man is a part of organic nature it appears a difficult and uncertain task to attempt to interpret this highest order of integration without attempting to determine the relations between it and the lower and simpler orders of integration on which it must be in part based.

BIOLOGICAL SOCIOLOGY AND SOCIOLOGICAL BIOLOGY

Some sociologists, *e. g.*, Comte, Spencer, Schäffle, have interpreted human society more or less in terms of biological conceptions. Spencer emphasizes the morphological aspects, the mechanisms, of society, while Schäffle is interested not merely in the structure but in the function of the mechanisms. Both authors carry the biological analogy into minute detail. Of course the question whether or not we shall call human society an organism must depend on our definition of an organism. The objections made by various sociologists to biological forms of interpretation in sociology are of some interest, and some of them suggest that some sociologists have not considered what organisms are. For example, the objection to the biological analogy has been based on the ground that there is no protoplasmic or physical continuity between human individuals. It may be pointed out that the blood cells, though parts, or organs of the organisms, are not continuous and that in the simpler forms cells may lose their continuity with other cells, migrate and establish continuity with a new group. On the other hand, many sociologists maintain that the tool in use becomes essentially an organ, or that in working with different tools the hand plus the tool become essentially different organs. If we grant this, human society consists not simply of human bodies, but of these bodies plus environmental factors, whether natural or in the form of man-made tools which permit communication. Are not two human beings conversing over the telephone or even by means of atmospheric sound waves brought into a dynamic correlation very similar to the dynamic correlation in the organism?

Again, it has been pointed out repeatedly that human society has no permanent organs, but essentially the same thing is true of many of the simpler organisms. In this connection it may also be pointed out that the tools, the fabrications, are the permanent organs of society. The human individual may be regarded as the dynamic, the metabolic factor in the pattern.

The objection has also been raised that the basis of human association is psychic, but unless our definition of the word is very narrow, the psychic factor exists in many forms of animal association as well as in human society. Certainly not all human association is intelligent and self-conscious in character, while many integrations among animals are more or less psychic, perhaps conscious in character.

Objections such as those that human society is not a big animal, that it has for example no stomach, no muscles, etc., are just as true for many organisms as for society. It has been said that the social mind has no sensorium. But do not the individuals in relation to each other and to environment constitute the sensorium of the social mind just as truly as cells and cell groups in relation to each other and to the external world constitute the sensorium of the individual mind?

And finally many sociologists who admit that the biological analogy may have a certain value are inclined to regard it as a crude and merely preliminary form of interpretation. Undoubtedly human behavior and its integration patterns differ in many respects from anything recognizable in other organisms, but the foundations of human behavior include all of biology, not simply the social behavior of animals, but the behavior of individuals and its mechanisms, and even the behavior of living protoplasm which constitutes the organism. How can we hope to analyze and interpret adequately the more advanced forms of integration in human society without knowledge of the foundations on which they rest?

It is perhaps not of great importance whether or not we call human society an organism but it is a highly significant fact that biological terms apply better than any others. Even though we decline to speak of the social organism we find it very difficult to dispense with the term organization, simply because the term expresses better than any other certain processes and phenomena in society as well as in the organism. The term "differentiation" is also used in the biological sense in sociology, likewise the term "function," and so on. The fact that these terms are universally recognized as practically indispensable must mean that the social process is in certain respects, at least, very similar to the organismic process.

The biologist, likewise, has found that certain sociological terms afford more satisfactory analogies for purposes of interpretation than any others. For example, the conception of the multicellular organism as a cell state, with division of labor among its constitutent cells is familiar to every student of elementary biology, and it would be difficult to express certain aspects of the pattern of organisms so clearly in any other terms. In preceding chapters (pp. 146, 258) I have called the more primitive axiate type of pattern an autocratic form of government and have pointed out that evolution has progressed toward democracy and representative government. Various neurologists and psychologists have found the conception of a parliament or deliberative assembly of very great value in interpreting the rôle of the cerebral cortex.

But there seems to be no good reason for stopping here. The sociologist is accustomed to call the relatively fixed and permanent social patterns institutions. Are there not patterns or orders within the organism fundamentally similar to social institutions in that they represent integrations of living units? Is not the organism itself an institution of some sort in the living protoplasm of one or more cells? If the physiological conception of axiate pattern developed in earlier chapters and elsewhere (Child, '15c, '21a) is correct the axiate organism is an institution resembling the state. It represents fundamentally a relation of dominance and subordination, i. e., of government and governed.

In short, whether we are primarily concerned with the organism or with human society, we cannot help but see the fundamental similarities in the processes of integration in the two patterns, and even though sociologists may continue to insist that sociology remain distinct from biology, the development in biology of the dynamic, in place of the older morphological viewpoint, will make this more and more difficult. In fact the definition of the organism to which the strictly physiological viewpoint of the preceding chapters leads us will serve almost equally well as a definition of society. The organism is a dynamic order, pattern, or integration among living systems or units. A social organization is exactly the same thing. The fundamental difference between the organism and social integrations among human beings is apparently one of degree or order of magnitude. Social integration is a dynamic integration of human organisms, and the human organism is an integration of cells, tissues and organs. Unquestionably these differences in the order of magnitude of the integration determine differences in detail in the processes concerned, but both cell and human being are living systems, and we believe that the human being is a product of evolution from the cell. We may expect therefore, to discover a fundamental similarity or identity in the more general laws and processes of integration from the one extreme of the cells or the simplest organism to the other of the great modern state or nation. The overlapping of biology and sociology and their use of each other's terminology indicate that this is the case, but from the dynamic viewpoint this fundamental similarity appears even more clearly than from any other. The morphological analogy between organism and society is at best very general and may readily be overworked. As the morphological mechanisms of the human body are different from those of a bacterium or an *Amœba*, so the morphological mechanisms of human society differ from those of the human body. But when we come to the problem of the nature of the integration process which makes the micro-örganism and the human being organisms and human society a "superorganismic" pattern, we find certain highly significant similarities. To some of these attention is briefly called in following sections.

INTEGRATION AMONG ORGANISMS IN GENERAL

Among animals and even among plants we find not only various degrees of organismic integration, from the simple cell to the multiaxiate or "colonial" plant and animal, but we also find certain superorganismic integrations. Some are unquestionably social, while others are near the border line between social relation and relation to environment in general. Biologically speaking, social integration represents for the individual a reaction to a particular factor in his environment, viz., another individual or group of individuals. We must search, therefore, for the foundations of social integration in the relations of the individual to his environment and more particularly his living environment.

The most general relations of this sort are the ecological relations between different species. Ecological communities represent integrations of various species of animals and plants based on the relations of each species to its environment, including both inorganic factors and the other species of the community. As regards the living environment, these relations are of various sorts. The one species or some of its products of metabolism or its body may be merely a source of food in the environment of the other. Even this relation may differ widely in character. The relation between the herbivorous animal and its food, for example, is passive and accidental on the side of the plant, but a definite feature of excito-motor behavior on the part of the animal. The relation of the parasite and its host is likewise usually based on a onesided reaction. The relation between the predatory animal and its prey, however, may involve reaction on both sides. The various forms of symbiosis, mutualism, inquilinism, "guest" relations, range from cases like the symbiosis of hydra and other simple animals with green algae in which both species are apparently passive and the relation a matter of chance, to cases among insect species in which each shows definite behavior with respect to the other. This is particularly the case as regards the ants and some of their "guests." Certain species of ants raid the nests of other species, capture and carry home the larvæ or pupæ, which are brought up to be "slaves." In some relations of this sort the one species is wholly dependent on the other for continued existence. For example, the eggs of certain species of plant lice from which ants obtain nutritive secretions during the summer are carried by the ants to their nests, cared for during the winter and in the spring the young aphids are carried to their food plants. Certain species of ant aphids are carried out to pasture in good weather and back to the ants' nests in bad weather, cold nights, etc. Also the ants move them from one pasture to another. The species of plant lice in which these mutualistic relations with ants occur react differently to the ants from other independent species, and their behavior shows adaptation in various ways to the ants. Students of ants have described many other mutualistic relations between ants and other insects (see, for example, Wheeler, '10, Chap. XIX, also '23.)

Discussion of the question whether any of these relations between species, or which of them are to be called social is unprofitable. It may merely be noted that at least some of them exhibit features which play a part in true social integrations. The more general ecological relations between different species of living organisms are largely or wholly material in character and as such they constitute the material basis of a relation of exchange, a commercial relation, but unregulated by communication between individuals. In the more intimate relations between species, e. g., some of those between ants and aphids, communication, excito-motor reaction, and often complex instinctive behavior of one or both species may occur.

It is perhaps justifiable to characterize as fundamentally nonsocial the general ecological relations existing between different species and having to do with material factors such as food, oxygen, or other factors concerned in vegetative life. Social relations are then theoretically distinguishable from such ecological relations in that they are fundamentally relations between members of the same species and involve communication of some sort. But it is probably impossible to make this distinction sharp, for in certain cases the ecological relations obviously approach a social character.

Certain sorts of integration may occur more or less indifferently between individuals of different but closely related species, and between members of the same species. For example, Allee ('20) has described aggregations among ophiurid starfish and among isopod crustacea which may include one or more species. The animals concerned tend to keep their bodies in contact with solid surfaces (positive thigmotaxis) and when such surfaces are reduced to a minimum in their environment they react positively to each other and form masses or bunches of individuals. Dr. Allee informs me that while such aggregations may consist of members of more than one species they form more readily and to a greater extent between individuals of the same species. This being the case, the aggregating individuals must be able to distinguish in some way and to some degree between other individuals of the same and those of other species. Apparently even in these physical aggregations of individuals there is a factor remotely akin to the social factor.

In many other relations between individuals of the same species the social character of the integration appears more clearly. Many animal species aggregate into herds, flocks, packs, schools, etc. The simplest forms of aggregation are temporary and shifting, consisting of individuals which happen to be near enough together to react to each other. Concerning many such aggregations we can say little more than that they originate in a gregarious instinct, but this is no more than saying that they exist because members of the species behave in a certain way. Aggregations of this kind may become more definite and distinct under certain special conditions, e. g., the integration of the herd of cattle through fear, the flocking of various species of birds and of insects, at the migratory season. Again, such aggregations may be based on the brood, the family, or they may have some sexual significance. The flying or "dancing" groups of various species of the gnats and midges which appear in spring and early summer apparently represent a rudimentary and temporary grouping, but one apparently involving some sort of reaction of the individuals to each other. For the formation of such groups a certain atmospheric humidity and absence of wind are obviously necessary. Such a group may divide or join with others, and individual insects may enter it or leave it. We can distinguish no indications of leadership and in some forms the group can be temporarily or permanently disintegrated by a sound of certain pitch and intensity. But the fact that such groups are at least often, perhaps always, composed of males only is evidence of their relation in some way to sex.

We also find animal groups with definite leadership; either temporary and shifting or more or less permanent. The migrating flocks of wild geese are led by a gander and assume a more or less definite arrangement of individuals in two lines diverging from the position of the leader. A more or less definite and fixed relation of leadership and led is commonly believed to exist in the wolf pack and in the aggregations of various other mammalian species. Such groups appear to be truly social. The behavior of the individuals is regulated to some extent by their relation to the group and this relation is dynamic, not material, i. e., it rests on communication of some sort, not necessarily volitional, but none the less real. Some such groups seem to show something approaching consciousness of the group, however rudimentary. In groups of various birds and mammals certain individuals function as sentinels while the others feed.

The family in one form or another is of wide occurrence among animals and the fundamental factor underlying the origin of the family, viz., sex, is a general biological phenomenon. The parental instinct appears in one form or another, and as a temporary and evanescent, or periodic phenomenon far down among the invertebrates, and the true family appears, at least as a temporary or periodic integration even in certain fishes and in many species among the higher vertebrates. Often the relations of the male to the family are little or nothing more than the primary sexual relation, but there are various species among both birds and mammals in which it is much more than this, and in some animals the male is permanently a member of the family.

The social integration among ants, bees, wasps and termites appears to represent in large measure modifications of the family. The various castes represent different degrees of development and differentiation of the sexes, in bees, wasps and ants primarily of the females, in termites of both sexes. In the differentiation of the castes heredity, the occurrence or non-occurrence of fertilization, at least in the bees, nutritive conditions during development and perhaps other factors are concerned. The bee and ant communities are social systems centered about the queen mother, matriarchal systems, with various complications associated with the differentiation of castes. With the development of the different castes within one sex, or as in the termites, in both sexes, the division of labor has gone further than the primary sexual division and so the community has come to resemble in certain respects a state rather than a family, but its relation to the family seems evident.

Wheeler ('18) has suggested the possibility of a very different origin of social life in the insects, viz., the exchange of nutritive substances, including secretions and excretions, between individuals, a relation which he calls trophallaxis. Unquestionably such exchange plays a part of great importance in many insect communities, but the interpretation of the relation of the community to sex, to the queen mother and to the offspring in terms of trophallaxis appears to offer some difficulties.

Within the communities of different species of ants and other social insects various institutions of more or less definite social character exist in addition to the nutritive exchange. Among the ants for example, we find agriculture, slavery, social care of the young, war, to mention only a few. As a predominantly instinctive, rather than an intelligent integration, the insect community is relatively rigid, but it involves dynamic communication, direct or indirect, between individuals and recognition of, and distinction between, individuals of different sex, caste, stage of development, nest, species, etc. Moreover, the fixity of the integrative behavior is by no means absolute, but modification does occur through learning. In the ordinary life of most social insects there is little indication of anything approaching real leadership, though some vestiges of it do perhaps appear at times. In general the integration of behavior appears to be largely the result of the uniformity of instinctive response of the individuals of each caste to any particular factor. The absence of leadership and the apparent dead level of individuality in each caste make social progress in any strict sense impossible. Probably progress in the insect community can occur only with evolution of castes and instincts, in whatever way this takes place.

That social integration among human beings is fundamentally psychic in character needs no proof. In its simpler forms it may be largely instinctive, but in its higher development it becomes conscious and intelligent and in modern society group self-consciousness has developed rapidly and is obviously of fundamental importance for the future progress of society.[1] Unquestionably human

[1] See for example McDougal, '20.

social integration is a matter of the behavior of human beings, particularly with respect to each other, and at the foundation of that behavior as of the individual organism, lie the physicochemical processes of excitation and transmission in human protoplasms and their significance as correlative factors in the organism. In human integration transmissive correlation within the cerebral cortex has become the chief factor, or to speak in psychological terms, the development of human society represents the progressive dominance of the idea and its effects upon behavior.

This brief and fragmentary consideration of relation and integration among organisms is sufficient to show that the fundamental factors in such integration are the excitatory or sensory impressions determined in individual organisms by other organisms and the effects of such impressions upon behavior. In its simpler forms such integration may be little or nothing more than a tropism or a trial-and-error reaction in which individuals react to each other simply as a part of their environment. In somewhat more highly developed forms of animal integration more or less blind and stereotyped instincts are brought into play by the sensory impressions, and the integration becomes more distinctly social in character, though not necessarily involving any conscious factor. Some forms of animal integration, particularly among the higher vertebrates, appear to involve some degree of consciousness of the group, doubtless vague and rudimentary. And finally, the higher forms of integration among human beings involve not only consciousness but self-consciousness of the group. With evolution of the nervous system and its behavior mechanisms the fundamentally psychic character of integration among individual organisms becomes always more distinct.

In preceding chapters I have attempted to show that the individual organism as an integration or pattern represents the behavior of a specific protoplasm with certain hereditary potentialities in a certain physical environment. The nature of such behavior depends of course upon the behavior mechanisms present in the specific protoplasm. That the integration of individual organisms into groups or patterns of a higher order of magnitude is fundamentally dependent on behavior is a self-evident fact. As the character of the particular organism depends primarily upon the specific constitution of its protoplasm and the behavior mechanisms resulting from this constitution, so the character of a particular integration among organisms depends primarily upon the sort of organisms concerned and the behavior mechanisms which they possess. With the development of excito-motor behavior and its mechanisms in the individual organism new potentialities of physiological integration arise and similarly with the evolution of excito-motor behavior and its mechanisms new potentialities of integration among organisms arise. We may analyze these into social and non-social, conscious and unconscious integration, etc., but the point which I wish to emphasize is that, from the viewpoint of behavior, synthesis is also possible. From the individual organism onward through various forms of integration of organisms, we are dealing with the reactions of specific living systems to their environments, including other living systems, and with the laws which govern those reactions. The degree of complication of mechanism differs enormously, but, if we admit that man is a part of organic nature, then we must also admit physiological continuity from the simple excitation-transmission gradient to the complex workings of the human mind in its social relations. And at this point the question arises whether the synthesis is completed with the recognition of such continuity. This question is dealt with in following sections.

FACTORS OF SOCIAL INTEGRATION

Association.—In the organism the association of cells or other parts in normal development usually represents rather an incomplete dissociation or separation than an active coming together of independent individuals. Under experimental conditions, however, isolated cells not too far distant from each other do move toward each other and aggregate into masses (Roux, '94; H. V. Wilson, '07, '11). In certain cases, *e. g.*, cells of sponges, these aggregates, if exposed to an environmental differential may become new individual organisms. In such cases active association does occur, supposedly through the action of chemical substances given off by the cells. The swarm spores of certain simple plants also undergo normally an active association to form multicellular individuals of more or less definite form and cell-configuration (R. A. Harper, '18 a, b).

The basis of social integration is likewise association of individuals and such association may be predetermined and passive, so far as the individual is concerned, or it may be active. For example, the individual is born into a group as a new cell arises by division in an organ, but he associates actively with other individuals, whether it be in a conflict of interests or under the compulsion of a common instinct, the stress of a common emotion, or the influence of a common purpose.

The question of the basis of the gregarious character of man has been much discussed. According to some authorities it originates in the family, according to others it results somehow from the essential likeness of human individuals. Some assume a gregarious impulse as given, *i. e.*, as of biological origin, others maintain that the human being was originally non-social and that association has arisen secondarily through natural selection, through fear of the non-human environment, etc. It seems scarely necessary, however, to base all human association on a single primary factor. Why may not the factor determining association differ under different conditions? As a matter of fact, we see association taking place on the basis of fear, of pleasure, of curiosity, and apparently of simple imitation, and in such associations instinctive factors may be far more important than intelligence and purpose. On the other hand, association may occur on an intelligent self-conscious basis, with a definite purpose in view.

Historically it appears probable that two factors have been largely concerned in development of association among human beings and their predecessors in evolution. In the first place, the developing consciousness must become increasingly subject to the feeling of fear, unrest, discomfort, or helplessness, as it becomes increasingly aware of the world about it and its mysterious and often injurious action. Association, whether instinctive, or conscious and purposive, lessens these feelings, perhaps in part by directing attention elsewhere, and the individual is more comfortable. Biologically it is undoubtedly possible for association to develop on a pure trial and error basis and it is not improbable that even among human beings a trial and error factor, *i. e.*, in the broad sense a pleasure-pain factor, plays a considerable rôle in the more primitive and rudimentary sorts of association.

A second factor in association, not only of human beings, but of many animals, is the family or its biological basis, the sex relation. Attention has already been called to the fact that the family in some form exists temporarily, periodically or permanently among many organisms and in the social insects constitutes the basis of a complex social integration; moreover, sex relation is of course a general biological phenomenon. This relation affords a biological basis for association of individuals and it is evident that, because of its universal occurrence it may serve as the starting point and play an important rôle in associations which really depend on other factors. For example, the association of male and female and later of their offspring with them, undoubtedly lessens the fear or discomfort arising in isolation and so may become the basis of the clan, of the blood-bond and of various other associations. But it serves as a basis simply because it represents a primitive biological relation between individuals, not because it is fundamentally social in any strict sense. In other words, we see various other associations developing historically out of the family, not because it is a fundamental or necessary factor in such associations, but simply because it antedates them. The boy's "gang" originates in a primitive and rudimentary sort of association just as truly as does the clan and many other social groups of primitive races, but the gang is quite independent of the family, while the primitive clan usually has some relation to it. In short, it seems possible that the conception of the family as the basis of social integration involves a confusion of historical sequence in development of human society, with cause and effect. From the biological viewpoint, association of individual organisms, whether human or non-human, appears to originate in many different ways, according to conditions, and the relation of the family to social association in any strict sense appears to be secondary and incidental rather than fundamental. The family may antedate historically various forms of association, but it is by no means necessary to their genesis.

Correlation between individuals. — In the integration which constitutes the biological organism physiological correlation between the unit parts, cells or cell groups integrated is a fundamental factor. The "organism as a whole" consists of all the parts plus all the physiological relations between them and the wholeness of the organism consists in the relations between the parts rather than in the parts themselves (Chaps. III, V). The distinction between material and dynamic correlative factors drawn in Chapter V has made it possible to advance another step in the analysis of the wholeness of the organism. Consideration of the biological data in the light of this distinction has forced us to the conclusion that certain dynamic factors, viz., excitation and its transmission in living protoplasm, constitute the fundamental factors in organismic integration (Chaps. V–XI). Excitation and its transmission constitute the basis of what we call behavior in organisms and if we admit that they are the fundamental factors in organismic integration we must also admit that the individual organism is a behavior pattern or integration in a specific protoplasm (Chap. XII). The metabolic or physiological gradient, which in its simplest form is essentially an excitation-transmission gradient, is the primary factor in determining the differentiation and integration of the living units into a whole. This gradient originates in a differential relation to environment, but once present it may persist through processes of reproduction and so be inherited.

Turning to social integration, it is evident that it, like organismic integration, depends primarily on correlation between the individuals constituting the social entity or group. Moreover, social correlation is fundamentally dynamic rather than material, that is to say, it consists primarily in the transmission from one individual to another of energy changes which affect the sense organs. The transmission in this case is not of course through a physically continuous protoplasm, but through other physical media, but this social correlative factor originates in excitatory and transmissive changes in one individual or group and results finally in excitatory and transmissive changes in the other individuals affected. This is true whether the correlation consists in the instinctive or intelligent behavior of one individual or group of which others become aware through sight, hearing or other senses, or whether communication occurs directly by signs, speech, direct, or transmitted by telegraph, telephone, etc., or by writing, books, or other indirect means.

We may say then, I believe, that social integration, like organismic integration, depends primarily upon dynamic correlation of excitatory-transmissive character. The excitatory and transmissive process as a whole may be enormously more complex than in physiological integration, and may consist in part of physiological processes in protoplasm and in part of transmission of energy changes in some physical medium intervening between the living individuals. Even in its simplest forms social correlation originates in the behavior of individual organisms or groups and in its highest forms among men it originates in an effective idea, with all that the term implies of physiological or psychic complexity. Organic continuity in the biological sense does not exist, but the individual plus the means of communication constitute the morphological organ of communication. Sociologists have often pointed out that the tool, the instrument, in fact, any fabrication, becomes in a sense an organ when used by man in the control of the environment. We may even go a step farther than this and say that speech makes the atmosphere, sight, the ether, an organ of social correlation, as truly as protoplasm is an organ of physiological transmission. But whether or not we admit such analogies, the important point is that the media of the natural environment, or man-made tools and instruments do provide a basis for dynamic continuity between individuals. This continuity is even more effective as a substratum for social correlation than the protoplasmic substratum of the individual for physiological correlation.

It is evident that even the simplest forms of social material correlation, *i. e.*, of barter and exchange, or commerce, are impossible without such dynamic correlation. We cannot conceive of social integration as originating in material exchange between individuals or groups without such transmissive correlation, direct or indirect. Material exchange, commerce, is unquestionably a factor of great importance in social differentation and integration, but that it is the primary factor, I think no one believes. Since the theory of formative substances was advanced by Sachs many biologists have maintained that physiological integration originates in such material transport alone, but this conception ignores completely the fact that irritability and capacity for transmitting excitation are fundamental properties of protoplasm, and that material exchange can become an ordering and integrating factor only when different regions, cells or parts have already become different. Similarly, material exchange is significant, as a social and integrating factor only secondarily, *i. e.*, when some sort and degree of differentiation and integration already exist.

From this viewpoint physiological and social integration both represent the integration of living systems into larger wholes through the agency of dynamic correlation. At the one extreme, the simple organism, the initiating factor is the relatively simple protoplasmic excitation resulting from relation to environment which is transmitted through protoplasm, at the other, intelligent integration among human beings, it is an idea and unless we assume psychic autonomy in the individual, this idea must have originated in some individual or individuals at some time through excitatory changes in relation to environment. To serve as a basis of social correlation such an idea must not only be communicated, but must be effective in determining the behavior of individuals with respect to others. Whatever the idea may be psychologically, it is certainly represented physiologically by excitatory and transmissive processes and the simple protoplasmic excitation which determines a temporary or permanent transmission gradient constitutes the first physiological step toward the idea.

Leadership, dominance and subordination. — The consideration of physiological integration in the individual organism has led us to a conception of physiological dominance and subordination as a fundamental factor in such integration (Chaps. IV, X). It has also been pointed out that this physiological relation of dominance and subordination arises as an essential feature of excitation and its transmission. In the simplest case the region of primary excitation dominates other regions to which the excitation is transmitted, because through the transmitted excitation it determines their physiological condition at least for the moment. When a physiological gradient has been established the region of highest metabolic rate, i. e., the region which is living most rapidly or intensely, is the dominant region. Because of its physiological condition it reacts more rapidly or more intensely to external factors than other parts and so influences the condition of other parts to a much greater degree than they influence it. Elsewhere I have endeavored to show that this relation of dominance and subordination is a fundamental factor in development and that nervous dominance and control in general and more specifically the dominance of the cephalic nervous system in the higher animals, is a physiological consequence of the relation of dominance and subordination in the simple physiological gradient (Child, '21 a).

Moreover, the dominant region is not merely a pacemaker in development and function, but is a factor in determining the differentiation of subordinate parts (Chaps. VIII–X). The cells of the organism differentiate along different lines, not because of inherent specific differences, but because of the differences in their relations to other cells and to the external world. Speaking in general terms we may say that the relation of dominance and subordination creates the axiate organism. Through this relation the course of development of individual cells or cell groups is determined and controlled. Different cells become different from each other and from that which they would have been in the absence of this relation.

In fact, an analysis of physiological integration leads us to a conception of physiological leadership, based primarily on dynamic factors. Physiologists have recognized clearly the existence of such dominance or leadership in the "pacemaker" of the heart and various other rhythmic organs (pp. 149–151) and the dominance of the growing tip and of other regions of relatively high activity in plants has long been known to the botanists (pp. 62, 139). The development of zoölogy along predominantly morphological lines has led to structural rather than dynamic conceptions of the animal organism, and the zoölogist has not always found it easy to attain any idea of "the organism as a whole." It is evident, however, that the orderly behavior of the organism in development and function must be determined either by an effective physiological dominance or leadership of some sort, or by some metaphysical principle such as Driesch's entelechy, and the evidence points us to the first alternative.

Sociology, like zoölogy, has not always been clear as regards the part played by leadership in social integration. Not infrequently a "social impulse," the "social mind" or the "ethnic mind," or some other basis of integration has been conceived as if it existed somehow apart from, and superior to, the individual. On the other hand, the fundamental importance of leadership for any except the most rudimentary social integration has been pointed out again and again. It seems evident that social integration cannot develop very far without some sort of leadership, whether personal or impersonal, autocratic or representative. But leadership is dominance of some sort, either of the person, the group or the idea, and involves subordination, voluntary or involuntary, of those who are led.

Rudimentary and temporary integrations among human beings may occur with very little evidence of leadership. For example, the crowd, the horde, etc., may be without definite leadership, but if we watch its formation we observe temporary, evanescent and shifting, leadership. The crowd began with a single individual or a small group and this individual or group represents for the time being the leader. Others observing, join the group and thus in their turn serve as leaders for still others and so the process goes on. But until some definite and more or less persistent leadership arises in it, such a crowd is a mere aggregation of individuals. It is, in fact, much like a cell aggregation without a definite axiate pattern, or like an unstimulated *Amœba*. The appearance of leadership may determine a more or less definite new pattern, as in the case of *Amœba* pp. 57–59).

The simplest sort of organismic pattern is the surface-interior pattern (pp. 38, 57, 93), which represents merely the differences between parts directly exposed to environment and those not so exposed. Here the only dominance or leadership is that of the surface, as contrasted with the interior. Certain simple social integrations resemble very closely this surface-interior pattern and even show a morphological differentiation in relation to it. For example, the wagon trains crossing the western plains in earlier days often made camp, when in hostile Indian country, by disposing the wagons in a circle with women and children inside this circle and the men, or part of them, patrolling the periphery. Where the methods of travel and transport are still primitive and subject to attack by bandits or hostile tribes some such kind of camp is still very generally found, and in some parts of the world the primitive village shows a somewhat similar surface-interior pattern.

In such pattern the periphery, because of its more direct relation to environment, dominates the interior in certain respects, but no other leadership is apparent in the pattern. Undoubtedly the origin of the idea of this sort of camp involved leadership, and the arrangement of the camp in a particular case may be determined by a leader, or where environmental conditions have made such a pattern necessary in the past, the idea in impersonal form, i. e., as custom, tradition, dominates. The pattern itself, however, is directly related to environment, and since there is no environmental differential in different radii which determines differences of reaction there is nothing more than surface-interior pattern. Moreover, there may be no fixed differentiation of individuals in such pattern. If the camp is composed entirely of men, each of them will probably take his turn in patrolling the periphery. As in the surface-interior organism, the differentation in such cases is directly determined by relation to environment.

If such a camp is attacked at one point of its periphery, it may become for the time being and in some degree axiate, with the region of greatest activity and dominance at the point of attack. Attack at another point of the camp determines reaction there and with the repulse of the attacks and recovery from the excitement reversion to the surface-interior pattern may occur. Such change resembles in some respects the formation of a pseudopod in *Amœba*, but the pseudopod usually represents a reaction of avoidance or escape rather than of resistance and so is more or less definitely localized on other portions of the surface than that directly subjected to disturbance.

Such social integration is of course very simple and rudimentary and, as noted above, is directly related to environment. Whenever human beings or the higher animals aggregate into a group, such surface-interior pattern must necessarily develop to some extent because of the different relations to environment of the superficial and other portions of the aggregation. Both biologically and socially it is the simplest form of integrative pattern possible among the living units concerned.

It is evident, however, that social integration cannot proceed very far without definite and relatively permanent leadership, embodied in a person, a group, or a body of tradition, custom, law, etc. As a matter of fact, we find the relation of dominance and subordination an essential factor in the progress of social, as of biological organization. In certain primitive forms of social pattern dominance may be exercised by an individual with a club, in others by the patriarch, the "old man" of H. G. Wells, in still others by the medicine man, the supposed possessor of magical or occult powers and so on. In all these cases, however, the dominance is essentially psychic and involves first the idea of fear, reverence, superstition, and second the effect of this idea in determining behavior. The excitation of protoplasm and its transmission is effective as an integrating factor, only as it alters the pirotoplasm and determines its behavior, and similarly the idea is effective socially, only as it determines behavior. With the progress of social integration the personal factor in dominance becomes more and more completely replaced by the impersonal factor, the idea, in the form of tradition, law, custom, etc. In earlier times the dominance of the monarch was to a considerable extent personal, but with the progress of time the monarch came to be more and more an institution, *i. e.*, the embodiment of an idea far greater than himself, to which he personally was subordinate. In all the more highly developed institutions of modern society, such as the nation, the church, the dominance of an idea as the effective agent in determining behavior is clearly evident.

Recognition of this dominance of ideas in social integration has been perhaps the chief factor in leading the sociologist to regard biological analogies as at best remote and of little practical value. Moreover, the conceptions advanced by certain schools of sociology of the group-mind, the social mind, the ethnic mind as the source of the dominant idea seem to separate sociology and biology still further. But when we examine the basis and processes of integration, rather than merely their morphological or functional results, the physiological integration of the organism and the psychic integration of human society seem to show certain fundamental similarities or identities.

The origin of the dominant idea. — Tracing briefly the origin of the dominant idea, it may be pointed out, first, that the group mind or social mind consists of the minds of the individuals composing the group plus all the relations between these minds. In the final analysis the first approach toward the dominant idea, whether instinctive or intelligent, must have originated in the mind of some individual, or possibly in the minds of several or many individuals at about the same time. Moreover, it must have originated either in the reaction of some individual or individuals to environmental factors different from those affecting other individuals. or in differences in individuals, such that under the same environment the idea or its foundation arose in the minds of one or more of them, but not in the minds of others.

In the one case the leadership or dominance results directly from the environmental differential. The man who has had experience along certain lines has usually developed ideas which the man without such experience is not likely to have. In the other case leadership depends on the intrinsic differences between individuals. The personal leader is a more or less "exceptional" individual, and a dominant idea may originate in a mind which reacts to a given environment in a way different from that of most minds. In this latter case the basis of the social integration is already present in the intrinsic differences between individuals, and all that is needed is a particular environment, in other words, "the right time" or "the psychological moment" to make the integration real and effective.

The intrinsic differences between individuals must of course have been determined in some way, either through differences in the past history of the individuals or by heredity. But we do not believe that the hereditary differences between individuals arose "spontaneously," without cause. They must have been determined originally by relations between a germ plasm and its environment, but we have at present no conclusive evidence that these relations are of the sort postulated by the Lamarckian theory. The important point is that the innate differences between individuals, which make of one a leader or the originator of a dominant idea, and of another a follower, must have originated at some time in the past in the relations between protoplasms and their environments. That is to say, in spite of its psychic character, dominance in social integration, whether personal or impersonal, is not independent of the external world in its origin. According to the biological viewpoint, each human being is what he is because of present and past relations to environment of his protoplasm and the protoplasms from which it has arisen. In short, dominance in social, as in physiological integration, must originate in reaction to an environmental differential.

The dominant idea does not remain unchanged, but undergoes more or less rapid change and development. It usually becomes more distinct and definite in certain respects, but may be greatly modified in the course of time by the additions and other alterations which it undergoes in the minds of the individuals composing the group. Through the action of so-called social heredity the dominant idea may become or include a great body of tradition, law, custom. In the case of a great modern nation, for example, the idea of the nation which, through its effect on the behavior of the individuals composing it, is the dominant factor in the integration, is now exceedingly complex and its content is very different from that of the dominant idea of tribe, clan, gang, etc., from which it has developed. It is commonly less effective in controlling, as a formal custom or tradition, the minuter details of individual behavior, as it does in many primitive societies, but at the same time it may be more effective as a dominant idea influencing intelligent behavior. The greater complexity of its content makes its influence on the behavior of human beings more varied and more far-reaching, consequently it is able to dominate and integrate much larger groups with much greater diversity of interests than is the primitive idea. The development of physiological dominance in the nervous system may be described in almost the same terms.

Since this relation is a factor in determining the behavior of the human individual, it is a factor in making him what he is. His individuality is more definite, more highly developed and differentiated because of his social relations. As in the organism, the changes in him go hand in hand with the development of integration. These changes may consist of repression or inhibition of certain potentialities and realization and increased development of others, but in any case it is sufficiently obvious that the human individual is not simply the product of heredity. His social relations, or more specifically, his subordination in some way and in some degree to more or less definite ideas play a fundamental part in determining the course of his thought, his sentiments and his behavior.

To sum up: it appears that leadership, dominance, the pacemaker, play essentially the same rôle in social as in physiological integration. Moreover, if the conclusions advanced are correct, there is physiological continuity, not simply from the physiological gradient to the fully developed organism, but to the dominance of the idea in intelligent social integration.

CHAPTER XVII

THE COURSE OF SOCIAL INTEGRATION AND THE ORIGIN OF NEW GROUPS

The great modern nation-states represent social integration on the largest scale and in the greatest complexity thus far attained. In the state, government, *i. e.*, a relation of dominance and subordination of some sort and some degree is a fundamental factor. Even in the most primitive associations dominance and subordination are present, but as transitory and shifting, rather than definite and persistent relations. The crowd may be swayed now by one leader or idea, now by another. A party lost in the woods may follow one leader for a time and then turn to another, *i. e.*, dominance may be a matter of trial. In the surface-interior integration, the circular camp mentioned above, the dominance of the individuals at the surface may be replaced in case of attack by the dominance of a single region of the periphery. But in any persistent orderly integration, such as the state, government, *i. e.*, a definite and persistent relation of dominance and subordination, exists and on it the orderly character of the state pattern depends. In fact, the state possesses social polarity and may be termed an axiate social pattern, with government representing the dominant region and the various classes and differentiations of its members in relation to the government the subordinate regions of various levels of the axis.

PRIMITIVE AUTOCRACY AND PROGRESS TOWARD DEMOCRACY

Physiologically the lower and simpler sorts of organismic pattern are essentially autocratic in character (pp. 146, 258). The dominant region controls other parts in development and function but is practically independent of them. For example, the apical region of a hydroid, the head of a planarian, is able to develop in the complete absence of other parts, but when other parts are present it dominates them, while they are able to affect it only when strongly excited and then only slightly. Such autocratic physiological dominance is apparently more highly developed in motile than in sessile forms. The motile form resembles an army advancing through hostile territory, the sessile form a primitive settled community.

288

We have seen, however, that in the course of evolution and in the individual development of higher animals and man there has been progress toward a physiological democracy with more or less representative government (pp. 257–258). The cerebral cortex of the higher vertebrates is a sort of physiological parliament, a deliberative assembly. Through lower centers it may receive reports from any part of the organism and its final action, the efferent impulse, depends upon these and upon its records of past events, i. e., memory.

That the evolution of the state and nation and of many, if not all other social groupings follows in general a similar course seems evident. This does not necessarily mean that the autocratic or even the oligarchic type of integration is characteristic of all social integrations or all states among primitive peoples, nor does it mean that the autocratic form of dominance always involves personal autocracy. With individuals of a low grade of intelligence the autocratic dominance of the impersonal idea, as given in the body of tradition, custom, tabu, etc., may be more complete and effective than that associated with any personality. And it is this sort of autocracy that appears to be the characteristic feature of the social integrations approaching or attaining state form, as well as of most other institutions, among the more primitive peoples. The idea dominates the individual and his effect upon it is practically nil. Such an integration may persist through long ages, but is rigid and unplastic and undergoes little or no evolutionary progress. Like the simpler organisms of the autocratic type, it represents a sort of integration, a pattern, which has attained the highest development possible with that particular protoplasm and environment (Herrick, '24, Chap. XII, first section). In the case of the social pattern, as in the case of the organism, changes in the protoplasm through intermixture of blood or otherwise, changes in social environment through contact with other tribes, peoples or races, or changes in physical environment, such as climate, may sooner or later be effective in modifying the dominant idea and so in bringing about social progress.

Even in the great nations of modern times this autocratic dominance of the idea has by no means disappeared. The events of recent years have afforded abundant evidence that national tradition, custom, sentiment, are still potent factors in controlling in an autocratic way the actions of individuals. But these same events have not been without effect in bringing about some degree of modification of the dominant ideas, that is, the dominance has not been entirely autocratic for all members of the group, even though it has been for some.

So far as the individual is concerned, this autocratic type of dominance of the idea is essentially unintelligent. As other parts of the more primitive axiate organism are subordinate to the apical region or head, so the individual is subordinate to such ideas and is practically without influence in modifying them. In fact, autocratic dominance, whether physiological or social, whether through physical force or of purely psychic character, is essentially compulsory and not the result of coöperation or representation, nor of compromise among conflicting views and interests.

Even in the more primitive axiate organisms the general autocratic dominance is not absolute, but within restricted limits relations of parts may be mutual to a greater or less extent and determined by local conditions. Within certain limits of distance transmission of local excitation may occur in any direction. Within such restricted areas there is some approach to physiological democracy. With the development of the process of excitation and of special transmitting paths of higher conductivity than the general protoplasm, the boundaries of such areas are extended, until in the higher vertebrates and man any part of the body may coöperate in determining the condition of the cortex, the content of consciousness and the resulting efferent impulses. There seems to be little room for doubt that it is the development, on the one hand, of the process of excitation, i. e., leadership, from its primitive, inefficient protoplasmic forms to the highly specialized and efficient nervous type, and on the other, of the processes and means of transmission, which have been the chief factors in making possible and determining the progressive evolution of the organism from physiological autocracy toward physiological democracy.

That the development of efficient, i. e., intelligent leadership and of the processes and means of communication between human beings and groups are the fundamental factors in the progress of social integration is very generally admitted by sociologists. Whether leadership be primarily a matter of exceptional individuals or consists in ideas worked out by the coöperation or conflict of many minds, is a matter of minor importance. Communication may take place in most diverse ways, e. g., by signs, speech, writing, and with the aid of various mechanical devices and agencies. But the important fact remains, that in social integration, as in the organism, the development of leadership and of communication are the foundations of progress.

It is evident that, as physiological democracy appears, first in limited areas of the organism, so coöperative or democratic and intelligent social integration appears first in small groups. Under primitive conditions the means of communication limit narrowly the size of the group, and even under the most favorable conditions of modern life, though we have greatly extended the range of democratic integration and believe that the best way to settle many questions is to talk them over, we still go to war to settle some of the larger questions. With the development of the means of communication the possibility of the appearance of new ideas or effective modifications of old ones increases and the range of effectiveness of ideas is extended until it becomes unlimited, so far as distance is concerned. At the present time the factors of greatest importance limiting human integration are differences of language, custom and race. As in the case of the higher organisms, mere distance is no longer an effective obstacle to integration, as it was in primitive life.

Even as regards the enormous and highly complex groups representing the great modern nations, integration has in many cases progressed far toward democracy, at least in political form of government, if not as yet in the intelligent coöperation of all individuals and in intelligent and purposive modification of the dominant ideas underlying the nation. But there can be no question that intelligent and purposive progress is gathering headway. In the relations between nations, however, the primitive, unintelligent, autocratic dominance of bodies of tradition, custom, sentiment, still plays a very large part.

SOCIAL ISOLATION AS A FACTOR IN THE FORMATION OF NEW GROUPS

The part played by physiological isolation in the reproduction of new individuals and the reduplication of parts was considered in Chapter X. The range of physiological dominance is limited in the simpler organisms, and in the earlier stages of development of the higher forms, because of the primitive character of communication. Parts may become physiologically isolated in four different ways, or more strictly speaking, four different factors may be concerned in physiological isolation. First, growth and resulting increase in size of the whole beyond a certain limit may carry some part beyond the range of dominance. Second, decrease in dominance through decrease in activity of the dominant region by advancing age, external factors, etc., may isolate parts most distant from the dominant region without increase in size of the whole. Third, difficulties or obstacles in the way of communication may isolate parts physiologically. And fourth, conditions affecting directly a subordinate part, increasing its activity, or determining new gradients in it to such an extent that the original dominance is no longer effective, also lead to physiological isolation.

The part isolated in any of these ways, if it is not too highly specialized, undergoes more or less dedifferentiation, and if the original gradients persist in it, or if new gradients are determined by local factors, it may become a new complete individual. The result of physiological isolation in such cases is the same as that of physical isolation. When physiological isolation is not complete, or when the part concerned is more or less specialized, it may give rise to a new part, a tentacle, a segment, a branch, as in plants, or a new zooid, as in colonial animals, and such reduplicated parts may be more or less integrated into a more complex individuality.

The higher the development of physiological correlation and primarily of transmissive correlation, that is, the better the means of communication, the less readily and frequently do such physiological isolation and reproduction occur and vice versa. In many organisms we see such isolations occurring in the earlier stages of development, when transmissive correlation is still primitive in character and shows a marked decrement, while in later stages isolation becomes impossible under normal conditions. And finally in the higher animals physiological isolation in normal life is limited to very early stages of development and even there usually gives rise to reduplicated parts, such as segments, rather than to complete individuals. The tumors, particularly the malignant forms, probably represent isolation of cells, but the nature of the conditions determining the isolation and the continued growth have not yet been determined for animals. Apparently the fourth factor in physiological isolation is largely concerned here, i. e., direct action, stimulation, irritation of the cells concerned until they become so active that they are no longer under control. But since cancer occurs chiefly in old individuals the decrease in dominance in consequence of advance in age is probably also concerned.

In the processes which we may call social reproduction and reduplication of groups, the factor of social isolation in its various forms and degrees plays a part essentially similar to that of physiological isolation in organisms. Moreover, in the simpler and more primitive sorts of social groupings four factors similar to those concerned in physiological isolation are involved. First, the growth of the group, the mere increase in size, tends toward isolation of the parts least effectively dominated. Growth in size is a factor in social re-production in primitive tribes and clans and even in many social groups in advanced civilization. A society founded for one purpose or another increases in size and becomes unwieldy, too large to han-dle its business efficiently, and splits up into several societies or into groups or sections, which remain more or less integrated into one whole. Social dominance in the simpler forms of the community or state is limited in range, and growth favors the appearance of new groups, either independent of the old, or as subdivisions of it.

Second, a decrease in dominance without increase in size of the group may constitute a factor in the origin of new social groups. This appears most clearly perhaps in groups integrated on the basis of a personal leadership. With advancing age, illness, or death of the leader, his dominance becomes less effective, and unless there is some one to take his place and continue the representation of that for which he stood in the mind of the group, a more or less complete disintegration of the group may occur, just as some of the simpler organisms separate into their constituent cells with the disappear-ance of dominance. Or as the original dominance weakens, factions may arise within the group, each with its own leader, and so deter-mine the origin of new groups as new gradients determine the ori-gins of new axes and individuals under similar conditions in organ-isms. Even in the nation or state, the government may decrease in effectiveness through the weakening or degeneration of the ruler, the royal family or the governing class, or through the ineffective representation of the dominant idea by the party or group in power, and disintegration of the whole, with the formation of independent, or partially independent smaller groups may result. Factors of this sort evidently played a part in the downfall of the Roman Empire.

Third, obstacles to communication are powerful factors in social reproduction. In its more primitive forms the working of such fac-tors is seen very clearly in the influence of geographic obstacles such as rivers, mountain ranges, deserts, etc., on social integration. The migration of part of a tribe or clan across a mountain range or a desert commonly leads to their integration into a new group, more or less independent of the old. Even a river may have the same effect to a greater or less degree. The more primitive the means of com-munication, the more effective are such obstacles and the more lim-ited the size of the integrated group or state. Even temporary ob-stacles, such as a flood, destruction of a bridge or other means of communication across a stream, may, if other conditions are favorable, *i. e.*, at a critical period, result in social isolation and reproduction. Again, capture or killing of official couriers, capture of ships, or railway trains, the stoppage of transmission of messages by cutting the wires or by any other means, all these and many other methods of obstruction of communication have played their parts upon occasion as factors in social reproduction of one kind or another.

And finally, the local conditions under which some portion of a social group finds itself may determine reproduction, that is, its in-integration as a new group in spite of the original dominance. A new leadership, personal or impersonal, of such force that it is able to maintain itself, persist and be effective in spite of the original governmental or other dominance, may arise in this portion. Such leadership may consist in the "exceptional" individual who promulgates new ideas, or the geographic, economic, or other conditions may determine the working out of a dominant idea or a modification of the old, which is effective as an integrating factor. In the separation of the American colonies from Great Britain, for example, factors of this sort played a part, though they were of course not the only factors. The origin of new religious sects often represents a social reproduction of this sort and numerous other examples will occur to the reader.

Of course in human society, as in the organism, more than one of these four factors of isolation may be concerned in any one case. A certain degree of social isolation through increase in size of the group, decrease in dominance, or obstructed communication, renders the isolated part of the group more susceptible to new personal leadership or to new ideas arising in relation to local economic or geographic conditions. All four factors may be concerned in a particular case and any one of the four may be predominant, and it seems to be true that all cases of social reproduction, *i. e.*, of the origin of new groups from parts of preëxisting groups, are determined by some one, or some combination of these four factors.

With the development in modern times of the mechanical means of communication, mere size, whether a matter of geographic area or of number of individuals, is practically eliminated, as it is in the higher organisms for essentially the same reasons, as a factor limiting social integration. The most important limiting factors at present are diversity of interests, language, custom, race, etc., *i. e.*, factors of more or less primitive autocratic character. The more fundamental social groupings, *e. g.*, the great nation-states, have therefore become relatively stable, persistent integrations, and national social development consists largely in the origin and differentiation of subordinate groups within the nation, in the complication of the correlation between them, and in the gradual modification of the dominant idea or ideas underlying each group from the nation itself down. As in the higher animals, isolation and reproduction occur chiefly in the specialized groups subordinate to the whole and result in diversity or reduplication of parts, rather than in the formation of new wholes.

The forms of physiological reproduction on which this consideration is based are all primarily asexual or agamic and do not necessarily involve the union of gametes or sex cells. If, however, we examine sexual or gametic reproduction from the physiological viewpoint, it seems to differ from asexual reproduction as a physiological process only in that the reproductive elements are so highly specialized in consequence of their past history as parts of an organism that isolation alone is not sufficient, except in cases of parthenogenesis, to bring about or initiate reproduction. In addition to isolation, certain specific changes, bringing about excitation or acceleration of living in the egg, and probably other changes as well, are necessary and the physiological relations between sperm and egg provide these. But in many cases in which the development of the egg is initiated in nature by the sperm, it can be initiated experimentally by various physical and chemical agents. Viewed physiologically then, sexual reproduction seems to be a process depending on isolation plus a more or less definite or specific excitatory factor.

The sex cells or gametes are cells so highly specialized that they have lost their capacity to react to isolation alone and in nature are dependent on each other for further existence and the development of a new individual. Sex is obviously a matter of protoplasmic constitutions or activities, and while some remote analogy to sexual reproduction may be found in the effects on society of mixture of races, or the effects of new ideas from without in initiating the development of new social groups it is not necessary to force any such analogy. Sex in biology represents certain protoplasmic differences and their results, including their significance as conditions of certain forms of reproduction. It is quite unnecessary for present purposes to attempt to determine whether analogous specializations and reproductions exist in society, and there appears to be no reason why they should exist. The only reason for bringing up the matter of sex in this connection is to point out that it is a specialized form of reproduction requiring special conditions for its occurrence and not a fundamental physiological factor in reproduction in general.   Even if we seek to parallel physiological and social integration and reproduction it is entirely unnecessary to look for anything analogous to sexual specialization in organisms as a basis for social reproduction.

The chief purpose of this incursion into sociology has been to call attention to the fact that between the organism and society *as processes of integration*, certain interesting and significant similarities or identities exist.   These result, I believe, from the fact that both the organism and society represent integrations of living protoplasmic systems through their relations to each other and to other environmental factors.   The similarity or identity of process seems to me the interesting point.   Whether society is an organism, whether it is morphologically or functionally similar to an organism, are matters of minor and chiefly academic interest.   But the recognition of similarity in processes of integration among living protoplasmic units or systems, from cells or parts of cells at the one extreme to human individuals at the other, constitutes one step in synthesis from the dynamic viewpoint.

QUESTIONS OF THE FUTURE

It has often been said that the purpose and end of science is to control and to predict, but in many fields of biology we are still a long way from attaining this end and the biological prophet does not always prove a safe guide.   Nevertheless, life is largely concerned with the question of the future, even though it be no more than a question, and it is of perhaps some interest to raise the question here.   In the preceding chapters we have been concerned with the problem of the integration of living action systems, or reaction systems of specific constitution into larger systems, patterns or wholes.   Consideration of the evidence has led us to the conclusion that from the simplest organism to the most complex social group, the process of integration is based upon the behavior of the living systems, *i. e.*, upon their reactions to their environment including each other.   Moreover, certain significant and apparently fundamental similarities, or in a broad sense identities, in the processes and course of physiological and social integration have been pointed out, and if these are admitted we seem to have some justification — though doubtless many sociologists will not agree — for regarding social integration as one aspect, plane or order of magnitude of biological integration.

The evolution of protoplasm and of the potentialities of behavior and physiological integration have been going on through millions of years, and the beginnings of social integration lie far back in this evolutionary history, but social integration among human beings is of comparatively recent origin. In the light of the various facts and conclusions we may, without assuming the rôle of prophecy, at least ask the question whether we can find in physiological integration any suggestions or indications for the future of human social integration. Attention has been called repeatedly in the preceding pages to the autocratic character of the more primitive process of physiological integration and to the progress of the organism toward a democracy with representative government vested in a deliberative organ connected through various centers with all parts of the body and in touch with the external world through the sense organs. This type of integration is the one which has thus far proved most successful and efficient, and it is in this type of integration that consciousness and self-consciousness have attained their highest development, involving in man conscious recognition of the organism as a whole. In such an organism there is governmental control, regulation and coördination of the various parts, but there is also conflict and competition. In starvation, for example, we find certain organs maintaining themselves at the expense of others. The different cells as specialized parts of the organism are not actually equal, even though they may be so potentially. Certain cells, e. g., the muscles, lose their ability to function and undergo degeneration when the nerves leading to them are cut. The progress of evolution then has apparently not been toward a socialistic or communistic form of integration. On the contrary, those types of integration which approach communism most closely, e. g., the colonial animals such as the sponges, hydroids, etc., and the multiaxial plants have been left far behind in the course of evolutionary progress and such success as they have attained appears to be due to the fact that they are not strictly communistic but possess some degree of autocratic or oligarchic dominance. Physiological anarchy in the simpler forms may result in disintegration of the organism as an organism, though its constituent cells may live independently or may give rise to new organisms like the old, or in its more extreme forms it may give rise to pathological growths such as cancer which destroy the organism because they do not react to its dominance.

In short, the course of evolution of physiological integration has been in the main toward democracy with representative government,

298 PHYSIOLOGICAL FOUNDATIONS

assisted so to speak by experts, the organs of special sense. Autocracy, on the one hand, and approaches toward communism on the other produce only relatively simple organisms. Whether these facts have any significance for the future of human society must remain a matter of opinion, but it seems at least to be true that the integration of human society is progressing psychologically, in later times, to some extent intelligently and self-consciously, toward what may be called a democracy of ideas, with representative government, i. e., dominance of the most effective ideas, as worked out by the intelligent coöperation and conflict of the minds composing the group. Even now integration in small groups for special purposes approaches this form. The pattern resulting from such integration represents in terms of social psychology something very similar to the pattern of the higher organisms in terms of physiology. In such a pattern, as in the organism, material and transportative, i. e., commercial relations in the broadest sense may play essential parts in determining the differentiations of groups within the whole, but they are not the fundamental factors in integration (Herrick, '24, Chap. XXI).

And finally it may be noted that socialistic, communistic and even anarchistic schemes of human relationship are such primarily with respect to material factors. Psychologically every one of them involves the dominance of an idea and often this dominance is of the primitive, autocratic type. Even the most advanced and intelligent socialistic or communistic schemes of human society are such only as regards material relations. Psychologically they are democracies, i. e., democracies of ideas involving dominance and subordination, coöperation, competition, conflict and representation. From this psychological viewpoint we can see no more indication of approaching socialism or communism in human society than in organismic integration. No matter what the form of material or commercial relation in human society, the fundamental factors in the future progress of social integration will be ideas; for even according to the socialistic and communistic schemes the ideal society will be socialistic or communistic only in general political form, but fundamentally it will be a democracy of ideas.

CONCLUSION

In the present book we have been concerned with the dynamics of the integration of living systems into systems or patterns of higher orders of magnitude. I have attempted to show that from the simplest organism to the most complex human society integration is based on the behavior of living protoplasms of specific constitution and therefore shows a certain fundamental similarity or identity in process and course of development and evolution. Differences appear with the differences in complexity of the behavior mechanisms, whether protoplasmic or social, but in spite of these differences the fundamental similarity is evident. The incursion into the sociological field is the result of the belief that the consideration of the organism as a process of integration and development of pattern on the basis of behavior affords a more adequate formulation for biological approach to sociological problems than mere morphological or functional analogies between an organism and society. How far that belief is justified the future must determine.

In this brief discussion of social integration consideration of many points which are of interest from the dynamic biological viewpoint has been impossible. For example, the progress and increase in fixity of differentiation, and the accompanying loss of the power or growth through decrease in birth-rate, or failure to add new members to the group, in short, the phenomena of senescence and even of death are not unknown in social groups. On the other hand, in the origin of new social groups by some form of isolation we often see extensive dedifferentiation and reorganization, accompanied by an increase in irritability and vigor of the group, in short, a social rejuvenescence. Biology has learned something of the conditions determining these phenomena and of the methods of control, at least in the simpler organisms, and the consideration of certain social problems in the light of our biological knowledge is of interest. Again the development of barter and exchange, of commerce and its control and regulation may well be examined in the light of what we know concerning chemical or transportative correlation in organisms.

Experimental biology aims at the control of processes and phenomena, and so of physiological integration. Intelligent social progress is based essentially on the experimental method as employed in biology. The earlier analogies drawn between society and the organism have been based on the data of descriptive anatomy and physiology, but the discussion of social integration in these two chapters is based primarily on the conclusions of experimental biology. I have attempted to show that the results of the experimental method as applied to the process of integration of living systems which constitutes the individual organism seem to throw some light on the integrations of organisms including human beings into larger and more complex patterns or groups. If I have succeeded in showing that the processes of physiological and of social integration have something in common, that they both represent aspects of the behavior of living things, the purpose of these chapters as well as of those preceding is attained.

BIBLIOGRAPHY

ALLEE, W. C.
   1920.   Animal Aggregations, *Proc. Amer. Soc. Zoöl., Anat. Rec.,* XVII.
ALLEN, G. D.
   1919 a.   Quantitative Studies on the Rate of Respiratory Metabolism in *Planaria,* I, *Amer. Jour. Physiol.,* XLVIII.
   1919 b.   Quantitative Studies, etc. II, *Amer. Jour. Physiol.,* XLIX.
   1920.   The Rate of Carbon Dioxide Production by Pieces of *Planaria* in Relation to the Theory of Metabolic Gradients, Proc. Amer. Soc. Zoöl., 1919, *Anat Rec.,* XVII.
ALVAREZ, W. C.
   1914.   Functional Variations in Contractions of Different parts of the Small Intestine, *Amer. Jour. Physiol.,* XXXV.
   1915 a.   The Motor Functions of the Intestine from a New Point of View, *Jour. Amer. Med. Assoc.,* LXV.
   1915 b.   Further Studies on Intestinal Rhythm, II, *Amer. Jour. Physiol.,* XXXVII.
   1916 a.   IV.   Differences in Rhythmicity and Tone in Different Parts of the Wall of the Stomach, *Amer. Jour. Physiol.,* XL.
   1916 b.   V.   Differences in Irritability and Latent Period in Different Parts of the Wall of the Stomach, *Amer. Jour. Physiol.,* XLI.
   1917 a.   VI.   Differences in Latent Period and Form of the Contraction Curve in Muscle Strips from Different Parts of the Frog's Stomach, *Amer. Jour. Physiol.,* XLII.
   1917 b.   VII.   Differences in Latent Period and Form of Contraction Curve in Muscle Strips from Different Parts of the Mammalian Stomach, *Amer. Jour. Physiol.,* XLII.
   1918 a.   X.   Differences in Behavior of Segments from Different Parts of the Intestine, *Amer. Jour. Physiol.,* XLV.
   1918 b.   XII.   The Influence of Drugs on Intestinal Rhythmicity, *Amer. Jour. Physiol.,* XLVI.
   1818 c.   XVI.   Differences in the Action of Drugs on Different Parts of the Bowel, *Jour. Pharm. and Exp. Ther.,* XII.
   1922.   *The Mechanics of the Digestive Tract.* New York.
ALVAREZ, W. C., and MAHONEY, LUCILLE J.
   1921.   Action Currents in Stomach and Intestine, *Amer. Jour. Physiol.,* LVIII.
ALVAREZ, W. C., and STARKWEATHER, E.
   1918 a.   XI.   The Metabolic Gradient Underlying Intestinal Peristalsis, *Amer. Jour. Physiol.,* XLVI.
   1918 b.   XIII.   The Motor Functions of the Cecum, *Amer. Jour. Physiol.,* XLVI.

1918 c. XVII. The Metabolic Gradient Underlying Colonic Peristalsis, *Amer. Jour. Physiol.*, XLVII.

1919. XVIII. Conduction in the Small Intestine, *Amer. Jour. Physiol.*, L.

ALVAREZ, W. C., and TAYLOR, F. B.

1917 a. The Effect of Temperature on the Rhythm of Excised Segments from Different Parts of the Intestine, *Amer. Jour. Physiol.* XLIV.

1917 b. Changes in Rhythmicity, Irritability and Tone in the Purged Intestine, *Jour. Pharm. and Exp. Ther.*, X.

BARTELMEZ, G. W.

1912. The Bilaterality of the Pigeon's Egg, *Jour. Morphol.*, XXIII.

BATESON, W.

1894. *Materials for the Study of Variation.* London.

BEHRE, ELINOR H.

1918. An Experimental Study of Acclimation to Temperature in *Planaria dorotocephala, Biol. Bull.*, XXXV.

BELLAMY, A. W.

1919. Differential Susceptibility as a Basis for Modification and Control of Early Development in the Frog, I, *Biol. Bull.*, XXXVII.

1922. Differential Susceptibility, etc. II, *Amer. Jour. Anat.*, XXX.

BERNSTEIN, J.

1899. Die Konstitution und Reizleitung der lebenden Substanz, *Biol. Zentralbl.*, XIX.

1912. *Elektrobiologie.* Braunschweig.

BIEDERMANN, W.

1896. *Electro-Physiology*, English Translation. London.

1903. Elektrophysiologie, *Ergebn. d. Physiol.*, Jahrgang II, Abt. II.

BORUTTAU, H.

1900. Die Aktionsströme und die Theorie der Nervenleitung, *Arch. ges. Physiol.*, LXXXI.

1901 a. Die Aktionsströme, etc., *Arch. ges. Physiol.*, LXXXIV.

1901 b. Alte und neue Vorstellungen über das Wesen der Nervenleitung, *Zeitschr. f. allgem. Physiol.*, I.

BOSE, J. C.

1902. *Response in the Living and Non-Living.* London.

1906. *Plant Response.* London.

1907. *Comparative Electro-Physiology.* London.

1913. *Researches on Irritability.* London.

BOVERI, T.

1901 a. Ueber die Polarität des Seeigeleies. *Verh d. phys-med. Gesell.* Würzburg, N. F., XXXIV.

1901 b. Die Polarität von Ovocyte, Ei und Larve des *Strongylocentrotus lividus. Zoöl Jahrbücher*, Abt. f. Anat. und Ont., XIV.

1910. Die Potenzen der *Ascaris*-Blastomeren bie abgeänderter Furchung. *Festschr. zum sechsigsten Geburtstage R.* Hertwigs, III.

BRACHET, A.

1911. Études sur les localisations germinales et leur potentialité réele dans l'oeuf parthénogénétique de *Rana fusca, Arch. de Biol.*, XXVI.

BUCHANAN, J. W.
1922. The Control of Head-formation by Means of Anesthetics, *Jour. Exp. Zoöl.*, XXXVI.

CAREY, E. J.
1920. Studies in the Dynamics of Histogenesis. I, II, *Jour. Gen. Physiol.*, II, III, 1920.
1921 a. Studies, etc. IV-VII, *Amer. Jour. Anat.*, XXIX.
1921 b. Studies, etc. VIII, *Amer. Jour. Physiol.*, 1921.

CARLSON, A. J.
1923. The Secretion of Gastric Juice in Health and Disease, *Physiol. Rev.*, III.

CHILD, C. M.
1900. The Early Development of *Arenicola* and *Sternaspis, Arch. f. Entwickelungsmech.*, IX.
1904. Studies on Regulation, V, VI, *Jour. Exp. Zoöl., I.*
1905. Studies on Regulation, VIII, IX, X, *Arch. f. Entwickelungsmechanik*, XIX, XX.
1907 a. An Analysis of Form Regulation in *Tubularia*, I, *Arch. f. Entwickelungsmech.*, XXIII.
1907 b. An Analysis, etc., II, *Arch. f. Entwickelungsmech*, XXIII.
1907 c. An Analysis, etc., IV, *Arch. f. Entwickelungsmech.*, XXIV.
1907 d. An Analysis, etc., V, *Arch. f. Entwickelungsmech.*, XXIV.
1909. Factors of Form Regulation in *Harenactis attenuata*, III, *Jour. Exp. Zoöl.*, VII.
1910 a. Physiological Isolation of Parts and Fission in *Planaria, Arch. f. Entwickelungsmech.*, XXX, II. Teil.
1910 b. Further Experiments on Adventitious Reproduction and Polarity in *Harenactis, Biol. Bull.*, XX.
1911 a. Experimental Control of Morphogenesis in the Regulation of *Planaria, Biol. Bull.*, XX.
1911 b. Studies on the Dynamics of Morphogenesis and Inheritance in Experimental Reproduction, I, *Jour. Exp. Zoöl.*, X.
1911 c. Studies, etc., II, *Jour. Exp. Zoöl.*, XI.
1911 d. Studies, etc., III, *Jour. Exp. Zoöl.*, XI.
1911 e. Die physiologische Isolation von Teilen des Organismus, *Vortr. u. Aufs. ü. Entiwckelungsmech.*, Heft, XI.
1911 f. The Regulatory Processes in Organisms, *Jour. Morphol.*, XXII.
1912 a. Studies, etc., IV, *Jour. Exp. Zoöl.*, XIII.
1912 b. Correlation in Regulation, *Proc. 7th Internat. Zoöl. Congress*, Boston, 1907. Published 1912.
1913 a. Studies, etc., V, *Jour. Exp. Zoöl.*, XIV.
1913 b. Studies, etc., VI, *Arch. f. Entwickelungsmech.*, XXXVII.
1914 a. Susceptibility Gradients in Animals, *Science*, XXXIX.
1914 b. The Axial Gradient in Ciliate Infusoria," *Biol. Bull.*, XXVI.
1914 c. Starvation, Rejuvenescence and Acclimation in *Planaria dorotocephala, Arch. f. Entwickelungsmech.*, XXXVIII.
1914 d. Studies, etc., VII, *Jour. Exp. Zoöl.*, XVI.

1914 e.   Studies, etc., VIII, *Jour. Exp. Zoöl.*, XVII.
1915 a.   Axial Gradients in the Early Development of the Starfish, *Amer. Jour. Physiol.*, XXXVII.
1915 b.   *Senescence and Rejuvenescence.* Chicago.
1915 c.   *Individuality in Organisms.* Chicago.
1916 a.   Axial Susceptibility Gradients in the Early Development of the Sea Urchin," *Biol. Bull.*, XXX.
1916 b.   Studies, etc., IX, *Jour. Exp. Zoöl.*, XXI.
1916 c.   Axial Susceptibility Gradients in Algæ, *Bot. Gaz.*, LXII.
1916 d.   Experimental Control and Modification of Larval Development in the Sea Urchin in Relation to the Axial Gradients, *Jour. Morphol.*, XXVIII.
1916 e.   Further Observations on Susceptibility Gradients in Algæ, *Biol. Bull.*, XXXI.
1916 f.   Age Cycles and Other Periodicities in Organisms. *Proc. Amer. Phil. Soc.*, LV.
1917 a.   Susceptibility Gradients in the Hairs of Certain Marine Algæ, *Biol. Bull.*, XXXII.
1917 b.   Experimental Alteration of the Axial Gradient in the Alga, *Griffithsia bornetiana, Biol. Bull.*, XXXII.
1917 c.   The Gradient in Susceptibility to Cyanides in the Meridional Conducting Path of the Ctenophore, *Mnemiopsis, Amer. Jour. Physiol.*, XLI.
1917 d.   Differential Susceptibility and Differential Inhibition in the Development of Polychæte Annelids, *Jour. Morphol.*, XVII.
1918.   Physiological Senescence in Hydromedusæ, *Biol. Bull.*, XXXIV.
1919 a.   Demonstration of the Axial Gradients by Means of Potassium Permanganate, *Biol. Bull.*, XXXVI.
1919 b.   The Axial Gradients in Hydrozoa, II," *Biol. Bull.*, XXXVII.
1919 c.   The Effect of Cyanides on Carbon Dioxide Production and on Susceptibility to Lack of Oxygen in *Planaria dorotocephala, Amer. Jour. Physiol.*, XLVIII.
1919 d.   Susceptibility to Lack of Oxygen During Starvation in *Planaria, Amer. Jour. Physiol.*, XLIX.
1919 e.   A Study of Susceptibility in Some Puget Sound Algæ, *Publ. Puget Sound Biol. Sta.*, II.
1920 a.   Studies, etc., X *Jour. Exp. Zoöl.*, XXX.
1920 b.   Physiological Isolation by Low Temperature in *Bryophyllum, Bot. Gaz.*, LXX.
1920 c.   Some Considerations Concerning the Nature and Origin of Physiological Gradients, *Biol. Bull.*, XXXIX.
1921 a.   *The Origin and Development of the Nervous System from a Physiological Viewpoint.* Chicago.
1921 b.   Certain Aspects of the Problem of Correlation, *Amer. Jour. Bot.*, VIII.
1921 c.   Studies on the Dynamics, etc., XI, *Jour. Exp. Zoöl.*, XXXIII.
1921 d.   The Axial Gradients in Hydrozoa, IV, *Biol. Bull.*, XLI.
1923 a.   The Axial Gradients in *Corymorpha palma*, Proc. Amer. Soc. Zoöl., 1922, *Anat. Record*, XXIV.

1923 b.　The Axial Gradients in Hydrozoa, V, *Biol. Bull.*, XLV.
1923 c.　Physiological Polarity and Symmetry in Relation to Heredity, *Genetics*, VIII.
1923 d.　The General Relation Between Susceptibility and Physiologic Condition, *Arch Int. Med.*, XXXII.

CHILD, C. M., and BELLAMY, A. W.
1919.　Physiological Isolation by Low Temperature in *Bryophyllum* and other Plants, *Science*, L.

CHILD, C. M., and HYMAN, L. H.
1919.　The Axial Gradients in Hydrozoa, I, *Biol. Bull.*, XXXVI.

COHN, E. J.
1918.　Studies in the Physiology of Spermatozoa, *Biol. Bull.*, XXXIV.

COLE, L. J.
1913.　Direction of Locomotion of the Starfish (*Asterias forbesi*), *Jour. Exp. Zoöl.*, XIV.

CONKLIN, E. G.
1897.　The Embryology of *Crepidula*, *Jour. Morphol.*, XIII.
1902.　Karyokinesis and Cytokinesis in the Maturation, Fertilization and Cleavage of *Crepidula* and other Gasteropoda, *Jour. Acad. Nat. Sci. Philadelphia*, Ser. II, Vol. XII.
1910.　The Effects of Centrifugal Force upon the Organization and Development of the Eggs of Fresh Water Pulmonates, *Jour. Exp. Zoöl.*, IX.
1922.　*Heredity and Environment*, Princeton, Fifth Edition.

CREMER, M.
1909.　Die allgemeine Physiologie der Nerven, Nagel's *Handbuch d. Physiologie d. Menschen*, IV.

DAY, LUCY M., and BENTLEY, M.
1911.　A Note on Learning in Paramecium, *Jour. Animal Behavior*, I.

DEWEY, J., A. W. MOORE and others.
1917.　*Creative Intelligence*, New York.

DRIESCH, H.
1891.　Entwicklungsmechanische Studien, I, II, *Zeitschr. f. wiss. Zoöl.*, LIII.
1893.　Entwicklungsmechanische Studien, III–VI, *Zeitschr. f. wiss. Zoöl.*, LV.
1899.　Studien über das Regulationsvermögen der Organismen, *Arch. f. Entwickelungsmech.*, IX.
1901.　*Die organischen Regulationen*, Leipzig.
1908.　*The Science and Philosophy of the Organism.* London.

DRIESCH, H., and MORGAN, T. H.
1895.　Zur Analyse der ersten Entwicklungsstadien des Ctenophoreneies, *Arch. f. Entwicklungsmech.*, II.

ENGELMANN, T. W.
1875.　Contractilität und Doppelbrechung, *Arch. ges. Physiol.*, XI.

EYSTER, J. A., and MEEK, W. J.
1921.　The Origin and Conduction of the Heart Beat, *Physiol. Rev.*, I.

FARMER, J. B., and WILLIAMS, J. L.
    1898.   Contributions to our Knowledge of the Fucaceæ, *Phil. Tr. Roy. Soc.*, CXC.
FISCHEL, A.
    1897.   Experimentelle Untersuchungen am Ctenophorenei, I, *Arch. f. Entwickelungsmech.*, VI.
    1898.   Experimentelle Untersuchungen, etc., II–IV, *Arch. f. Entwickelungsmech.*, VII.
    1910.   Ueber die Differenzierungsweise der Keimblase, *Arch. f. Entwickelungsmech.*, XXX.
    1914.   Ueber das Differenzierungsvermögen der Gehirnzellen, *Arch. f. Entwickelungsmech.*, XL.
FLEXNER, S.
    1898.   The Regeneration of the Nervous System of *Planaria torva* and the Anatomy of Double-Headed Forms, *Jour. Morphol.*, XIV.
GALIGHER, A. E.
    1921.   Axial Metabolic Gradients in the Early Development of the Sand Dollar, *Dendraster excentricus*, *Publ. Puget Sound Biol. Sta.*, III.
GLASER, O. C.
    1907.   Movement and Problem Solving in *Ophiura brevispina*, *Jour. Exp. Zoöl.*, IV.
GOLDFARB, A. J.
    1909.   The Influence of the Nervous System in Regeneration, *Jour. Exp. Zoöl.*, VII.
GOWANLOCH, J. N.
    1923.   Reversal of Vertebrate Heart Beat, Proc. Amer. Soc. Zoöl., 1922. *Anat. Record*, XXIV.
GURWITSCH, A.
    1905.   Ueber die Zerstörbarkeit des Protoplasmas im Echinoderm-enei, *Anat. Anz.*, XXVII.
GRAVE, C.
    1900.   *Ophiura brevispina*, *Mem. Biol. Lab. Johns Hopkins Univ.*, IV.
HARPER, R. A.
    1918 a.   The Evolution of Cell Types and Contact and Pressure Response in *Pediastrum*, *Mem. Torrey Bot. Club*, XVII.
    1918 b.   Organization, Reproduction and Inheritance in *Pediastrum*, *Proc. Amer. Phil. Soc.*, LVII.
HARRISON, R. G.
    1918.   Experiments on the Development of the Fore Limb of *Amblystoma*, a Self-differentiating Equipotential System, *Jour. Exp. Zoöl.*, XXV.
    1921.   On Relations of Symmetry in Transplanted Limbs, *Jour. Exp. Zoöl.*, XXXII.
HARVEY, E. N.
    1912.   The Question of Nerve Fatigue, *Carnegie Inst. Yearbook*, No. 10.
    1920.   An Experiment on Regulation of Plants, *Amer. Nat.*, LIV.

HEILBRUNN, L. V.
  1923.   The Colloid Chemistry of Protoplasm, I and II, *Amer. Jour. Physiol.*, LXIV.
HERING, E.
  1876.   *Ueber das Gedächtniss als eine allgemeine Funktion der organisierten Materie.* Wien.
  1879.   Beiträge zur allgemeinen Nerven- und Muskelphysiologie II, Mitteilung, *Sitzungsber Akad. Wiss. Wien, Math. Naturwiss. Kl.*, Bd. LXXIX, III Abt.
  1888.   *Zur Theorie der Vorgänge in der lebenden Substanz*, Prag. English translation: Theory of the Functions of Living Matter, *Brain*, XX, 1897.
  1899.   *Theorie der Nerventätigkeit.* Leipzig.
HERMANN, L.
  1867 a.   *Untersuchungen über das Stoffwechsel der Muskeln ausgehend vom Gaswechsel derselben.* Berlin.
  1867 b.   *Weitere Untersuchungen zur Physiologie der Muskeln und Nerven.* Berlin.
  1879.   Allegemeine Nervenphysiologie, *Handbuch d. Physiol.*, II Bd, 1 Teil.
  1899.   Zur Theorie der Erregungsleitung und der elektrischen Erregung, *Arch. ges. Physiol.*, LXXV.
HERRICK, C. J.
  1920.   Irreversible Differentiation and Orthogenesis, *Science*, LI.
  1922.   *An Introduction to Neurology.* Third Edition. Philadelphia.
  1924.   *Neurological Foundations of Animal Behavior.* New York.
HERTWIG, O.
  1894.   *Zeit und Streitfragen der Biologie.* Heft 1. Jena.
HERTWIG, R.
  1905.   *A Manual of Zoölogy.* Second American Edition from Fifth German Edition. Translated by J. S. Kingsley. New York.
HILL, A. V.
  1912.   Absence of Temperature Changes During the Transmission of a Nervous Impulse, *Jour. Physiol.*, XLIII.
HINRICHS, MARIE A.
  1923 a.   Modification of Larval Development in *Arbacia* on the Basis of Differential Susceptibility to Light. *Proc. Amer. Soc. Zoöl.*, *1923, Anat. Rec.*, XXVI.
  1923 b.   Demonstration of the Axial Gradient by Means of Photolysis, *Proc. Amer. Soc. Zoöl.*, *1923, Anat. Rec.*, XXVI.
HOLMES, S. J.
  1911.   *The Evolution of Animal Intelligence.* New York.
  1916.   *Studies in Animal Behavior.* Boston.
HOORWEG, J. H.
  1898.   Ueber die elektrischen Eigenschaften der Nerven, *Arch. ges. Physiol.*, LXXI.
HÖRMANN, G.
  1899.   *Ueber die Kontinuität der Atomverkettung, ein Strukturprinzip der lebenden Substanz.* Jena.

HURD, A. M.
  1919. Some Orientating Effects of Monochromatic Lights of Equal Intensities on *Fucus* Spores and Rhizoids, *Proc. Nat. Acad. Sci.*, V.
  1920. Effect of Unilateral, Monochromatic Light and Group Orientation on the Polarity of Germinating *Fucus* Spores, *Bot. Gaz.*, LXX.

HUXLEY, J. S.
  1921. Studies in Dedifferentiation, *Quart. Jour. Micr. Sci.*, LXV.
  1922. Dedifferentiation in *Echinus* Larvæ and its Relation to Metamorphosis, *Biol. Bull.*, XLIII.

HYDE, IDA H.
  1904. Differences in Electric Potential in Developing Eggs, *Amer. Jour. Physiol.*, XII.

HYMAN, L. H.
  1916 a. An Analysis of the Process of Regeneration in Certain Microdrilous Oligochætes, *Jour. Exp. Zoöl.*, XX.
  1916 b. On the Action of Certain Substances on Oxygen Consumption, I, *Amer. Jour. Physiol.*, XL.
  1917. Metabolic Gradients in *Amœba* and Their Relation to the Mechanism of amœboid Movement, *Jour. Exp. Zoöl.*, XXIV.
  1918. Suggestions Regarding the Causes of Bioelectric Phenomena, *Science*, XLVIII.
  1919 a. On the Action of Certain Substances on Oxygen Consumption, II, *Amer. Jour. Physiol.*, XLVIII.
  1919 b. Physiological Studies on *Planaria*, I, *Amer. Jour. Physiol.*, XLIX.
  1919 c. Physiological Studies, etc., II, *Amer. Jour. Physiol.*, L.
  1919 d. Physiological Studies, etc., III, *Biol. Bull.*, XXXVII.
  1919 e. On the Action of Certain Substances on Oxygen Consumption, III, *Biol. Bull.*, XXXVII.
  1920 a. Physiological Studies, etc., IV, *Amer. Jour. Physiol.*, LIII.
  1920 b. The Axial Gradients in Hydrozoa, III, *Biol. Bull.*, XXXVIII.
  1920 c. On the Action of Certain Substances on Oxygen Consumption, IV, *Publ. Puget Sound Biol. Sta.*, II.
  1921. The Metabolic Gradients of Vertebrate Embryos, *Biol. Bull.*, XL.
  1923 a. Oxygen Consumption with Respect to Level, Size and Regeneration and Electrical Polarity in *Corymorpha*, Proc. Amer. Soc. Zoöl., 1922, *Anat. Record*, XXIV.
  1923 b. Physiological Studies, etc., V., *Jour. Exp. Zoöl.*, XXXVII.

HYMAN, L. H., and BELLAMY, A. W.
  1922. Studies on the Correlation between Metabolic Gradients, Electrical Gradients and Galvanotaxis, *Biol. Bull.*, XLIII.

HYMAN, L. H., and GALIGHER, A. E.
  1921. Direct Demonstration of the Existence of a Metabolic Gradient in Annelids, *Jour. Exp. Zoöl.*, XXXIV.

INGVAR, S.
  1920. Reaction of Cells to the Galvanic Current in Tissue Cultures, *Proc. Soc. Exp. Biol. and Med.*, XVII.

JENKINSON, J. W.
  1907.   On the Relations Between the Symmetry of the Egg and the Symmetry of the Embryo in the Frog (*Rana temporaria*), *Biometrika*, V.
  1909.   On the Relation Between the Symmetry of the Egg, the Symmetry of Segmentation and the Symmetry of the Embryo in the Frog, *Biometrika*, VII.
  1911.   On the Origin of the Polar and Bilateral Structure of the Egg of the Sea Urchin, *Arch. f. Entwickelungsmech*, XXXII.
JENNINGS, H. S.
  1899 a. Studies on Reactions to Stimuli in Unicellular Organisms, II, *Amer. Jour. Physiol.*, II.
  1899 b. Studies, etc., III, *Amer. Nat.*, XXXIII.
  1902.   Studies, etc., IX, *Amer. Jour. Physiol.*, VIII.
  1903.   Rotatoria of the United States, II, A Monograph of the Rattulidae, *U. S. Fish Commission Bull. for 1902*.
  1904.   Contributions to the Study of the Behavior of Lower Organisma, *Carnegie Inst. Publ.* No. 16.
  1905.   The Method of Regulation in Behavior and other Fields, *Jour. Exp. Zoöl.*, II.
  1906.   *The Behavior of the Lower Organisms*, New York.
  1907.   Behavior of the Starfish *Asterias forreri* de Loriol, *Univ. Cal. Publ. Zoöl.*, IV.
  1908.   The Interpretation of the Behavior of the Lower Organisms, *Science*, XXVII.
  1909.   Tropisms, *C. R. VIᵉ Congrès Internat. de Psychol.* Geneve.
  1910.   Diverse Ideals and Divergent Conclusions in the Study of Behavior in Lower Organisms, *Amer. Jour. Psychol.*, XXI.
KAPPERS, C. U. A.
  1917.   Further Contributions on Neurobiotaxis, IX. An Attempt to Compare the Phenomena of Neurobiotaxis with other Phenommena of Taxis and Tropism, *Jour. Comp. Neurol.*, XVII.
  1922.   Dixième contribution a la théorie de la Neurobiotaxis, *L'encephale*, No. 1.
KEETON, R. W., KOCH, F. C., and LUCKHARDT, A. B.
  1920.   Response of the Stomach Mucosa of Various Animals to Gastrin Bodies, *Amer. Jour. Physiol.*, LI.
KEETON, R. W., LUCKHARDT, A. B., and KOCH, F. C.
  1920.   The Response of the Stomach Mucosa to Food and Gastrin Bodies as Influenced by Atropine, *Amer. Jour. Physiol.*, LI.
KEILLER, V. H.
  1910.   A Histological Study of Regeneration in Short Head Pieces of *Planaria simplicissima*, *Arch. f. Entwickelungsmech.*, XXXI.
KELLOGG, V. L.
  1901.   *Elementary Zoölogy*, New York.
KNIEP, H.
  1907.   Beiträge zur Keimungsphysiologüe und Biologie von *Fucus*, *Jahrb. f. wiss. Bot.*, XLIV.

KOCH, F. C., LUCKHARDT, A. B., and KEETON, R. W.
    1920.   Chemical Studies on Gastrin Bodies, *Amer. Jour. Physiol.*, LII.
KÜSTER, E.
    1906.   Normale und abnorme Keimungen bei *Fucus, Ber. deutsch. Bot. Gesell.*, XXIV.
LANKESTER, E. R.
    1900.   *A Treatise on Zoölogy*, Part III.
LAPICQUE, L.
    1907 a. Première approximation d'une loi nouvelle de l'excitation électrique baseé sur une conception physique du phénomene, *C. R. Soc. Biol.*, LXII.
    1907 b. Polarisation de membrane dans les électrolytes du milieu physiologique reproduisant la loi de l'excitation électrique des nerfs, *C. R. Soc. Biol.*, LXIII.
    1907 c. Plan d'une théorie physique du fonctionnement des centres nerveux, *C. R. Soc. Biol.*, LXIII.
    1907 d. Considerations prealables sur la nature du phénomene par lequel l'électricité excite les nerfs, *Jour. Physiol. Pathol. gèn.*, IX.
    1907 e. Recherches quantitatives sur l'excitation électrique des nerfs traiteé comme une polarisation, *Jour. Physiol. Pathol. gèn.*, IX.
    1908 a. Orthorhéonome a volant, Excitabilité des nerfs différents pour les ondes électriques lentes ou rapides, *C. R. Soc. Biol.*, LXIV.
    1908 b. Sur le mécanisme de la curarisation, *C. R. Soc. Biol.*, LXV.
    1908 c. Sur la théorie de l'excitation électrique, *Jour. Physiol. Pathol. gèn.*, X.
    1909 a. Definition expérimentale de l'excitabilité, *C. R. Soc. Biol.*, LXVII.
    1909 b. Conditions physiques de l'éxcitation électrique, I, II, *Jour. Physiol. Pathol. gèn.*, XI.
LAPICQUE, L. et M.
    1903.   Variation de la loi d'excitation électrique pour les muscles de la grenouille suivant la rapidité de la contraction, *C. R. Soc. Biol.*, LV.
    1912.   Curarisation par la veratrine; antagonismes dans la curarisation, *C. R. Soc. Biol.*, LXXII.
LAPICQUE, L. et R. LEGENDRE.
    1913.   Relation entre le diametre des fibres nerveuses et leur rapidité fonctionelle, *C. R. Acad. Sci.*, CLVII.
LAPICQUE, L. et J. PETETIN.
    1910.   Nouvelles recherches sur un modèle de la polarisation en vue de la théorie physique de l'excitation, *Jour. Physiol. Pathol. gèn.*, XII.
LASAREFF, P.
    1918.   *Recherches sur la theorie ionique de l'excitation.*, Premiere Partie. Moscow.
LEVI, G.
    1897.   Ricerche citologiche comparate sulla cellula nervosa dei vertebrati, *Riv. di Patol. nerv. e ment*, II.

1906. Studi sulla grandezza delle cellule, 1, Ricerche comparative sulla grandezza delle cellule dei mammiferi, *Arch. ital. Anat. e Embr.* V.

1908. I gangli cerebrospinali, Studi di istologia comparata e di istogenesi, *Supplem. al Arch. ital Anat. Embr.*, VII.

1916. I fattori che determinano il volume degli elementi nervosi, *Riv. di Patol. nerv. e ment*, XXI.

1919. Nuovi studi sull' accrescimento delle cellule nervosi, *Atti Reale Accad. Sci. Palermo*, XI.

LEWIS, MARGARET R.
1915. Rhythmical Contraction of the Skeletal Muscle Tissue Observed in Tissue Culture, *Amer. Jour. Physiol.*, XXXVIII.

LEWIS, MARGARET R., and LEWIS, W. H.
1917. The Contraction of Smooth Muscle Cells in Tissue Culture, *Amer. Jour. Physiol.*, XLIV.

LILLIE, F. R.
1901. Notes on Regeneration and Regulation in Planarians, II, *Amer. Jour. Physiol.*, VI.

1906. Observations and Experiments Concerning the Elementary Phenomena of Embryonic Development in *Chætopterus, Jour. Exp. Zoöl.*, III.

1908. Polarity and Bilaterality of the Annelid Egg, Experiments with Centrifugal Force, *Biol. Bull.*, XVI.

LILLIE, R. S.
1909 a. On the Connection between Stimulation and Changes in the Permeability of the Plasma Membrane of the Irritable Element, *Science*, XXX.

1909 b. On the Connection between Changes of Permeability and Stimulation and on the Significance of Changes in Permeability to Carbon Dioxide, *Amer. Jour. Physiol.*, XXIV.

1909 c. The General Biological Significance of Changes in the Permeability of the Surface Layer of the Plasma Membrane of Living Cells, *Biol. Bull.*, XVII.

1911. The Relation of Stimulation and Conduction in Irritable Tissues to Changes in the Permeability of the Limiting Membranes, *Amer. Jour. Physiol.*, XXVIII.

1913. The Rôle of Membranes in Cell Processes, *Pop. Sci. Mo.*, February.

1914. The Conditions Determining the Rate of Conduction in Irritable Tissues and Especially in Nerve, *Amer. Jour. Physiol.* XXXIV.

1915. Conditions of Conduction of Excitation in Irritable Cells and Tissues and Especially in Nerve, II, *Amer. Jour. Physiol.*, XXXVII.

1916 a. The Theory of Anesthesia, *Biol. Bull.*, XXX.

1916 b. The Conditions of Physiological Conduction in Irritable Tissues, III, *Amer. Jour. Physiol.*, XLI.

1917. The Formation of Structures Resembling Organic Growths by Means of Electrolytic Local Action in Metals and the Physiological Significance and Control of that Type of Action, *Biol. Bull.*, XXXIII.

1918. Transmission of Activation in Passive Metals as a Model of the Protoplasmic or Nervous Type of Transmission, *Science*, XLVIII.
1919. Nervous and other Forms of Protoplasmic Transmission. *Sci. Mo.*, May and June.
1920 a. The Recovery of Transmissivity in Passive Iron Wires as a Model of Recovery Processes in Irritable Living Systems. I, II. *Jour. Gen. Physiol.*, III.
1920 b. The Nature of Protoplasmic and Nervous Transmission. *Jour. Physical Chem.*, XXIV.
1920 c. The Transmission of Physiological Influence in Nerve and other Forms of Living Matter. *Scientia*, Vol. XXVIII.
1922. Transmission of Physiological Influence in Protoplasmic Systems, Especially Nerves. *Physiol. Rev.*, II.
1923. *Protoplasmic Action and Nervous Action.* Chicago.

LILLIE, R. S., and BASKERVILL, MARGARET L.
1921. The Action of Neutral Isotonic Salt Solutions in Sensitizing Arbacia Eggs to the Activating Influence of Hypertonic Sea Water. *Amer. Jour. Physiol.*, LVII.

LILLIE, R. S., and JOHNSTON, E. N.
1919. Precipitation Structures Simulating Organic Growths. *Biol. Bull.*, XXXVI.

LOEB, J.
1890. *Der Heliotropismus der Tiere.* Würzburg.
1891. *Untersuchungen zur physiologischen Morphologie der Tiere, I, Ueber Heteromorphose.* Würzburg.
1892. *Untersuchungen, etc., II, Organbildung und Wachstum.* Würzburg.
1899 a. *Einleitung in die vergleichende Psychologie.* Leipzig.
1899 b. On Ions which are Capable of Calling Forth Rhythmical Contractions in Skeletal Muscle. *Festschr. f. Prof. Fick.* Braunschweig.
1906. *Vorlesungen über die Dynamik der Lebenserscheinungen.* Leipzig.
1915 a. Rules and Mechanisms of Inhibition and Correlation in the Regeneration of *Bryophyllum calycinum*. *Bot. Gaz.*, LX.
1915 b. The Stimulation of Growth, *Science*, XLI.
1916 a. Further Experiments on Correlation of Growth in *Bryophyllum calycinun*. *Bot. Gaz.*, LXII.
1916 b. *The Organism as a Whole.* New York.
1917 a. Influence of the Leaf upon Root-formation and Geotropic Curvature in the Stem of *Bryophyllum calycinum* and the Possibility of a Hormone Theory of these Processes. *Bot. Gaz.*, LXIII.
1917 b. A Quantitative Method of Ascertaining the Mechanism of Growth and Inhibition of Growth in Dormant Buds, *Science*, XLV.
1917 c. The Chemical Basis of Regeneration and Geotropism, *Science*, XLVI.
1917 d. The Chemical Basis of Axial Polarity in Regeneration, *Science*, XLVI.

1917 e. The Chemical Basis of Morphological Polarity in Regeneration, *Proc. Soc. Exp. Biol. and Med.*, XV.

1918 a. The Law Controlling the Quantity of Regeneration in the Stem of *Bryophyllum calycinum. Jour. Gen. Physiol.*, I.

1918 b. The Chemical Mechanism of Regeneration, *Ann. Inst. Past.*, XXXII.

1918 c. The Law Controlling the Quantity and Rate of Regeneration, *Proc. Acad. Nat. Sci.*, IV.

1918 d. *Forced Movements, Tropisms and Animal Conduct.* Philadelphia.

1919. The Physiological Basis of Morphological Polarity, I, II, *Jour. Gen. Physiol.*, I.

1920 a. Quantitative Laws in Regeneration, I, II, *Jour. Gen. Physiol.*, II.

1920 b. The Nature of the Directive Influence of Gravity on the Arrangement of Organs in Regeneration, *Jour. Gen. Physiol.*, II.

1923. Theory of Regeneration Based on Mass Action, I, II, *Jour. Gen. Physiol.*, V, VI.

LOEB, J., and BANCROFT, F. W.
1912. Can the Spermatozoön Develop Outside the Egg? *Jour. Exp. Zoöl.*, XII.

LUCAS, K.
1917. *The Conduction of the Nervous Impulse.* London.

LUCKHARDT, A. B., HENN, S. C., and PALMER, W. L.
1922. On the Specificity of Gastrin and Pancreatic Secretin, *Proceedings Amer. Physiol. Soc., Amer. Jour. Physiol.*, LIX .

LUCKHARDT, A. B., KEETON, R. W., KOCH, F. C., and LA MER, V.
1920. Gastrin Studies, II, *Amer. Jour. Physiol.*, L.

LUND, B. L.
1918. The Toxic Action of KCN and its Relation to the State of Nutrition and Age of the Cell as Shown by *Paramœcium* and *Didinium, Biol. Bull.*, XXXV.

LUND, E. J.
1918 a. Quantitative Studies on Intracellular Respiration, I, II, *Amer. Jour. Physiol.*, XLV.

1918 b. Quantitative Studies, etc., III, IV, *Amer. Jour. Physiol.*, XLVII.

1921 a. Quantitative Studies, etc., V, *Amer. Jour. Physiol.*, LVII.

1921 b. Control of Organic Polarity by the Electric Current, I, *Jour. Exp. Zoöl.*, XXXIV.

1922. Experimental Control of Organic Polarity by the Electric Current, II, *Jour. Exp. Zoöl.*, XXXV.

1923. Experimental Control of Organic Polarity, etc., III., *Jour. Exp. Zoöl.*, XXXVII.

MACALLUM, A. B.
1911. Oberflächenspannung und Lebenserscheinungen, *Ergebn. d. Physiol.*, XI.

MACARTHUR, C. G., and JONES, O. C.
1917. Some Factors Influencing the Respiration of Ground Nervous Tissue, *Jour. Biol. Chem.*, XXXII.

MacArthur, J. W.
    1920.   Changes in Acid and Alkali Tolerance with Age in Planarians,
             Amer. Jour. Physiol., LIV.
    1921.   Gradients of Vital Staining and Susceptibility in *Planaria*
             and other Forms, *Amer. Jour. Physiol.*, LVII.
MacDonald, J. S.
    1905.   The Structure and Function of Nerve Fibers, *Proc. Roy. Soc.*,
             B, LXXVI.
Mangold, O.
    1920.   Fragen der Regulation und Determination an umgeordneten
             Furchungsstadien und verschmolzenen Keimen von *Triton*,
             Arch. f. Entwickelungsmech., XLVII.
Mast, S. O.
    1911.   *Light and the Behavior of Organisms.*   New York.
Mathews, A. P.
    1901.   The Relation between Conduction and the Inorganic Salts of
             the Nerve, *Jour. Boston Soc. Med. Sci.*, V.
    1902.   The Nature of Nerve Stimulation, *Science*, XV.
    1903 a. The Nature of Nerve Irritability, *Science*, XVII.
    1903 b. Electric Polarity in Hydroids, *Amer. Jour. Physiol.*, VIII.
    1904.   The Nature of Chemical and Electrical Stimulation, I, *Amer.
             Jour. Physiol.*, XI.
    1905.   The Nature of Chemical and Electrical Stimulation, II, *Amer.
             Jour. Physiol.*, XIV.
Mayer, A. G.
    1906.   Rhythmical Pulsation in Scyphomedusæ, *Carnegie Inst. Publ.*
             No. 47.
    1908.   Rhythmical Pulsation in Scyphomedusæ, II, *Carnegie Inst.
             Publ.* No. 102.
    1916.   Nerve Conduction and Other Reactions in *Cassiopea*, *Amer.
             Jour. Physiol.*, XXXIX.
McCallum, W. B.
    1905.   Regeneration in Plants, I, II, *Bot. Gaz.*, LX.
McDougall, W.
    1920.   *The Group Mind.*   New York and London.
Meisenheimer, J.
    1912.   Experimentelle Studien zur Soma- und Geschlechtsdifferen-
             zierung, II.   Jena.
Moore, A. R.
    1919.   The Respiratory Rate of the Sciatic Nerve of the Frog in Rest
             and Activity, *Jour. Gen. Physiol.*, I.
    1923.   Galvanotropism in the Earthworm, *Jour. Gen. Physiol.*, V.
Morgan, T. H.
    1897.   Regeneration in *Allolobophora fœtida*, *Arch. f. Entwickelungs-
             mech.*, V.
    1901 a. Factors that Determine Regeneration in *Antennularia*, *Biol.
             Bull.*, II.
    1901 b. Regeneration in *Tubularia*, *Arch. f. Entwickelungsmech.*, XI.

1902. Experimental Studies of the Internal Factors of Regeneration in the Earthworm, *Arch. f. Entwickelungsmech.*, XIV.
1905. Polarity Considered as a Phenomenon of Gradation of Materials, *Jour. Exp. Zoöl.*, II.
1906. The Physiology of Regeneration, *Jour. Exp. Zoöl.*, III.
1907. *Experimental Zoölogy.* New York.
1908. Some Further Records Concerning the Physiology of Regeneration in *Tubularia*, *Biol. Bull.*, XIV.
1919. *The Physical Basis of Heredity.* Philadelphia.
MORGAN, T. H., and DIMON, A. C.
1904. An Examination of the Problem of Physiological "Polarity" and Electrical Polarity in the Earthworm, *Jour. Exp. Zoöl.*, I.
MORGAN, T. H., STURTEVANT, A. H., MULLER, H. J., and BRIDGES, C. B.
1923. *The Mechanism of Mendelian Heredity.* Revised Edition. New York.
NERNST, W.
1908. Zur Theorie des electrischen Reizes, *Arch. ges Physiol.*, CXXII.
NEWMAN, H. H.
1917 a. On the Production of Monsters by Hybridization, *Biol. Bull.*, XXXVII.
1917 b. *The Biology of Twins.* Chicago.
1918. Hybrids Between *Fundulus* and Mackerel, *Jour. Exp. Zoöl.*, XXVI.
1923. *The Physiology of Twinning.* Chicago.
NOLL, F.
1900. Ueber die Umkehrungsversuche mit *Bryopsis*, *Berichte deutsch bot Gesell.*, XVIII.
NORMAN, W. W.
1900. Do the Reactions of the Lower Animals against Injury Indicate Pain Sensations? *Amer. Jour. Physiol.*, III.
PATTERSON, J. T.
1913. Polyembryonic Development in *Tatusia novemcincta*, *Jour. Morphol.*, XXIV.
PENFIELD, W. G.
1920. Contraction Waves in the Normal and Hydronephrotic Ureter, *Amer. Jour. Med. Sci.*, CLX.
PFEFFER, W.
1897. *Pflanzenphysiologie.* Zweite Auflage. Bd. I. Leipzig.
PREYER, W.
1886. Ueber die Bewegungen der Seesterne. *Mitt. A. d. Zoöl. Station zu Neapel*, VII.
PRIZIBRAM, H.
1906. Kristallanalogien zur Entwicklungsmechanik der Organismen, *Arch. f. Entwickelungsmech.*, XXII.
1921. Die Bruch-Dreifachbildungen im Tierreiche, *Arch f. Entwickelungsmech.*, XLVIII.
RAND, H. W.
1911. The Problem of Form in *Hydra*, *Science* XXXIII.
1912. The Problem of Organization, *Science*, XXXVI.

REGEL, F.
1876. Die Vermehrung der Begoniaceen aus ihren Blättern, *Jen. Zeitschr.*, X.

REICHERT, E. T.
1913. The Differentiation and Specificity of Starches in Relation to Genus, Species, etc., *Carnegie Inst. Publ.*, No. 173.

REICHERT, E. T., and BROWN, A. F.
1909. The Differentiation and Specificity of Corresponding Proteins and Other Vital Substances in Relation to Biological Classification and Organic Evolution. The Crystallography of Hemoglobin, *Carnegie Inst. Publ.*, No. 116.

RIGGS, L. K.
1919. Action of Salts upon the Metabolism of Nerve, *Jour. Biol. Chem.*, XXXIX.

RITTER, W. E.
1919. *The Unity of the Organism.* Boston.
1921. The Need of a New English Word to Express Relation in Living Nature, *Jour. Phil. Psychol. Sci. Meth.*, XVIII.

ROBBINS, H. S., and CHILD, C. M.
1920. Carbon Dioxide Production in Relation to Regeneration in *Planaria dorotocephala*, *Biol. Bull.*, XXXVIII.

ROMANES, G. J.
1885. *Jellyfish, Starfish and Sea Urchin.* New York.

ROUX, W.
1885. Beiträge zur Entwickelungsmech. des Embryo. III, *Breslauer ärztliche Zeitschr.*, Jhg. 1885.
1887. Beiträge, etc., IV., *Arch. f. mikr. Anat.*, XXIX.
1894. Ueber den Cytotropismus der Furchungszellen des Grasfrosches (*Rana fusca*), *Arch. f. Entwickelungsmech.*, I.
1895. Gesammelte Abhandlungen. Leipzig.
1905. Die Entwickelungsmechanik: Ein neuer Zweig der biologischen Wissenschaft, *Vortr. u. Aufs. ü. Entwickelungsmech.*, I.
1912. *Terminologie der Entwicklungsmechanik der Tiere und Pflanzen.* Leipzig.

SATANI, Y.
1919. Experimental Studies of the Ureter, *Amer. Jour. Physiol.*, XLIX.

SEMON, R.
1904. *Die Mneme als erhaltendes Prinzip in Wechsel des organischen Gesehehens.* Leipzig.

Sheaff, H. M.
1922. A Method for the Quantitative Estimation of Minute Amounts of Gaseous Oxygen and its Application to Respiratory Air. *Jour. Biol., Chem.*, LII.

SHELFORD, V. E.
1918. The Reactions of Goldfish to Certain Habit-forming Drugs, *Jour. Amer. Pharm. Assoc.*, VII.

SHELFORD, V. E., and ALLEE, W. C.
1914. Rapid Modification of the Behavior of Fishes by Contact with Modified Water, *Jour. Animal Behavior*, IV.

SHOREY, MARIAN L.
1909.   The Effect of the Destruction of Peripheral Areas on the Differentiation of the Neuroblasts, *Jour. Exp. Zoöl.*, VII.

SIVICKIS, P. B.
1923.   Studies on the Physiology of Reconstitution in *Planaria lata*, with a Description of the Species, *Biol. Bull.*, XLIV.

SMITH, STEVENSON.
1908.   The Limits of Educability in Paramœcium, *Jour. Comp. Neurol.*, XVIII.

SPEMANN, H.
1918.   Ueber die Determination der ersten Organanlagen des Amphibienembryo, I–VII, *Arch. f. Entwickelungsmech.*, XLIII.

1921.   Die Erzeugung tierischer Chimären durch heteroplastische embryonale Transplantation Zwischen *Triton cristatus* und *tæniatus*, *Arch. f. Entwickelungsmech.*, XLVIII.

STAHL, E.
1885.   Ueber den Einfluss der Beleuchtungsrichtung auf die Teilung der Equisetumsporen, *Ber. deutsch. Gesell.*, III.

STEVENS, N. M.
1902.   Regeneration in *Antennularia ramosa*, *Arch. f. Entwickelungsmech.*, XV.

1910.   Regeneration in *Antennularia*, *Arch. f. Entwickelungsmech.*, XXX.

STOCKARD, C. R.
1907.   The Artificial Production of a Single Median Cyclopian Eye in the Fish Embryo by Means of Sea Water Solutions of Magnesium Chloride, *Arch. f. Entwickelungsmech.*, XXIII.

1909.   The Development of Artificially Produced Cyclopian Fish. The Magnesium Embryo, *Jour. Exp. Zoöl.*, VI.

1910.   The Influence of Alcohol and Other Anesthetics on Embryonic Development, *Amer. Jour. Anat.*, X.

1911.   The Experimental Production of Various Eye Abnormalities and an Analysis of the Development of the Primary Parts of the Eye, *Arch. f. vergl. Ophthalmol.*, I.

1921.   Development Rate and Structural Expression, *Amer. Jour. Anat.*, XXVIII.

TASHIRO, S.
1914.   The Metabolic Gradient in the Nerve Fiber, *Proc. Amer. Physiol. Soc., Amer. Jour. Physiol.*, XXXIII.

1915 a.   The Metabolism of Resting Nerve and Its Correlation with the Direction and Rate of Nerve Impulse, *Proc. Amer. Physiol. Soc., Amer. Jour. Physiol.*, XXXVI.

1915 b.   On the Nature of the Nerve Impulse, *Proc. Nat. Aca. Sci.*, I.

1917.   *A Chemical Sign of Life.* Chicago.

TASHIRO, S., and E. M. HENDRICKS.
1921.   Can an Indicator Method be Used for Measurement of CO_2 Production from Isolated Nerve. *Proc. Soc. Biol. Chemists, Jour. Biol. Chem.*, XLVI.

318 BIBLIOGRAPHY

TAYLOR, F. B., and ALVAREZ, W. C.
1917. The Effect of Temperature on the Excised Segments of Different parts of the Intestine, *Amer. Jour. Physiol.*, XLIV.

TERNI, T.
1914. Sulla correlazione fra ampiezza del territorio di innervazione e volume delle cellule gangliari, *Anat. Anz.*, 1914.
1919. Sulla correlazione, etc., 2, *Arch. Ital. Anat. Embr.*, XVII.

TORREY, H. B.
1907. The Method of Trial and the Tropism Hypothesis, *Science*, XXVI.

UEXKÜLL, J. VON.
1905. Studien über den Tonus, II, *Zeitschr. f. Biol.*, XLVI.

VALENTIN, G.
1861. *Die Untersuchung der Pflanzen- und Thiergewebe in polarisirtem Lichte.* Leipzig.
1871 a. Beiträge zur Mikroskopie, II. Die doppeltbrechenden Eigenschaften der Embryonalgewebe, *Arch. f. mikr. Anat.*, VII.
1871 b. *Die Physikalische Untersuchung der Gewebe.* Leipzig.

VERWORN, M.
1906. Die Vorgänge in den Elementen des Nervensystems. Sammelreferat, *Zeitschr. f. allgem. Physiol.*, VI.
1913. *Irritability.* New Haven.

VÖCHTING, H.
1878. *Ueber Organbildung in Pflanzenreich.* Bonn.
1884. *Ueber Organbildung*, etc. Bonn.
1887. Ueber die Bildung der Knollen, *Bibl. Bot.*, H. 4.
1900. Zur Physiologie der Knollengewächse, *Jahrb. wiss. Bot.*, XXXIV.

WAELSCH, L.
1914. Ueber experimentelle Erzeugung von Epithelwucherungen und Vervielfachungen des Medullarrohres (Polymyelie) bei Hühnerembryonen, *Arch. f. Entwickelungsmech.*, XXXVIII.

WALLER, A. D.
1897. *Lectures on Physiology. First Series. On Animal Electricity.* London.
1903. *Signs of Life in their Electrical Aspect.* London.

WERBER, E. D.
1916. Experimental Studies Aiming at the Origin of Monsters, I, *Jour. Exp. Zoöl.*, XXI.
1917. Experimental Studies, etc., II, *Jour. Exp. Zoöl.*, XXIV.

WHEELER, W. M.
1910. *Ants.* New York.
1918. A Study of Some Ant Larvæ with a Consideration of the Origin and Meaning of the Social Habit among Insects, *Proc. Amer. Phil. Soc.*, LVII.
1923. *Social Life Among the Insects*, New York.

WHITMAN, C. O.
1895. Evolution and Epigenesis. *Woods Hole Biol. Lect.*, 1894.

WILHELMI, HEDWIG.
1922.   Ueber Transplantation von Extremitätenanlagen mit Rück-
         sicht auf das Symmetrieproblem, *Arch. f. Entwickelungsmech.*,
         LII.
WILSON, E. B.
1892.   The Cell Lineage of *Nereis, Jour. Morphol.*, VI.
1893.   *Amphioxus* and the Mosaic Theory of Development, *Jour.
         Morphol.*, VIII.
1894.   The Mosaic Theory of Development, *Woods Hole Biol, Lect. for
         1893.*
1896.   On Cleavage and Mosaic Work, *Arch. f. Entwickelungsmech.*,
         III.
1903.   Experiments on Cleavage and Localization in the Nemertine
         Egg, *Arch. f. Entwickelungsmech.*, XVI.
1904.   Experimental Studies on Germinal Localization, I, II, *Jour.
         Exp. Zoöl.*, I.
WILSON, H. V.
1907.   On Some Phenomena of Coalescence and Regeneration in
         Sponges, *Jour. Exp. Zoöl.*, V.
1911 a. Development of Sponges from Dissociated Tissue Cells, *Bull.
         Bur. Fish.*, XXX.
1911 b. On the Behavior of Dissociated Cells in Hydroids, Alcyonaria
         and *Asterias, Jour. Exp. Zoöl.*, XI.
WINKLER, H.
1900 a. Ueber Polarität, Regeneration und Heteromorphose bei *Bryop-
         sis, Jahrb. f. wiss. Bot.*, XXXV.
1900 b. Ueber den Einfluss äusserer Faktoren auf die Teilung des Eies
         von *Cytosira barbata, Ber. deutsch. bot. Gesell.*, XVIII.
WINTREBERT, P.
1920.   La contraction rythmeé aneurale des myotomes chez les em-
         bryons de Selachiens, I, *Arch. Zoöl. exp. gén.*, LX.
WOOD-JONES, F.
1912.   *Coral and Atolls.* London.
ZIEGLER, H. E.
1898.   Die Furchungszellen von *Beroe ovata, Arch. f. Entwickelungs-
         mech.*, VII.

INDEX

Abnormal, the: as equilibration, 219, 220; the conception of, 220; in reconstitution, 243. *See also* Normal.

Acceleration: excitation as, 49; differential, 84, 85, 86.

Acclimation: in relation to physiological condition, 77; differential, 82, 84, 109.

Aggregation: among animals, 273; among cells, 277.

Alimentary tract, physiological gradient in, 90.

ALLEE, W. C., aggregation among animals, 273.

All-or-none reaction, 186, 196.

ALVAREZ, W. C., gradient in alimentary tract, 90, 141.

Amœba: behavior of, 2; surface-interior pattern in, 57, 132; temporary axiate pattern in, 58, 204, 242, 246, 254; reversibility of excitation in, 200; behavior of, in terms of tropism theory, 232; protoplasmic memory in 249; progressive integration in behavior of, 260.

Antennularia, determination of polarity in, 54, 116.

Arbacia: susceptibility gradient in blastula of, 79, 81; differential inhibition in, 83; differential acclimation in, 84; reduction gradient in, 87, 88; apolar larva of, 106.

Armadillo, polyembryony in, 163.

Association: among cells, 277; among human beings, 278; factors in human, 278. *See also* Integration, social.

Asterias forbesii: bilaterality in behavior of, 63; modification of development, 105, 106.

Asymmetry: forms of, 39, 40; in behavior, 66; locomotion in relation to spiral, 71; of amphibian leg, 127, 128; inverse, 167. *See also* Gradient, physiological; Symmetry.

Autocracy: in physiological dominance, 146, 258, 270, 288; in social integration, 288; of the dominant idea, 289. *See also* Dominance, physiological; Dominance, social.

BARTELMEZ, G. W., bilaterality of pigeon's egg, 130.

Begonia, adventitious buds in, 122.

Behavior: as reaction to environment, 1; integration of, 2, 3; protoplasmic and organismic, 2, 4; as realization of hereditary potentialities, 3, 11; physiological and historical aspects of, 4, 5; as basis of organismic pattern, 10, 22, 195; excito-motor, 11, 226, 229, 251; in relation to excitation and transmission, 15, 52, 191, 197; coördination in, 35; in relation to polarity and symmetry, 61; of echinoderms, 64; versatility in, 68; origin of nervous system in protoplasmic, 111; in relation to excitation-transmission gradients, 197; as regulation, 226, 228; in relation to life, 227, 238; usefulness of, 227; useless and injurious, 228; potentialities of, 228; trial and error in, 230, 260; tropisms in, 230, 263; reflex, 233; evolution primarily concerned with mechanisms of, 236; creative character of, 241; fixed and modifiable, 252; nervous system and modifiability of, 256; in relation to cerebral cortex, 257; instinctive, 264, 267; intelligent, 265; in social integration, 267, 271, 277; foundations of human, 269.

BELLAMY, A. W.: differential modification of development of frog, 106, 108; ovarian egg of frog, 98, 99.

BERGSON, H., élan vital, 241.

BERNSTEIN, J., theory of excitation-transmission, 176.

Block: as factor in physiological isolation, 156; of nerve impulse, 159.

BORUTTAU, H., theory of excitation-transmission, 176.

BOSE, J. C., theory of excitation-transmission, 176.

BOVERI, T.: polarity as gradation, 74; polarity of sea urchin's egg, 129.

BRACHET, A., bilaterality in frog's egg, 130.

Brissopsis lyrifera, bilaterality and locomotion in, 66, 67.

Bryophyllum: action of gravity on, 54; dominance in, 158; physiological isolation by block in, 159.

Bryopsis, determination of polarity by light in, 115.

CAREY, E. J.: mechanical factors in differentiation, 50; mechanical factors in rhythmic response, 185.

CARLSON, A. J., secretin and gastrin, 7 footnote.

Cassiopea xamachana: dominance in, 64; transmission in, 64, 187.

Cell, the: in relation to organism, 2, 8, 25; as elementary organism, 20; whole germ plasm inherited by, 22, 25; behavior of, 58, 59, 60, 71; gradient in, 76 footnote, 79, 80, 87, 88, 98, 99, 100; as surface-interior pattern, 93, 131, 132; accumulation of fat in, 97; changes in gland, 97; epithelio-muscle, 111; isolation of sexual, 170; aggregation, 277.

Cerebral cortex, 257, 265, 289.

Chœtopterus pergamentaceus, structure of egg of, 99, 100.

Chronaxie, 177.

COLE, L. J., starfish rays not physiologically equivalent, 65.

Conduction. *See* Transmission.

Conifer, reaction to removal of tip in, 62.

CONKLIN, E. G.: reaction to environment in development, 23; hypothesis of elastic structure in eggs, 136.

Correlation, physiological: kinds of, 34; transportative, 44; dynamic, 47; yolk as factor in transportative, 101; as basis of equilibration, 217, 251.

Correlation, social: among different species, 272; as factor in social integration, 279, 290; dynamic, 280; material, 281.

Corymorpha: decrease of polarity in short pieces of, 117; biaxial forms in 117, 118; obliteration of gradient in, 119; determination of new gradient

in, 119, 120; adventitious budding in, 123, 124.

Crystal: hemoglobin, 26; organismic pattern as analogous to, 26.

Ctenophore: gradient in plate row of, 90; dominance and subordination in plate row of, 141; pacemaker in plate row of, 149; rate of transmission in plate row of, 190.

Cyclopia: in *Planaria*, 107, 108; in fishes and amphibia, 108.

DAY, L. M., and BENTLEY, M., behavior of *Paramecium*, 261.

Decrement: in transmission of excitation, 51, 152, 186, 195, 198; in nerve fiber, 191; in certain regions of reflex arc, 197.

Democracy: in physiological integration, 146, 258, 270, 288, 290; in social integration, 288, 291, 297; appears first in small groups, 291.

Dero limosa, susceptibility gradient in, 80, 81.

Development: mosaic, 11, 146, 244; of *Fucus*, 60; of hydroid, 63; differential modification of, 80, 104; teratological, 86; non-specificity of differential modifications of, 86; adventitious, 122; as behavior, 193; constancy in, 211; normal and abnormal, 216, 217; as regulation, 223, 224, 226; as realization of new patterns, 241; as modification by experience, 248; of leadership and communication in social integration, 290. *See also* Differentiation.

DEWEY, J., sterility of conception of organism as primarily independent of external world, 30.

Dichotomy: as equal division of dominant region, 126; in plants, 161, 162; experimental, 161; in armadillo, 163; physiological processes in, 165; conditions favoring, 165; different degrees of, 166.

Differentiation: in relation to specific and dynamic factors, 53, 100, 282; in relation to physiological gradients, 80, 95, 102, 109; in relation to theory of qualitative nuclear division, 95; definition of, 96; in relation to oxidation-reduction, 97; in *Chœtopterus* egg, 99, 100; of nervous system,

relation to behavior, 61; as coördinate system, 73; in relation to protoplasmic structure, 75; in relation to rate of development, 75; in relation to rate of reconstitution, 75; in relation to susceptibility, 80, 104; obliteration of, 82, 106; in relation to permeability, 80; in relation to oxidation-reduction, 87; in relation to electric potential difference, 87; in relation to galvanotaxis, 89; in relation to respiration, 90; quantitative character of, 91; developmental changes in, 92; as basis of localization and differentiation, 95; in eggs, 98, 129; constancy of, 211; cerebral cortex in relation to, 257; resemblance of, to state, 270; in social integration, 284. *See also* Gradients, physiological; Pattern, organismic.

Pattern, organismic: scale of, 4, 8, 44; as a physiological unity and order, 4; as factor in behavior, 5, 10, 33, 61, 252; in relation to environment, 8, 10, 30, 42, 193, 212, 239; evolutionary modification of, 9; as behavior pattern, 10, 23, 193, 205; dynamic character of, 17; predeterministic and epigenetic conceptions of, 20; stereochemical theories of, 25, 26; dominance and subordination in, 34; polarity and symmetry in relation to, 36; excitation and transmission in relation to, 50; alteration of, by behavior, 70; modifiability of, 239; tropisms in relation to, 263. *See also* Pattern, axiate; organismic; protoplasmic; surface-interior.

Pattern, protoplasmic: nature of, 8; in relation to organismic pattern, 9, 34, 40, 41. *See also* Pattern, organismic.

Pattern, social: institution as, 270; similar to organismic, 270; among animals, 271; factors of, 277; dominance as factor of, 281, 285; surface-interior, 283; axiate, 288; evolution of, 288, 297, effect of isolation on, 291. *See also* Dominance, social; Integration, social.

Pattern, surface-interior: as relation to environment, 24, 132; in simplest organisms, 38; in relation to behavior, 57; only persistent pattern

in *Amœba*, 58; in relation to gradients, 93; cell pattern as, 93; in all organisms, 94; origin of, 131; in cell masses, 132; nucleus in relation to, 133; in social integration, 283.

PATTERSON, J. T., twinning in armadillo, 163.

PENFIELD, W. G.: gradient in ureter, 91 footnote; functional dominance in ureter, 141.

Pentacta frondosa, bilaterality and locomotion in, 67.

Permeability: gradients in, 86; of neuroblasts, 111; change of, in excitation, 179, 180.

Phialidium gregarium: development of, 63; susceptibility gradients in development of, 79, 80; differential inhibition in, 82; differential reduction of KMnO₄ in, 87, 88; adventitious budding in, 123, 125; polarity of egg of, 129.

Photolysis, as means of demonstrating gradients, 76 footnote, 109 footnote.

Physiological state: conception of, 240, 259, 260; law of resolution of, 263.

Planaria: behavior of different cells of, 25, 111, 243, 246; polarity and symmetry in, 33, 39, 242; gradient in rate of reconstitution in, 76; photolytic susceptibility of, 76 footnote; localization of parts under different conditions, 103; differential inhibition of head development in, 107, 108, 243; biaxial forms in, 117, 119, 159; dominance in reconstitution of, 142; self-differentiation of head in, 142; reconstitution at different body levels of, 152; physiological isolation in, 153; decrease of dominance in, 156; experimental dichotomy in, 161; negative geotaxis in, 228; reaction to food in, 262.

Polarity: stereochemical theories of, 25, 26, 130; in *Planaria* and *Marchantia*, 33; in relation to organismic pattern, 36; of *Fucus* egg, 27, 58, 115, 135, 202, 203; as factor in behavior, 61; reversal of, in hydroids, 63; as gradient, 74; obliteration of, 82, 106, 136; of *Sternaspis* egg, 98, 129; of frog egg, 99; of *Chœtopterus* egg, 99, 100, 129; of neuroblasts, 111; experimental determination of,

114; inheritance of, in eggs, 129; social, 288. *See also* Gradients, physiological; Pattern, axiate; Symmetry.

Polarization, electric, as factor in transmission, 175, 177, 179.

Polytomy, 168.

Potential, electric: axial differences in, 87; in relation to metabolism, 89; in relation to transmission, 179.

Predeterminism: elementary organism in relation to, 19; organism in terms of, 20, 26; fundamental difficulty of, 29, 30; in relation to neo-vitalism, 31.

Protoplasms: behavior of, 2, 24; specific differences in constitution of, 6, 7; non-specific factors in, 7, 25; integration of, in organisms, 8, 41; in relation to environment, 12, 13.

PRZIBRAM, H.: crystalline and organismic form, 26 footnote, 110, 127; reduplication of parts, 127.

RAND, H. W., physiological dominance in hydra, 141.

Recovery: in relation to physiological condition, 77; differential, 84, 109.

Reduction: of KMnO₄, 87; of methylene blue, 87.

Reduplication: of amphibian legs, 126; of parts in general, 127. *See also* Dichotomy.

Reflex: dominance and subordination in, 36, 138; as functional unit, 112, 234; physiological gradient as simplest, 112, 256; in behavior, 233; in relation to course of development, 233; in relation to trial reaction and tropism, 235; modifiability of, 235, 262; integration of, 256.

Regulation: of function, 214, 219, 220; of form, 214, 221; as return to normal, 215, 218; definitions of, 216; as equilibration, 217, 218; usefulness of, 219; normal and abnormal in, 219, 220; in development, 221; as repair process, 221; development as, 223; physiological gradient as mechanism of, 224; in physiological integration, 225; life as, 226; in relation to behavior, 228, 232; historical aspects of, 235; modification of, 242, 243.

REICHERT, E. T., differentiation of starches, 26.

REICHERT, E. T., and BROWN, A. F., crystalline forms of hemoglobin, 26.

Reproduction: of main axis in conifer, 62; physiological isolation in agamic, 153; dichotomous, 160; polytomous, 168; gametic, 170, 295; social, 292. *See also* Isolation, physiological.

Rhythmicity: in muscle, 184, 185; in nervous discharge, 185.

RITTER, W. E.: on integration and differentiation, 2 footnote; protoplasms *versus* protoplasm, 6; fundamental importance of chemical correlation, 46.

ROMANES, G. J., nerve impulse in *Aurelia*, 64.

ROUX, W.: qualitative nuclear division, 21, 95; conception of development, 210, 216; definition of regulation, 216; normal and regulatory development, 221.

Sea urchin: axiate pattern in, 67; polarity in egg of, 129. *See also* *Arbacia*.

Self-differentiation: of head in *Planaria*, 142; of cephalic nervous system, 143, 144; in development in general, 244.

Self-excitation, 15, 184, 185.

SEMON, R., mnemic conception, 248.

SHELFORD, V. E., reactions of fishes to toxic substances, 220.

Size: of nerve cell and of animal, 144; in relation to physiological isolation, 155; conditions limiting, 169, 192, 291; in relation to social reproduction, 292.

SMITH, S., behavior of *Paramecium*, 261.

Society: organs of, 268; as superorganismic pattern, 271; as process of integration, 296.

Sociology: concerned with animals as well as man, 267; biological, 268; leadership in, 283.

SPEMANN, H., "organizer" in amphibian development, 144.

Spirostomum, susceptibility gradient in, 80.

Sponge: reduction gradient in, 87, 88; determination of new polarity in, 119.

Standardization: of conditions in evolution, 211, 212, 220, 222, 223, 228; of behavior mechanisms, 236.

INDEX

Starfish: polarity and symmetry in, 38; locomotion of, 65; versatility of 68; modification of development in, 105.

Stenostomum: susceptibility gradient in, 80, 81; physiological isolation in, 154, 155.

Stentor, differential susceptibility to ultraviolet radiation, 76 footnote.

Sternaspis, polarity in egg of, 98, 129.

STOCKARD, C. R.: cyclopia in fishes, 108; twinning in fishes, 166.

Stolen, of hydroid as inhibited gradient, 124.

Stomotoca atra, reduction gradient in egg of, 88.

Subordination, physiological. *See* Dominance, physiological.

Substances, formative: in relation to polarity and symmetry, 28; chemical correlation fundamental in theories of, 45, 281.

Summation, in reflex arc, 198.

Susceptibility: in relation to physiological condition, 76; differential, 76, 80, 104; to ultraviolet radiation, 76, 109; significance of, 77; non-specific and specific features of, 77, 78, 91; axial differences in 80; methods of demonstration of, 80.

Symmetry: stereochemical theories of, 25, 26, 28, 110, 122, 130; in *Planaria* and *Marchantia,* 33; in relation to organismic pattern, 36; in relation to dorsoventrality, 37; forms of, 38; behavior in relation to radiate, 63; behavior in relation to bilateral, 68; as gradation, 74; as physiological gradient, 74; in relation to susceptibility, 76; modifications of, in *Arbacia,* 83, 84, 106; obliteration of bilateral, 105, 106; inverse, 126, 128, 167; origin of, in eggs, 130. *See also* Gradients, physiological; Pattern, axiate.

TASHIRO, S., metabolism of nerve fiber, 178, 182.

Tolerance: in relation to physiological condition, 77; to toxic substances, 220. *See also* Acclimation.

Transmission: as excitation of one region by another, 49; in relation to organismic pattern, 50; decrement

in, 51, 186, 195; in scyphomedusæ, 64; nature of, 173; theories of, 175, 176, 178; in relation to metabolism, 181, 182; models of, 181; without decrement, 188; in relation to behavior, 191, 253; in relation to modifiability, 254; in social integration, 272, 276, 280. *See also* Excitation.

Trial and error: theory of, in motor behavior, 230; mechanisms of, 231; in relation to tropism and reflex, 235, 263; modifiability of, 260.

Trophallaxis, 275.

Tropism: definitions of, 230, 231; mechanism necessary for, 232, 263; in relation to trial reaction and reflex, 253; modifiability of, 263.

Tubularia: gradient in rate of reconstitution in, 75; localization of parts under different conditions, 102; decrease of polarity in short pieces of, 117; biaxial forms in, 117, 118; dominance and subordination in, 141; localization of hydranth in, 143; physiological isolation in, 155; decrease of dominance in, 156; tentacles in reconstitution of, 169.

Twinning: in armadillo, 163; physiological processes in, 165; *situs inversus viscerum* in, 167; mirror-imaging in, 167. *See also* Dichotomy.

Ureter: gradient in, 91 footnote; functional dominance in, 141.

VERWORN, M., theory of excitation-transmission, 177.

Vitalism: elementary organism in relation to, 19; organism in terms of, 31; chief service of, 31; invalidity of Driesch's argument for, 31.

WALLER, A. D., metabolism in relation to bioelectric phenomena, 176.

WEISMANN, A.: determinants, 19, 21; theory of qualitative nuclear division, 21, 95, 210.

WHEELER, W. M., trophallaxis, 275.

WILSON, H. V., development from fragments, 243.

WINTREBERT, P., rhythmic contraction of myotomes, 184.

WOOD-JONES, F., dominance and subordination in coral, 62, 156.

(